Financial Management for Engineers

Dr. Peter Flynn
Poole Chair in Management for Engineers
Department of Mechanical Engineering
University of Alberta

Fourth Edition
Copyright 2009

Publisher
Gautam Rao

Editor
Amy Jenkins

Flynn, Peter
Financial Management for Engineers

Published by
Castle Rock Research Corp.
2340 Manulife Place
10180 – 101 Street
Edmonton, AB T5J 3S4

1 2 3 FP 10 09 08

Printed in Canada

Dedicated to the memory of Dr. V. S. Rao

Author's Note:

Engineers often become managers: an estimated 33 to 50% of engineers will end up in a management role in their career.

Engineering education doesn't focus much on management, because engineering schools have so much technology that they must teach to ensure that graduates aren't a threat to society. Engineers work with expensive and powerful systems, and need a broad background in technology to understand how to get value from those systems without creating a hazard to society.

The result is that engineers who go into management are often stumbling about with poor background and inadequate skill sets. This was true of me. I was a supervisor after two years of work, and was running a company (a partially owned affiliate of a large publicly traded company) before I was 40. I couldn't read a balance sheet and had only a vague understanding of receivables. I would have done a better job if I had a better background in financial management.

Management involves a broad range of skills, from people management to technology to marketing, and always includes financial management skills. Engineers apply science to create commercial value, and as discussed in these notes commercial value is measured by money. These notes, and the course for which they were developed, focus on understanding financial concepts so that sound management decisions can be made. I hope that anyone who reads these notes won't be as ignorant as I was when I ran a company and couldn't understand its balance sheet.

These notes aren't designed to make you an accountant, and at times accounting precision is waived in favor of extracting the meaning of statements. They are meant to help anyone who moves into management, and will also help those who are managed understand what decisions are being taken, and why.

I dedicate these notes to my wife Jeanett, my sons Morris and Henry, and her daughters Chelsey and Ashley. I have had a wonderful time in many management roles, but none compared in pleasure to the roles of husband and father.

A Joke from the Internet:

A man is flying in a hot air balloon and realises he is lost. He reduces height and spots a man down below. He lowers the balloon further and shouts "Excuse me, can you help me? I promised my friend I would meet him half an hour ago, but I don't know where I am".

The man replies "Yes, you are in a hot air balloon, hovering approximately 30 feet above this field. You are between 40 and 42 degrees North Latitude and between 58 and 60 degrees West longitude."

"You must be an engineer," says the balloonist. "I am" replies the man. "How did you know?" "Well", says the balloonist, "everything you have told me is technically correct, but I have no idea what to make of your information, and the fact is, I am still lost."

The man below says, "you must be a manager". "I am" replies the balloonist, "but how did you know?" "Well" says the man, "You don't know where you are, or where you are going. You made a promise which you have no idea how to keep and you expect me to solve your problem. The fact is you are in the exact position you were in before we met, but now it is somehow my fault."

Table of Contents

Engineering, Business, and Society

Key Concepts

- Engineering is typically practiced in large groups. It tries to create commercial value.
- The value placed on goods and services, commercial value, is measured by money. Many social values are difficult or impossible to measure by money.
- Regulation is the mechanism by which market directed economies impose social values on business.
- Different classes of regulation protect business from business, individuals from business, and society from business.
- Financial analysis is one key element of a manager's required skill set.

Chapter 1: Engineering, Business, and Society

1.1   Why Should Engineers Learn Business?

Engineering is typically an institutional enterprise trying to achieve commercial goals measured by money. Because engineers work in groups and organizations, they will be managed by someone who will typically set or confirm goals and monitor progress. Technical companies are very frequently managed by engineers, who need to understand a range of management skills to serve in this role. Inevitably, a significant percentage of engineers migrate into management tasks. How well you are managed will have an enormous impact on the quality of your life, and if you become a manager, how well you manage will strongly impact others.

The work engineers do will most frequently be judged against commercial criteria in which money is the measure of commercial value (money has limitations in measuring some values, but not commercial values, which is further discussed in Appendix 1.1). Even for projects that are not driven by an overall need to make money, such as a weapons system or a bridge, concepts of budget, schedule, and cost effectiveness arise within the project. Business, or organizational, success comes from the efforts of many, and engineering can only be practiced when it is part of overall business or organizational success. The history of engineering is full of elegant technical work that foundered because businesses or organizations could not successfully apply it.

Business activities are no better or worse than technical activities. Not everyone will find happiness in management roles. For those with no interest in business or management, work can be more enjoyable if an engineer knows the issues and concerns of one's manager and the overall needs of the organization or business. Hence, a basic knowledge of business and management is part of a good career.

One or two survey courses are not intended to make an engineer an expert on business or management. Rather, the intent is to introduce the concepts and language of various elements of the manager's skill set. Management is a generalist higher-level activity, and anyone who enters management needs to work with others, such as accountants, auditors, lawyers, and technical specialists. An overview of business and management will ideally make an engineer who goes into management more confident when dealing with others. Specialized areas of knowledge frequently have a unique jargon that can deter understanding by others. Engineers who know the underlying issues of business and management are far more likely to be able to cut through jargon and get the benefit of help from others. Hence, the objective of this text is to help engineers understand the basic concepts of financial management, achieve confidence in dealing knowledgably with others, and recognize that there is more to learn.

1.2   Business, Engineering, and Society

Business and a profession such as engineering operate within a given society and, ultimately, are subordinate to social rule. At times, social values have significantly impacted commercial and professional issues.

Social values have modified the pattern and growth of business and the application of technology. In China, social forces led to the deferral of industrialization when entrepreneurial values and behavior came in conflict with social standards of harmony. In the United States, the concentration of business has been the subject of significant legislation. This led to **trust busting**, which is legislation for the destruction of a monopoly so society can operate as a free market. Rockefeller's Standard Oil and other major enterprises in the 1910s and 20s broke up as a result of trust busting. More recently, a vigorous debate over the potential breakup of Microsoft emerged when it was accused of inappropriately using its dominant market position. Society as a whole, or more typically various subsets, has attempted less successfully to limit the application of technology. For example, the Luddites smashed early weaving machines out of a fear of unemployment, medieval guilds went to great lengths to establish a monopoly on manufacture, and some unions resisted technological changes such as the automated bearing overheat detector as a replacement for the caboose.

Professions are created by legislation and enforce a code of social conduct by requiring training and licensing. Many also use disciplinary actions to regulate business standards.

Labor law attacks the concept that the corporation or company is a "person" (a separate legal identity) with equal power to any other real human person. The uneven power between companies and individuals is addressed in unionized settings by specific requirements about collective bargaining, including the application of majority rule on a unionized workforce, and in non-union settings by labor standards. Labor standards limit the ability of the individual to "bargain away" certain minimum standards; the limit is in place because of the perceived inequality in bargaining power between an individual and an employer.

Environmental issues are frequently a clear social tradeoff of the impact of higher prices on consumers with vastly different abilities to pay versus degradation of a common resource. Social wealth has historically had a significant correlation to the level of environmental standards; therefore, air and water pollution standards are far more stringent in Western Europe and North America than in India or China.

Subtler social issues are also impacted by business. Like other mammalian (and especially primate) groups, humans have a tendency to rank the status of members. How business deals with individuals creates powerful forces within a society in terms of status and rank. Much of the 20th century was driven by concepts of societal organization that on some level are a reflection of the impact of the inequalities in income and status that arose from the Industrial Revolution.

1.3   *The Role of Regulation*

At a practical level, market capitalism restricted by specific regulation is the accepted framework for commercial activity in most industrialized countries. One theme of the past decade has been the reduction and streamlining of regulation to enable enterprises to operate more efficiently. However, this has not eliminated the need for regulation. One way to think of regulation of business is that it is addressing three types of concerns:

- Protecting businesses from the actions of other businesses.
- Protecting individuals from business actions.
- Protecting society from business actions.

Rockefeller and the Hudson's Bay Company had similar approaches to pricing: make very large profits in areas where one has a monopoly, and price below cost where one has competition. The result was a spiraling reduction of competitors that went bankrupt. Extensive legislation exists in all industrialized countries (called combines legislation in Canada and fair trade or antitrust legislation in the US) to ensure that uneven pricing or other business practices are not employed to reduce competition.

Even though a huge corporation and an individual are each persons in the eyes of the law, they are clearly not of equal power. At times of medium to high unemployment, the threat of job loss is overwhelming to most employees. Labor legislation, such as rules governing the payment of overtime and the scheduling of work, is intended to enshrine certain rights and practices in law so that individuals do not have to bargain on a one-on-one basis and face the threat of job loss. Similarly, safety legislation imposes a social standard on employers to ensure that risk of accident (which is never zero) passes a test of social acceptability.

Also as noted above, most manufacturing processes involve some use of common sinks such as the atmosphere, rivers, oceans, and landfills to reject heat and waste. Most would judge a pure "zero discharge" standard as unaffordable, and most would also judge that no restrictions on emissions leads to unacceptable environmental damage (for which there is ample historical evidence). Environmental regulations are the outcome of that tradeoff, and they represent the protection of society as a whole from the practices of business.

The efficiency and effectiveness of regulation is an ongoing issue that is of tremendous importance to society as a whole and to individuals. In recent history, there have been blatant examples of excessive regulation that led to gross inefficiencies, with all of society paying the cost. Airlines, trains, trucking, and telecommunications are four areas where costs clearly dropped as the extent of regulation was reduced. On the other hand, under-regulation leads to abuses by the unscrupulous. In some countries, there are stunning examples of abuse of workers that critics associate with a failure to enforce labor standards. In the former Soviet block countries, environmental degradation was severe due to ineffective regulation and has had long-lasting consequences in terms of nuclear contamination and birth defects. Engineers need to accept that the debate over how much regulation is the "right" level will take place throughout their career, and they can and should participate in this debate as part of their contribution to society.

1.4   The Skill Set of a Good Manager

Organizations are complex entities that can be likened to a living organism: many systems need to function properly at the same time to sustain health. In living systems, some systems are more urgent than others: breath in humans is the system with the shortest time frame, while some skin problems can go without treatment for years without significant harm. In an organization, many systems of differing urgency also have to function as well: money has to flow into an organization and be spent on appropriate end uses, such as research, product development, manufacturing, and marketing, to sustain the life of the organization. Just like doctors monitor one or more of the functions of their patients and ensure they are working properly, managers oversee the various aspects of their company.

The following knowledge and skills are required by an effective manager:

- Financial analysis: understand and apply concepts of financial statements and cash flow analysis. Understand the difference between income and cash flow, the role that non-cash expense items make to cash flow, and the role of tax on cash flow.
- Financial management: understand how money enters a company and the relationship between the risk that money is exposed to and the reward that is expected by the entity that advanced the money; understand debt versus equity and the concept of the leverage of equity return.
- Operations management: direct an ongoing operating entity to make a profit and typically also grow. The focus is on continuous improvement and pushing responsibility downward.
- Project management: direct a one-time effort to achieve a pre-defined level of quality within a targeted budget and schedule. The focus is on planning, tracking to plan, taking corrective action, hitting the schedule and budgeting numbers, and doing it right the first time.
- Quality management: understand the principals for maintaining an appropriate level of quality in goods, services, or projects.
- Marketing: understand the identification of needs and the targeting of prospective customers, plus an analysis of the "benefit in use" to a customer; ability to design a promotion and sales program based on identified need; understand the alternative channels to market: distributor, agent, direct sale, and the pricing implications of each; understand fair-trade practices and common violations of combines legislation.
- Sales: understand the rudiments of selling; ability to discuss features and benefits, overcome the objections, and know what "asking for the order" or "closing" means.
- People management: understand management styles and variations in human personality, leadership issues of motivation, direction, and discipline, and supervisory issues of clear communication and active listening; have some sense of the needs people bring to work, and be competent in a wide range of communications, including one-on-one to customers, suppliers, and key contacts, to subordinates, superiors, and peers, and group communications that include a work team, an entire company, or an entire industry and its affected stakeholders; ability to form and share a vision.
- Human resources: understand the legal framework in which people work, the nature of deemed or actual employment contracts, the concept of severance, the role of unions, and typical benefits issues (including typical pension issues).
- Company organization: understand the alternative forms of organizing a company and when each form is most appropriate.
- Contracting: understand the role of the contract and the requirement to protect the interests of the company; ability to acquire or license technology by contract and have some sense of deal structure.

- Developing, buying, and selling technical know-how: understand what is needed to protect intellectual property; understand patents and licensing issues.
- Historical and social insight (senior management): understand issues in the context of history (e.g., union labor relations) and society (e.g., the ongoing evolution of environmental controls). Business issues evolve in the context of history and competing forces within society, and people's reactions and actions today reflect their place in society as well as the history of an issue. Strategic planning: understand the direction a company should take at the highest level; for example, should a pipeline company merge with a chemicals company so that the steady revenue of a regulated utility offsets the cyclical earnings in chemicals? Should a basic chemicals plus specialties business divest itself of the basic chemicals? Should a telephone provider buy a cable company or focus on offering cable type services through ADSL in competition to the cable company?

Depending on the management assignment, not all of these are required. For example, some oil company employees do not need sales skills, since marketing of the product is done remotely through exchanges rather than by some form of personal selling. Usually, only very senior management makes strategic decisions in conjunction with a board of directors. In some larger companies, all decisions on sources of financing are made by a remote treasury department. However, the greater the familiarity with this overall skill set, the more enjoyable a career in engineering will be. As engineers move into management, they will need and can get further training (formal and informal) in each area.

Appendix 1.1: Money as a Measure of Value and Societal Standards

People are constantly faced with questions of competing or conflicting values. At the individual level, you face these choices every day. Should I spend more to rent an apartment with a separate bedroom or reduce the rent by getting a roommate? Should I buy an old car and face the prospect of higher maintenance charges or buy a new car and have higher payments? Should I buy dinner out and have more time for studying or take the time to eat in and save the money?

At an institutional level, managers make many value choices. For example, should nickel powder be produced at a cost of X and a recovery of Y versus nickel briquettes at a lower cost and higher recovery, but with a lower sale value (price)? Should the company hire two more laborers, pay overtime, buy a second machine, or run a nightshift?

At a societal level, people also face these choices every day. Should a wilderness area be drilled for gas, or are the features of the area so unique that no development should be permitted? In a country with governmental health insurance, what is an appropriate waiting list for heart bypass surgery?

Money is a measure of commercial value, and as such it is an excellent guide to decisions that involve only commercial values. What is worth more: a pound of feathers or a pound of iron? This question is easily answered if the time frame is today, since you can look up the "market" price of feathers and iron and get a definitive answer. If the time frame is 1, 5, or 25 years from now, the question is far more difficult to answer, since you must forecast the relative price of feathers and iron far into the future. This takes much more analysis and involves uncertainty, but money is still the measure that captures the commercial value (the value of money itself has a time component, as will be discussed in much greater detail later in Chapter 7).

The price of something (its commercial value) is usually set by a balance of supply and demand. There are many exceptions to this. For example, public goods and services such as services provided by a regulated utility are granted a monopoly and a set rate of return in exchange for cost-based pricing. Also, in Canada, services provided by a doctor are not determined by supply and demand. However, the vast majority of goods and services are private and allowed to fluctuate and respond to short-term and long-term changes in supply and demand. Predicting future price is often the most important element in an investment decision.

At the individual and social level, many questions cannot be measured by money because they involve values other than commercial values. The question "Which bank pays the highest interest on a $1 500 GIC" is easy to answer, but the question "Should I save $1 500 toward my retirement or go on a trip to the mountains with my spouse and children" cannot be answered by any reference to money. Similarly, the question of whether to save money and have a roommate or spend more for a bedroom for yourself cannot be answered by money alone. Clearly, the shared apartment is cheaper, but what is the value of privacy? Not all people will give the same answer to these value questions. Part of the joy of knowing others is understanding their values, which are in some way different from one's own.

Social questions such as the value of wilderness versus jobs do not have a clear monetary measure. Some economists argue that one can assign an economic value to wilderness, in part by imputing the value from decisions that people make regarding the cost of accessing wilderness. This may have a theoretical grounding, but in a practical sense, these monetary values are rarely considered when these issues are discussed, usually in a political forum.

One clear function of society is to impose some non-monetary values on activities. Society outlaws crime and defines a wide range of standards of behavior such as labor standards or environmental compliance. Money is not the only issue considered when standards are set. For example, when the length of the workweek or the number of paid holidays per year is considered, ideally, both monetary and non-monetary factors are considered. Some business activists believe that an individual business should factor non-monetary values into its decisions; for example, do not trade with country X because of its human rights record, redress historical imbalances in the work force unilaterally, or go beyond a required standard of environmental performance in some area. Businesses can normally assess commercial values very well, but can get very confused by a mix of commercial and societal values, since there is not a consistent mechanism to consider and resolve the societal values. The major purpose of politics and government is to assign societal values and ensure that the important ones are met. Ideally, this is done with informed public debate.

A model of society assessing standards and setting the importance of non-commercial values is followed in most of the world. This frees business to maximize commercial value (measured by money) within the constraints of the standards. Some standards, once set, can be monetized, and this hybrid approach has worked very well in environmental issues. Thus, instead of forbidding any new emissions of SO_2 into an air basin, businesses are given the option of offsetting this by reducing emissions somewhere else in the basin by an amount equal to what is proposed to be added. This kind of offset program quickly leads to a market in emissions, which can be traded, and helps to ensure that the least expensive cleanup is done first and the most expensive last. The extension of this concept to CO_2 is under active development for North America. Note that the fundamental non-monetary value (that SO_2 or CO_2 must be restricted to x level) still comes from society.

The model of society assessing standards and setting the importance of non-commercial values works best if all "persons" in a society can contribute to the discussion. Hence, the role of business is to make clear the cost of a new standard, since this will ultimately be built into the cost of goods or services and be borne by consumers. When businesses or interest groups either dominate or are excluded from the process of setting social standards, the quality of the standards is reduced.

As business has become increasingly globalized, the problem of setting standards has become more difficult. This is because standard setting still largely occurs at a national level. The emergence of the European Union is an exception to this, but one can think of the EU as a large super nation that is not truly global. From the perspective of society, a standard that is grossly out of line with a trading partner will raise costs and drive jobs out of the country with the higher standard. From the perspective of business, one can interfere with a balanced evaluation of an appropriate standard by threatening to pull work out of high standard countries. Historically, there have been times when business power has far exceeded the power of society to regulate it, but this normally balances out over time. Watching this drama unfold is one of the exciting elements of business at the turn of the century.

Problems

1.1 Reflect on what you think your own happiness versus income curve looks like. Let the y-axis be personal happiness in the broadest human sense and the x-axis be income level. Speculate on what you think your curve will look like at age 25, 55, and 85, and plot these as well. Graph these curves (hand sketch is fine), and give one page or less of comments on your thoughts.

1.2 Comment on income level as a relative versus an absolute source of personal satisfaction, i.e., to what extent does a sense of personal satisfaction relate to the absolute level of income versus the relative level of income (how much a person makes compared to others)? In forming your thoughts, reflect on both your parents' and grandparents' generation's absolute income levels (the absolute value of the income they received rather than its value relative to the income of others) and their relative happiness. Also, comment on the statement that salary is a lousy motivator but an excellent demotivator (one page or less).

1.3 Look at the list of management skills in chapter 1. Discuss briefly one situation from your summer or part-time employment in which one of these skill sets was deficient, and describe the negative impact this had on your workplace (half to one page).

1.4 In section 1.3, three types of regulation of business were discussed. Give an example of each type of regulation. Say whether, in your opinion, each example of regulation is efficient and effective, and identify whether society would benefit from a change.

1.5 Would you expect emission standards (for example, from automobiles) to be more stringent (lower emissions) or less stringent (higher emissions) in India versus Canada and the US? Say why, and relate your answer, to the extent that your knowledge permits, to the evolution of emission standards in North America over the last 100 years.

1.6 Take one issue in contemporary society today in which you see society as a whole struggling to define a value that is not purely commercial. Examples include preserving wilderness versus commercial activity that creates wealth and jobs or tighter environmental standards versus the cost they impose on consumers. For the issue you select, briefly say what the issue is, what the competing positions are (at least two), who is advocating the various positions, and how society will eventually make a decision to resolve the conflict between various positions (who will make the decision and how). (1 page or less).

1.7 In the late 1990s, the US Justice Department prosecuted Microsoft for hindering competition. The Justice Department argued that Microsoft abused its large market share to, among other things, require customers to take "tied" deals. This meant in order to obtain Microsoft operating software at a competitive price, Microsoft's Internet Explorer program had to be installed on the computer. The Justice Department furthered argued that this kind of practice, and the large market share that Microsoft holds, in part due to such practices, is harmful to society. Microsoft argues that their large market share is the result of innovation and superior products, and that attempts to break up the company or limit its practices will harm innovation and hence society. The arguments on both sides parallel arguments from 100 years earlier regarding monopoly positions held by Standard Oil of New Jersey and United States Steel. Give your opinion on the Microsoft case (one to two paragraphs).

Introduction to Financial Statements

Key Concepts

- Bookkeeping uses a double-entry system to track all financial transactions. Accounting sorts these into accounts so that appropriate management decisions can be made.

- Accounting does not use standardized names for accounts.

- Accounts are used to align the timing of revenue from a sale with the related expenses.

- Companies require two kinds of excellence in management. Operational management ensures that goods or services are efficiently produced and sold at a competitive price that yields a profit. Financial management ensures that a company has the funds it requires to remain in business, and that the needs of those providing funds are properly met.

Chapter 2: Introduction to Financial Statements

2.1 Overview of Financial Statements

Professions typically develop standard documentation that is crucial to the practice of the profession and so ubiquitous as to impact more than 90% of the group. For example, all doctors would know the form and purpose of a medical chart in a hospital. Within engineering, chemical engineers are virtually universally exposed to Process Flow Diagrams and Piping and Instrumentation Diagrams. Mechanical engineers would understand exploded parts diagrams, electrical engineers would all be exposed to circuit diagrams, and architects and civil structural engineers would all know plan and elevation drawings. All engineers in construction would be exposed to critical path schedules. The standard documents of businesses are financial statements, and these are so important that anyone in a commercial environment should have a basic knowledge of them.

Financial statements are a form of scorekeeping, and are designed to answer some very important questions about commercial activity:

- Does the company create value?
- Does it have enough resources to stay in business?
- Where is the company's money going?

These questions arise in family finance as well as business finance and are relevant from a corner store to a multinational corporation. Just as in other fields of study, conventions and practices have evolved to help present data that contributes to insight. The key objective in learning about financial statements is to see how to extract useful information from the data.

2.2 Bookkeeping and Accounting

For almost all enterprises in which engineers are involved, money is an appropriate measure of value. For that reason, transactions that involve money are carefully recorded within almost all businesses. Bookkeepers note every transaction that takes place within a business. Some types of transactions that are recorded are included in the following list:

Type of Transaction	Recorded Transaction
Product or service sales for cash	cash revenue
Product or service sales to be invoiced and paid at a later date	deferred revenue
Asset sales (e.g., selling used equipment that has been replaced)	revenue
Purchase of raw materials for cash or future payment	accounts payable
Purchase of services from third parties (e.g., legal help)	legal fees
Purchase of fixed assets (e.g., land, buildings, machines)	assets
Payment of salaries	salaries
Payment of office expenses such as rent and utilities	operating expenses
Payment of taxes	tax
Borrowing of money	loans
Repayment of borrowed money	loan repayment
Investment of new funds (equity) into the business	share capital
Dividend to investors	dividends
Repurchase of shares in the company (retirement of equity)	share capital repurchase

Typically, each transaction measurable by money is recorded first in a journal, which is a chronological listing of transactions. Within bookkeeping and accounting, there is a double entry, since each transaction has two sides. For instance, if an asset is bought for cash, cash on hand goes down (a credit), and the value of assets goes up (a debit). There is a parallel between energy accounting (in ordinary thermodynamics, energy is neither created nor destroyed; hence, it is a zero sum game) and financial accounting in that each one uses a "balance" approach to see if energy gains and losses or financial credits and debits balance.

Journal entries are classified into one of five categories:

- Revenue—money received for delivering a good or service.
- Expense—the annual costs that are incurred in order to run the business.
- Assets—the value of things that have a useful life greater than one year.
- Liabilities—money that has a legal obligation to be repaid, such as debt.
- Shareholder's equity (capital)—money that owners put into a company.

Transactions are assembled into standard financial statements, which managers analyze to make appropriate decisions. Hence, the progression is from transaction to financial statement to management analysis to decision making to implementation, and from bookkeeper to accountant to manager.

A key part of any business is deciding what accounts will be used to track items such as revenue, expenses, assets, and liabilities. This is a matter of management judgment; accounts are picked to help manage a business. For example, tracking revenue by product line requires that each product that is sold be recorded in a different account. Tracking revenue and expenses over time gives insight into how a business is changing. This can only be done if accounts are consistent over time. Hence, once a business picks a set of accounts, it should change them only if there is a pressing need.

What Accounts Does a Business Need?

The accounts in a business should be selected to help stakeholders understand the business and help managers choose appropriate actions. The categories of inventory that a business tracks illustrate this point.

Consider two businesses: one makes aircraft, and the other pasteurizes and bottles milk. Both are manufacturing businesses that sell goods to customers, but their needs for tracking inventory are very different.

The aircraft company will have raw materials inventory and a very large manufacturing floor on which many airframes are being assembled. Because there is so much work on the floor at any one time, it makes sense to ask the question "How much value is there in process?" If this value goes up month after month, management might well ask the manufacturing manager why work is not getting completed. Senior management would likely emphasize getting work off the floor and into the hands of customers. To get this information, the aircraft company would have to track two different kinds of inventory: raw materials and "work in progress." This would require an accounting entry every time material is moved onto the shop floor. Thus, if $48 000 of hydraulic pumps and valves are moved out of raw materials inventory onto the shop floor for a specific aircraft, an accounting entry would be required to reduce raw materials and increase work in progress. This is not free; the cost of recording an accounting entry might be as much as $25 per entry. However, the value of the information is worth it. The aircraft firm would not only track work in progress, but would also likely track the costs against each aircraft so that the expense of each aircraft could be determined and compared to the sale price set by marketing. An aircraft company may or may not track finished product inventory, depending on whether it is making a standard product or manufacturing each aircraft to a specific customer order and specification.

For the milk bottling business, tracking milk as work in progress is meaningless: it would be the time that milk is going from a tank into a milk jug, likely less than 10 seconds. What meaningful information is conveyed by recording milk going from raw material to the shop floor (the bottling process)? The milk company might have value in tracking raw material inventory separate from finished product inventory, but work in progress is meaningless.

The key message here is that managers and accountants work to pick accounts that have meaning to a specific business. What is the right set of accounts? The one that best helps managers manage a business.

Same Concept, Different Name

Accounting is a profession with a high degree of guidelines and rules. Each country has its own set of Generally Accepted Accounting Principles (GAAP), although there is considerable effort to develop a single international accounting guideline, called International Financial Reporting Standards (IFRS). Accounting became much more rule bound after several notable scandals involving questionable accounting, of which the Enron collapse is the most notable. However, there are still some concepts that have many different names in the accounts of publicly traded companies. Profit, net income, and gain all have the same meaning. Overhead costs are costs that are not directly associated with making a specific product or delivering a specific service, such as legal and head office costs. They can also be called indirect costs, fixed costs, general and administrative costs (G&A), or sales, general, and administrative costs (SG&A). Similarly, depreciation and amortization, which used to have slightly different meanings, are now used interchangeably. The important message for a manager is to understand the concept, which is the same from company to company. If one company reports profit and another reports gain, it means the same thing.

Ratios, discussed in Chapter 6, are used to provide useful management information from financial statements, and these show as much variability as the names of accounts. An example of a ratio is profit margin on sales in which the numerator is income and the denominator is sales. Some companies use operating income in the numerator, some use net or total income, and some use net income minus preferred share dividends. Some use total sales in the denominator, and some use net sales (total sales minus an allowance for returns or warranty claims). If the ratios are being used internally to guide management action, the variation is not important; what is important is that the ratio is calculated the same way year over year. When a ratio is used to compare companies, it is important to use consistent numbers.

Sometimes, engineering students who take financial management express frustration because they want an exact universal definition or how to calculate a ratio. The best advice is to "get over this" because there is some imprecision in both the language and definition of ratios. Look to the meaning behind the number or the ratio, and always think about the management implication of the numbers.

2.3 *Timing Issues and Materiality*

Over time, accounting has developed procedures that allow financial data to be highly usable in making management decisions. For example, careful steps are taken to ensure that revenues and expenses are recognized in the same time period.

Consider a business that makes large vessels that are used in high-pressure processes in the petrochemical industry. It can take months or even years to fabricate one of these vessels. Steel is purchased early in the manufacturing cycle, and fittings such as nozzles and valves are purchased along the way. Direct labor charges are incurred over the course of the manufacturing of the vessel. If all costs for the job were expensed at the same time (if the company did its accounts by showing expenses and revenues as they were realized), the company would show a loss over many months. This is because no revenue would be coming in while the vessel was being fabricated. Then the company would show an enormous profit in the month that payment for the vessel is received. It would be virtually impossible for management to determine how the company was really doing financially, since the months that losses were incurred might or might not be offset by the future sale.

To avoid this confusion, accounting has developed techniques to defer expenses until the corresponding sale is booked, or in accounting terms, accrued. Thus, money spent on steel is held in an asset account (for example, raw materials inventory or work in progress, the name given to work on the shop floor). Direct labor charges can also be accumulated in work in progress. If the vessel is not shipped as soon as it is made, it can be held in a finished goods inventory. Then, at the point of actual transfer of the vessel from the manufacturer to the customer, called the **point of sale**, the revenue for the sale is booked. The value in the finished goods inventory (all the accumulated costs of making the vessel) is converted from an asset (inventory) to an expense (cost of goods sold, also know as COGS, which is discussed at some length in Chapter 3).

Similarly, when custody of the vessel changes hands, the payment for the vessel is rarely done at the same time; most business terms are "net 30 days," meaning the customer is asked to pay 30 days after the invoice, which is usually issued on the day of sale or one day after. Paying an invoice ideally requires three pieces of paper to be assembled, with three different signatures:

- A requisition ("I want this"), often signed by a maintenance person or engineer.
- A purchase order ("I bought this"), usually done by a purchasing agent.
- A receiving slip ("I got this"), usually signed by a warehouse person.

In an ideal situation, three different signatures make the probability of fraud far lower. Small companies can process this paper within 30 days. However, large companies often take up to 50 days to pay invoices because they process the paperwork so slowly. Even though the cash has not been received from the customer, the sale is booked, and an offsetting asset is created: a **receivable**, which is money due from a customer.

These procedures help to line up revenue and expenses into the same time period so that management can determine the key question: is the company creating value? The financial statements give insight into the business and allow informed management decisions. The accounting is complicated. For example, the same steel might move through many accounts: raw materials inventory, work in progress, finished goods inventory, and ultimately COGS, and the same product will go from sale and receivable to cash. However, this complexity is more than offset by the insight that the information provides.

Consider again the business that fabricates large vessels and makes perhaps 20 per year. If all expenses and revenues were booked in the period they were realized, then some months the business would have a huge loss (months in which it had bought the material for several vessels, but had sold none), and in some months, the business would have a huge gain (a customer might pay for many vessels at once). In trying to make sense of the business, the manager would be looking at monthly income statements with wildly fluctuating levels of profit and loss. However, by applying simple accounting rules and recording the costs associated with the manufacture of a vessel in the same time period as the sale is booked, a manager gets a consistent income statement that is a true picture of the business.

The key concept to understand is that expenses such as the purchase of goods or the direct cost of labor are deferred by being held in asset accounts until the time that a sale is booked; at that time, the asset accounts are reduced and an expense, such as the cost of goods sold, is recorded. At the same time, revenue from a sale is recorded, even thought the actual cash has not been received from the customer. When the revenue from a sale is aligned with its direct costs (the material and labor in the items that were sold), it is possible to see if there is an excess of revenue over expense (which is called the contribution margin), and whether that is enough to cover the indirect costs (e.g., indirect costs that are incurred regardless of level of sales, such as administration, office, legal, and marketing costs). These concepts are developed in Chapter 3.

Another concept in accounting is **materiality**, which shows up in determining whether errors need correction. It is inevitable that mistakes will occur in accounting given the thousands of transactions that are recorded daily. If the mistake is minor and correcting it is unlikely to add any insight into the business, it is judged to be not material, and the correction is not made. Thus, a miscoded $50 part on a $1.2 million vessel will not be corrected if the books have been closed, i.e., completed. However, an error of $50 000 would likely be corrected by a **post-period adjustment**. Companies often define standards for materiality.

What is a Sale, and When is it Accrued? (Revenue Recognition)

Accounting defers expenses in inventory accounts (an asset) and does not recognize these as an expense until a sale is booked, or recognized for accounting purposes. At that time, the revenue from the sale will be recognized, even though the customer has not sent the check; hence, the company has an asset, a receivable, to recognize income that the customer has not sent yet. As noted in Section 2.3, the purpose of "storing value" in inventory and receivables is to ensure that revenue and expense are recognized in the same time period. This lets a company know whether it is winning (revenue exceeds expenses) or losing.

Annual sales level is an important number to shareholders and analysts. The late 1990s and early years of 2000 saw companies facing extreme pressure to maintain growing sales; otherwise, their stock values would drop. In this climate, the definition of what a sale was became subject to abuse. The traditional test, when material was shipped from the dock, was sometimes adjusted to treat what customers had ordered, or even worse, what customers had indicated they might order, as a sale. Nortel is cited as a classic example of these abuses.

The response has been to give a stricter definition of what a sale is: it is not a sale until the customer has received it. This accounting standard has created its own problems because a company knows when something has left its dock, but it is much more difficult to know when a customer has received it. At year-end, in order to assess annual sales under the new standard, a company has to phone or e-mail its customers to see if shipped orders showed up at their docks.

One can wonder if the new criterion is an overreaction. The problem of misstated sales was real, but the fix is quite cumbersome. Perhaps settling on an honest application of the traditional value of point of sale, when goods leave the shipping dock, would be good enough.

2.4   *Financial Analysis and Financial Statements*

For business, there are four standard documents that are universal and apply from the smallest enterprise to huge multinational corporations:

- Income statement: how much value was created in a given time period (recognizing that there is a difference between cash and value)? The time period is typically a month, quarter, or year.
- Statement of retained earnings: of the value made since the business started, how much has been kept in the business versus being paid out in dividends to the owners? The value is cumulative, but it also shows how much money was kept in the business in the last year.
- Balance sheet: how much does the company have at a given point in time (assets), and where did the money come from to acquire this (with two sources, called liabilities and equity)? The balance sheet is at a point in time, since how much a business has changes day by day as customers buy goods and pay their bills, and the business buys raw materials or assets and pays its bills and payroll.
- Statement of cash flow: how much money flowed into the business in a given time period, and what did the company do with it? The statement of cash flow is usually prepared on the same basis as the income statement, i.e., monthly, quarterly, or annually.

To understand an existing business, you must understand historical and current versions of these documents. Reasons to understand a business are to manage it (hopefully for the better, be it growth, short-term profitability, or some other sensible goal) or to justify purchasing it. To start a business, especially if you want outside financing, you must project these statements forward, called **pro forma statements**.

To understand an existing business, you must understand historical and current versions of these documents. Reasons to understand a business are to manage it (hopefully for the better, be it growth, short-term profitability, or some other sensible goal) or to justify purchasing it. To start a business, especially if you want outside financing, you must project these statements forward, called pro forma statements.

The purpose of analyzing financial statements is to guide action. The actions can range from buying a stock to founding a company, but in all cases, studying these statements make a manager's actions appropriate and helpful.

2.5   *Operational versus Financial Management*

Financial statements let managers observe and make judgments about two distinct elements of management: operational and financial.

Operational management is the way in which a company uses resources such as materials, assets, and staff to deliver a product or service that meets a customer's needs. Delivering more value while consuming fewer resources is what operational management is all about. Most managers have operational roles: they design, build or operate assets, or sell products in an efficient way that creates value because it is as good as or better than competitors.

In a practical sense, all businesses use some combination of debt (other peoples' money) and equity (the owners' money) in order to operate. **Financial management** involves combining appropriate amounts of debt and equity, meeting obligations to lenders and suppliers, and rewarding equity owners with a combination of growth and/or dividends so that a company stays healthy and, if needed, it can attract more debt and equity in order to grow.

To understand the difference between the two, consider two companies that make identical manufactured products. Company A has less wasted raw materials, uses less labor per unit, has less inventory, has more sales, has lower marketing costs, and has fewer units returned for warranty claims than Company B. Shareholders in Company B would want to ask management why Company A was so much better at using resources, assets, and staff to make and sell goods. Shareholders in Company A would congratulate management on their operational skills: they can operate the physical elements of the business well, creating value in the process.

Now, imagine that Company A has paid excessively high dividends over the years, depleting its cash reserves and increasing its debt to the point where one bad year will put it into bankruptcy, which occurs when a company cannot service its interest and principal payments on its debt. Company B, although inferior from an operational point of view, has built up cash reserves, has a low debt level, and can ride out a bad year. The management of Company A would be considered financially reckless, while Company B's management has been quite conservative. If Company A goes into bankruptcy, the shareholders typically get nothing, and they would be quite right in criticizing their poor financial management skills.

The key objective of financial analysis is to be able to make good judgments and decisions about operational and financial management issues.

2.6   *Accounting versus Managing*

It is helpful for a manager to have a sense of how transactions move through bookkeeping into accounting statements, but it is not necessary that a manager be the master of the details of this. An engineer who becomes a manager can trust that bookkeepers and accountants have followed guidelines in preparing financial statements in much the same way that an accountant driving over a bridge can trust that an engineer followed proper guidelines in designing the bridge. It is important for managers to know what critical management is contained in financial statements and how to use that information to guide appropriate management decisions. The focus of chapters 3 through 6 of this text is on what financial statements indicate about a business and what actions they suggest.

Problems

2.1 a) Take the following list of accounts and for steps 1, 2, 3, 4, 5, and 7, show equal entries in two separate accounts.

The accounts are as follows: cash, accounts payable (money a company owes to its suppliers), inventory of raw materials, work in progress (the value of the goods that are on the shop floor being manufactured into a product), inventory of finished products, cost of goods sold, sales revenue, and accounts receivable (money due to be collected from a customer). Assume that the terms on which you buy materials and sell products are standard commercial terms, i.e., you issue or receive a purchase order, which triggers an invoice, and the invoice is paid 30 days later.

Step 1: Order and receive $1,000 of steel from a supplier.

Step 2: Pay the supplier (typically 30 days later).

Step 3: Move the steel onto the shop floor, and start fabrication.

Step 4: Incur $1,000 of shop labor costs in making the product.

Step 5: Finish fabrication of an item with a cost of $2,000 of which the raw steel's cost is $1,000 and shop floor labor is $1,000, and move it to finished product inventory.

Step 6: Sell the material to a customer for $2,500. Note that four entries, not two, are necessary for this step.

Step 7: The customer pays (typically 30 days later).

2.1 b) What book value do you think the item would have sitting in finished product inventory, the cost incurred in making it ($2,000) or its likely sale price ($2,500)?

2.2 Based on your experience of the home you grew up in or the home you have made, which of the concepts of financial statements do you think arise in a personal setting, i.e., how much time is spent determining and discussing the concepts? Comment briefly on your answers.

Income statement: how much money (value) have I made in a given time period?

Statement of retained earnings: of the money made since I started, how much has been kept versus being paid out?

Balance sheet: how much do I have at a given point in time, and where did the money come from to acquire this?

Statement of cash flow: what did I do with my cash?

The Income Statement and Statement of Retained Earnings

Key Concepts

- Net income, also called profit or earnings, is a measure of the creation of value over a period of time. It is not a measure of cash.

- Net income is revenue minus expense. Expenses are broken into three categories: variable, fixed, and other. As a first approximation, variable costs are proportional to sales level, fixed costs are independent of sales level, and other income includes one-time and unusual items outside the normal ongoing business of the company.

- Contribution margin, the money left over from a sale after paying variable cost, is an important financial measure and can be used to give guidance on discounting.

- Some expenses do not relate to current cash expenditure. Depreciation is an example of a non-cash expense that reflects the wearing out of long-term assets.

- Depreciation rates are set by management judgment. Too high a rate of depreciation depresses reported net income until an asset is fully depreciated and then causes a sudden bump in net income. Too low a rate of depreciation means an asset is not fully expensed when it is taken out of service, causing an extraordinary writedown that then depresses net income.

- The calculation of taxable income is different than a company's net income reported in its financial statements. Governments specify depreciation rates to be used for purposes of calculating tax.
- Cash flow is net income plus non-cash expenses, so the cash a company generates is different than the value it creates. Companies make short-term decisions, such as whether to stay in business, based on cash, but make long-term decisions, such as investment in new assets, based on forecasted net income.
- Start-up companies strive to reach breakeven. Two breakeven points are critical: cash breakeven, when the company generates positive cash flow, and book breakeven, when the company creates value.
- Earnings before interest and taxes (EBIT) and earnings before interest, taxes, depreciation, and amortization (EBITDA) are important measures of the inherent ability of a business to generate value.
- Vertical and horizontal analysis of multi-year income statements gives powerful insight into a company.
- The statement of retained earnings tracks, on a cumulative basis, how much of a company's earnings are kept in the company. Earnings not kept in the company are distributed to owners of the company as dividends.

Chapter 3: The Income Statement and Statement of Retained Earnings

3.1   The Purpose of the Income Statement

The purpose of the income statement is to measure profitability of a business within a given time period. **Profit** (also known as **gain** or **net income**) is a measure of the creation of value within a business. A business that is unprofitable in the long term does not create commercial value and, hence, should not exist. As noted in Chapter 1, the test of profit must be restricted to commercial enterprises only, since there are many areas of life where value is not measurable by money.

Income statements are primarily focused on operating businesses. Imagine a very large power company that operates 20 power plants in different locations and is building two new plants. The company will track the revenue and expenses of the 20 power plants and the general company overhead very carefully and prepare an income statement to determine whether value is being created. It will also carefully track the project costs for the two new power plants under construction, but it will store the costs of building new power plants in an asset account until the new units actually start producing power. This leads to a somewhat different mindset for managers of projects versus managers of operating companies.

Project versus Operations Management

Projects such as the construction of a new power plant tend to have unique characteristics and can be thought of as one-time events that never reoccur in exactly the same way. While some of the technology of power generation is common between plants, every new power plant will have some unique features related to its location and to the constant evolution of technology. What is critical in any project is schedule and budget: getting the project done on time at the intended cost.

The press sometimes places more emphasis on projects that overrun cost targets than those that are late in starting up. For many large engineering projects, this is the wrong focus. Consider a 500 MW base load power plant producing power for a market with an average price of $60 per MWh. Daily cash revenue from such a power plant is $0.7 million per day, and the avoided costs when not running would likely be negligible since fuel contracts are often "take or pay," i.e., the fuel supplier contracts an annual amount of fuel and insists on payment whether the fuel is used or not. A three-month delay in starting up a 500 MW power plant is equivalent to a $65 million cost overrun.

While projects are concerned with schedule and budget, they are somewhat indifferent to the precise timing of expenditure. Whether a $30 million payment for a turbine occurs in December or January is not significant to a multi-year construction budget. It is a project's total cost, not its cost per year, that is important.

Operations management has a different focus, and timing of expenses and revenue is very important. A company with many operating power plants is very interested in knowing whether it is selling the power for more than the total expense of generating the power. To answer this, it carefully lines up revenue and expense in the same time period. Therefore, whether an expense or a sale occurs in December or January is very important if the company is reporting its annual statement with a year-end of December. The income statement for a company is not focused on total cost, as occurs with a project, but with total cost and revenue within a given time period.

A further concept is important in understanding the difference between project management and its accounting treatment versus operation management. Interest can be thought of as a cost of renting money, so it is an expense. However, the interest cost on a project that has not started up is not treated as an expense as it is incurred, but rather is accumulated and treated as part of the capital cost of a project. For very large projects that take many years to build, this accumulation of interest during construction, sometimes referred to as IDC, can be a large number. The value of both the project and its accumulated interest then becomes an expense over time through depreciation, a concept discussed later. Depreciation of an asset does not occur until the asset is available for use or able to produce.

3.2 The Time Scale of the Income Statement

For most businesses, the key time period for financial statements is monthly, with a quarterly and an annual roll-up. Publicly traded companies (those whose shares trade on a stock exchange) will usually publicly report quarterly income but not monthly income. Income over a time frame of less than a month is rare for a manufacturing business, but might be relevant for a retail business, especially near peak buying times such as Christmas. For the purposes of financing a new business or purchasing an existing business, one would typically go to a lender or investor with a pro forma month-by-month projection for the first one or two years and an annual forecast thereafter for up to five or 10 years in total. The important concept is that financial statements exist in order to inform stakeholders and management and to guide action. They should pick a time frame relevant to meaningful action.

What is an Appropriate Time Scale for the Income Statement?

Income information usually does not have significant meaning on a very small time scale. "How much did our business make in the last year (or month)?" is a very relevant question. How much it made in the last 15 seconds is irrelevant because the fluctuation of income and the inability to match income and expense become overwhelming. This may sound obvious, but sometimes, management may demand forecasts of income over too small a time scale, which can lead to severely dysfunctional behavior in a business.

One example of this was a large metal and fertilizer producer that was weathering a period of low metal prices with a poorer stock performance than competitors. Senior management was concerned and unclear on how to deal with the issue. The notion arose that the company lacked good middle management, and that the test of good management was the ability to predict weekly income. The most likely source of this belief was that senior management was dealing with their frustration by looking at results on a week-by-week basis and seeing variability that it did not understand. Metal sales for this company were by container load, and each container had a value of $2,000,000 to $25,000,000. All metal was presold before shipment, and either covered by long-term contract with companies that had excellent credit ratings or by an irrevocable letter of credit that said in essence, "Once custody passes from our hands to yours, your bank is irrevocably directed to pay us the full amount of the sale from funds set aside for this purpose." Hence, the true sales risk was negligible. However, the point of custody transfer was when a dockside crane at a port first lifted the container. The metal remained in the producer's custody during the rail shipment to the port and while on the dock. Although there was no risk to the ultimate sale, there was a great deal of risk that a container scheduled to be loaded on a Friday might not actually get lifted until Monday, causing a large sale to shift from one week to the next. Senior management's belief that a pro forma income statement was a crucial item on a week-by-week basis was mistaken. The impact was to shift middle management's attention from the important work of selling metal at a high price to the unimportant work of understanding crane schedules in a remote port. The crane evaluation was unimportant because the sale was not at risk; the only concern was in which week it would be booked, or recorded as a sale. By picking too short of a time period for an income statement, senior management had, in effect, diverted resources from useful to useless and defensive work.

For many large continuous process industries such as petroleum refineries, chemical plants, and power plants, even monthly income statements will show "bumps" associated with annual planned shutdowns. Most large processing plants will have a turnaround every year or every other year in which the entire process is shut down, vessels and equipment are inspected, and repairs, maintenance, and changes to debottleneck the plant are implemented. Turnarounds typically last 15 to 45 days, so monthly income is clearly impacted.

3.3   The Form of the Income Statement

There are many small variations in an income statement. A typical form is as follows:

Gross Revenue (from sale of products or services)

Minus	Allowance, e.g., for bad debt, warranty, returns, and adjustments
Gives	Net revenue
Minus	Cost of goods sold
Gives	Contribution margin (aka gross margin)
Minus	Sales, general, and administrative (aka operating) expense
Gives	Operating income
Plus	Other income
Gives	Net income (aka earnings, gain or profit, or loss if negative)

Note that allowances for items such as bad debt or returns as a reduction of gross revenue do not appear in all income statements, and many statements simply show one entry for revenue, reflecting total sales income. Both variants are used in this text.

3.3.1   Tax

Companies, like individuals, pay income tax on net income. Taxes are based on consolidated income, which means they are calculated on a company-wide basis since in the eyes of the law the company is equivalent to a person. Income statements are frequently prepared by product line through the contribution margin and by division within a company to the net income stage. This is understood to be net income before tax, and the calculation of tax is not performed until divisional data is rolled up into a company-wide income statement.

In this chapter, net income is treated as before-tax net income. Tax is discussed in Section 3.4.3.1 under depreciation and in more detail in Chapter 7.

3.4   Revenue and Expense in the Income Statement

As discussed in Chapter 2, it is important to recognize revenue and its related expense in the same time period. This is done by holding a major expense. For example, for materials for a sale that will not occur for many months into the future, they are held in an inventory account until the sale occurs, at which time the cost is transferred to an expense. Similarly, even though a customer will not pay for 30 to 60 days (the sale is booked when the title to the goods passes to the customer), a payable is recorded, and the revenue is recognized in the same period as the various expenses associated with the good or service that was sold. This approach prevents wild fluctuations in the numbers on an income statement.

3.4.1   Revenue and Net Revenue

Revenue is typically sales. In some businesses, gross revenue is immediately reduced by an allowance, which reflects an expectation that not all sales will end up creating real revenue. Note that many companies do not have any allowance; revenue equals sales. However, items that can be reflected in an allowance as an estimate of costs are bad debt, warranty work, and returns of shipping errors. **Bad debt** is either a payable that is not collectable or can only be collected at a steep discount, i.e., the business on average recovers only a fraction of the total value of the sale from "bad debt" customers. **Warranty** work is an obligation on the sellers' part to provide service during some initial period. **Returns** is the name given to adjustments for wrong shipments and returned goods that for some reason cannot be put back into inventory such as a company that ships clothing items to customers. Since the actual cost of bad debt, warranty, or returns will be at least slightly different from the historical forecast, the actual cost can be annually adjusted for accuracy. Consistency from year to year is important so that the true cost of bad debt, warranty, or returns can be seen, since a significant increase in any of these should trigger management investigation of the cause. The actual accounting for an allowance can be complex, but the concept is simple: it is an anticipated cost.

3.4.2   Cost of Goods Sold and Contribution Margin

When a business spends on an item that will last longer than a year, the item is called an **asset**. The term **depreciation** records the cost of this expenditure. All other expenditures for items that do not last longer than a year, such as salaries, rent, utilities, and materials, are called **expenses**. As discussed in Chapter 2, spending on materials is booked as an expense at the time the sale of an item is recorded so that costs and revenue are aligned.

It is highly useful to a business to note expense in two categories: **variable costs**, those that are mainly proportional to sales, and **fixed costs**, those that are mainly independent of the sales level.

Cost of goods sold (COGS), sometimes called **direct cost**, is the direct or incremental cost of making or purchasing an item. In some cases, COGS is the materials input only, while in other cases, it is the materials plus the direct manufacturing labor. What is important is consistency, since the relationship between sales revenue and COGS is extremely important in tracking and controlling a manufacturing business.

Some businesses have large COGS costs relative to final sale price. Consider a vessel manufacturer working in specialty alloy materials. The costs of the materials are a substantial part of the final cost of the item, so compared to the price, it will be a significant number. However, the value of nickel, cobalt, molybdenum, and chrome can vary widely, with significant shifts over short periods of time. Tracking contribution margin in such a case is a means of determining the effectiveness of either a manufacturing group (including purchasing) in holding costs down or of a sales group in keeping prices moving up in relation to increased costs. If margin falls, then prices are not keeping up with costs. Another example is a company that installs an expensive compressor and related equipment into a package that can be shipped into the field. Again, material costs are high relative to the input of the company.

Other businesses have very low COGS values. These are businesses that add a large amount of value to simple raw materials. Think of a pharmaceutical company that buys simple organic chemicals and uses sophisticated reactions and purification to produce complex drugs, backed by highly expensive research and drug trials.

It is important to note that a high-margin business is not better than a low-margin business. What is critical for any business is that value is created, which is what the income statement measures. Whether COGS is high or low is not critical; it is the bottom line that matters.

Note that in rigorous accounting, one would use cost of goods sold for manufacturing, cost of service for a service company such as an Engineering Procurement Construction Management (EPCM) firm, or cost of sales for a retail business. In this text, COGS is used for the cost of a good, service, or retail item.

As a first approximation, COGS varies in direct proportion to the level of sales. For example, if a vessel fabrication business sold two vessels, it would buy twice as much alloy material and welding rods and perhaps hire twice as much labor. In the real world, few costs are purely variable. Even if you are assembling components into a product, you can sometimes get a volume discount as your purchase level increases, and you will likely find some economies of scale in production labor. Hence, the contribution margin will have some variability with level of sales. Nevertheless, the assumption that COGS is a measure of the variable cost of an incremental sale is a good assumption for small changes in sales volume.

Contribution margin (also called margin and sometimes gross profit) measures what is left over from a sale to contribute to the fixed costs of a business. Contribution margin is usually calculated on a product-by-product basis within a business and can be a powerful guide of where to focus company efforts. Contribution margin is calculated in dollar terms on an income statement, but it is most often cited as a percentage within a company, with the percentage being contribution margin over revenue. You may hear the phrases "Our margin on unit X dropped by 1%" or "One of our key objectives for next year is to increase margin on product line Y by 3%." Companies carefully look at year-to-year changes in margin.

Sample Problem 3.4.1 Calculating Margin

A medical supply company has done extensive research to prove the validity of a medical diagnostic analyzer. It sells the analyzer for $37,500. All components for the analyzer are purchased and assembled by contract labor. Component cost is 19,200. Assembly and testing labor is 40 hours at a net cost (including salary and benefits) of $44 per hour. Expressed as a percentage, what is the contribution margin for the analyzer?

The company sold 128 analyzers in the last 12 months. It is considering reducing the selling price of the analyzer by 10% to make the unit more competitive against another company's product. If the price is discounted, what is the margin percentage? How many units would the company have to sell in the next 12 months to achieve the same dollar value of contribution margin? What percentage increase in unit sales does this represent?

Solution:

Calculate the direct cost (COGS) of the analyzer.

Parts	$19,200
Labor	$1,760 (40 hours × $44 per hour)
Total COGS	$20,960

Then:

Margin ($) is Selling price – COGS.

Margin (%) is Margin ($) ÷ Selling price

	At Original Price ($)	At Discounted Price ($)
Selling price	37,500	33,750
COGS	20,960	20,960
Margin	16,540	12,790
Margin (%)	44.1	37.9

In the last 12 months, the analyzer product generated

Contribution margin = 128 units × $16,540 CM per unit = $2.117 million

If the product price is reduced 10%, then the same margin will be generated by

Units = $2.117 million ÷ $12,790 CM per unit = 166 units (rounding up)

The required increase in unit sales is

$$\frac{166 \text{ units}}{128 \text{ units}} = 30\%$$

3.4.2.1 Using Concepts of Contribution Margin

There are two key reasons why people go to all the effort to determine margin and why they pay such attention to it.

First, margin is one good measure of the ability of a sales/marketing group to take price, i.e., to continue to extract value from the customer for the goods that are sold. This assumes that manufacturing, including purchasing, is being vigilant in both sourcing material at competitive cost and producing goods efficiently. If this is so, falling margin usually means either that customers are not willing to continue to pay the same value relative to cost or that a sales and marketing organization is going "soft" and has lost the will to extract price. A good manager will also consider whether purchasing and manufacturing is competitive. In rare cases, it may be a warning that quality is dropping if the loss of margin is associated with high returns or warranty claims, although one can also see this from the line item in the income statement associated with warranty and returns.

There is tremendous pressure in most companies to increase sales and hit budgeted sales targets, but this can lead to a "sales at any price" mindset in a sales force in which discounting of price is seen as the primary mechanism to induce additional sales. Companies will sometimes counter this by tying commission for sales staff not to total sales but to total contribution margin. For example, a salesperson who makes many sales at a low price and a salesperson who makes fewer sales at a higher price would get the same reward. The fortunes of the company are tied to total margin contribution, not to total sales.

If margin is dropping, management should ask the following probing questions to try to understand why:

- Is margin dropping because of an increase in costs, i.e., is the cost of goods sold going up? If so, why is this the case? Is there a legitimate increase in the cost structure of suppliers? For example, if the price of oil doubles, some costs can be expected to go up; goods that are delivered over long distances, for instance, will have higher shipping charges. If the price of a raw material such as nickel goes up, then the cost of stainless steel components will go up. However, suppliers want more net income, and sometimes, the cost of raw materials goes up simply because the supplier is trying to extract more price. Management should know this and decide how much to resist the price increase with the current supplier or look for alternate suppliers.

- If margin is dropping because costs are rising, can the increased cost be passed on to the customer through a price increase? The normal test of cost recovery is not a fixed dollar value of contribution margin but a fixed percentage, meaning the contribution margin created in a company is expected to stay proportional to the costs. If an increased cost cannot be passed on to the customer, management should probe why this is the case. Does a competitor have a lower cost structure or a different supplier? Or, as sometimes occurs, is a sales force simply reluctant to push through the increase?

- If margin is dropping and costs are not rising, is the problem that a competitor is pushing down the price? If this is the case, then does the competitor have some advantage (better manufacturing equipment, lower raw material cost, cheaper labor rate), or is it just that the competitor wants more market share and is willing to earn less value (margin) to get that share? The long-term pattern in a product's life cycle is that margins start high when a product or service is novel and erode over time as more and more companies try to supply the product or service based on lower cost. However, management should be aware of such trends because they affect the long-term health of a product line and the company itself.

The second reason margin is so important is that it is used in pricing marginal sales. Imagine that you are selling a product in North America, say a gearbox, and your factory is running at 80% capacity. Your product has a contribution margin of 24%, or a COGS of 76% (assuming warranty and bad debt is very low). You would like to have a wider customer base and want to try to break into Europe. What introductory price can you use to try to build up a customer base? Any discount less than the margin percentage still means that the incremental sale is contributing to the company, so if you discount your gearbox 20% to try to get a new incremental customer in Europe, your company will still be further ahead (cash positive) because the cost of the incremental sale is 76% of the normal sale price, and the incremental revenue from the discounted sale is 80% of the normal sale price. The 4% difference is incremental cash that goes to cover the fixed costs of the company.

This exercise may seem trivial for one product, but imagine a company that has hundreds of products, each with a different margin and a mandate to expand into a new market. The vice president of marketing might, for example, authorize his sales staff to discount up to half of the contribution margin on sales in the new territory, which would mean he would not have to review each individual pricing decision. The theory is that once the new customers try and like the new products, they will continue to buy the products at the normal price, returning the company's margin to historical levels. Initial discounts are often labeled as temporary to underline this concept to the new customer.

Pricing based on margin is a widespread practice when a company is trying to build new sales. However, it has some dangers that indicate one should take this approach with caution:

- Is there any extra cost associated with the marginal sale? For example, if a cost that is normally a part of SG&A increases due to a new sale, then pricing solely based on margin and COGS is not a true measure of the impact of the sale. Using the gearbox example, if two new shipping clerks need to be added to arrange special packaging for a sale to Europe, then a deeply discounted sale may not be cash positive to the company. Losing cash on a sale is rarely justified and should require some higher level of authorization within a company.

- Is the sale truly marginal? Often, people think that an overseas sale has no implications on their sales volume in a home market, but this is not always the case. For example, imagine you sell many gearboxes to Europe. If they come back to North America in a finished product (say a hydraulic pump assembly) and this reduces your sales to North American customers that pay full price for the gearbox, then you do not have an incremental sale, but rather a lower margin sale displacing a higher margin one. At one time in the petrochemical industry, deep discounting of Pacific Rim sales ended up damaging North American customers as cheap resin came back into the North American market both on resale and as manufactured product.

- Will high-paying customers learn that the company is discounting to a less valued customer? Nothing frightens a marketing manager more than the thought that the discount given to get a new customer will become known to "long and faithful" customers, who will be indignant that they do not get "most favored" status. Treating discounts that are not related to volume of purchase as temporary and sticking to this is one way to minimize this risk.

- Is the sale a dump? At one time, it was a common practice for a company to have high margins from customers in its own country (with the market often protected by a tariff) and to sell at slightly above marginal cost in foreign markets. This practice became known as dumping, and both national legislation and international trade treaties (e.g., the WTO) have arisen to prohibit this practice. Discounts to build market share that become permanent (because the market being discounted is seen as distant) constitute dumping. The cost of defending a dumping action is prohibitive, and penalties are severe in that retroactive damages can be extracted.

Despite these cautions, analyzing pricing against margin and giving flexibility to discount based on margin, especially for new sales, are widespread practices.

Margin plays a key role in rigidly setting prices in certain businesses. For instance, many warehouse distribution centers carry a varying line of products and will simply mark up the product, selling it at a fixed multiple of the cost. Thus, if a distributor carries hundreds of products at a margin of 20% and is asked to carry a new product, he will price the product at cost times 1.25 (equivalent to cost divided by 1 minus margin). This kind of approach allows rapid pricing in response to customer enquiries, without senior management intervention. Similarly, skid-packaging businesses that make production equipment, such as compressors mounted on a transportable base, often work to a fixed margin based on the component cost of a skid; they do this because the labor to assemble the skid cannot be exactly estimated but usually runs a fixed percentage of the component cost. Thus, a company making compressor packages might have a rule of thumb that skids will sell for a fixed markup over the cost of components, and an engineer can price a new skid by pricing the components and applying the markup. This again helps in rapid response to bids and budgetary enquiries. One final example of margin-based pricing is retail: many retail stores, such as department or jewelry stores, that carry a wide diversity of products simply mark up their cost to a retail price, much as a distributor does.

Sample Problem 3.4.2 Using Contribution Margin to Make Decisions about Discounting

Potentialco and Leaderco are operating in an oil equipment manufacturing industry. They are both based in Canada, and all their sales until now have been within Canada. Each has an opportunity to expand their market by selling 10% of their capacity at a 20% discount to Asia-based customers. Potentialco is operating at 80% capacity, and Leaderco is at 100% capacity utilization. Assume that the SG&A costs and other income stay the same. Also, there is no room for exceeding capacity (which means that Leaderco would have to cut back on existing customers to build overseas sales). Given these assumptions, evaluate the impact of expanding the market to Asia, and comment on whether this is an appropriate strategy.

	Potentialco ($000)	Leaderco ($000)
Revenue	460,000	650,000
COGS	322,000	455,000
Contribution margin	138,000	195,000
SG&A	50,125	73,520
Operating income	87,875	121,480
Other income	−1,000	−1,150
Net income	86,875	120,330

Solution:

Leaderco is operating at full capacity, and it would see lower sales and lower profitability by taking on the overseas sales at a discount, since the sales in Asia would be taken by sacrificing domestic sales at a higher price and margin. Sales revenue drops by 20% times 10%, making the contribution margin and net income go down. The only circumstance in which it would make sense for Leaderco to sell into Asia is if it were convinced that a severe downturn was coming in Canada but not in Asia, and that having a market in Asia would help in the future. This is unlikely in the oil service equipment business, so selling into Asia is a questionable strategy for Leaderco.

For Potentialco, now operating at 80% capacity, additional sales of 10% capacity would take the company to 90% utilization of capacity. At regular price, moving from 80% to 90% capacity would

give sales of $517,500 ($460,000 × $\left(\frac{0.9}{0.8}\right)$. However, the extra sales are at a discount, and total

sales are $460,000 from domestic customers and 80% of ($517,500 − $460,000). The extra sales do not earn the same contribution margin as domestic sales, but overall contribution margin and net income increase. Potentialco can diversify its market and increase its income at the same time because it has unused production capacity.

	Potentialco ($000)		Leaderco ($000)	
	Existing	With Asia	Existing	With Asia
Revenue	460,000	506,000	650,000	637,000
Revenue growth (%)		10		−2
COGS	322,000	362,250	455,000	455,000
Contribution margin	138,000	143,750	195,000	182,000
Contribution margin (%)	30	28.4	30	28.6
SG&A	50,125	50,125	73,520	73,520
Operating income	87,875	93,625	121,480	108,480
Other income	−1,000	−1,000	−1,150	−1,150
Net income	86,875	92,625	120,330	107,330
Net income growth (%)		6.6		−10.8

New sales initiatives that involve discounting require an analysis of the impact on the income statement. Two other factors need to be considered. First, selling in an international market at a lower margin than one sells in the domestic market is called dumping and can lead to a claim for damages under World Trade Organization agreements. Steep discounts should be short term. The second consideration is the possible reaction of the domestic customers if they learn of steep discounting to offshore customers. They could demand the same pricing and become angry rather than satisfied customers. Discounting to increase sales is a complex question with many facets to be considered.

3.4.2.2 Margin in Public Annual Reports

Margin is an extremely sensitive business fact, and many companies do not like to reveal their true marginal (variable) costs. The simple reason for this is that a competitor will then know a pricing level that will cause the company to lose cash on every sale. The power of this is enormous. Historically, the Hudson's Bay Company and Standard Oil, among others, exploited monopolies in some areas, extracting high price and margin, and dumped their products in areas where they had competition at less than the marginal cost of production of their competitors. The competitors ended up losing cash on every sale and soon were sold or bankrupt. In some businesses where raw material price swings create a wide variation in COGS (for example, the manufacture of petrochemicals from ethane, propane, naphtha, and gas oil feedstocks), exact knowledge of marginal cost would enable predatory pricing.

In publicly released documents, such as the annual financial statements of publicly traded companies, variable and fixed costs are blended, and what is called COGS is often a blend of some variable and fixed costs. In these documents, margin (sometimes called operating margin or contribution margin) is calculated based on total costs including COGS. In addition, information by product line is very rarely given and only at an aggregate level.

One major use of income statements is to assess changes in a business by product or product line through analysis of margin. Anyone who is buying a business with more than one product or service should insist on income statements that break down aggregated company data into COGS by product lines, and anyone selling a business with a good operating history will find it to their benefit to provide such information, since it powerfully conveys the strength and good future earning potential of the company.

3.4.3   Indirect Expense: Sales, General, and Administrative (SG&A) Cost

The next element of the income statement is **indirect expenses**. As with other elements of the income statement, this can go by different names: indirect cost, overhead, fixed cost, general cost, general and administrative (G&A) cost, or sales, general, and administrative (SG&A) cost. In this text, SG&A will be used to mean all indirect expenses other than those in other income. What is classified as COGS versus SG&A involves judgment; the important concept is consistency from year to year and product line to product line, since inconsistency for either of these factors can lead to wrong actions.

The items in SG&A are the costs that are not directly related to the making of a product or the delivery of a service. For example, a company will have a president (or general manager or managing director) regardless of the level of product manufacturing and sales that are achieved. This is an expense of being in business. An example of SG&A is telecom services; today, phone, fax, or email is table stakes, which means you cannot even start to be in business unless you have these items. Another example is business and property taxes and the fees to report to a provincial or federal regulator of companies, which a company must pay regardless of its profitability or its level of sales. Accounting costs are in SG&A because a business must keep books regardless of its sales level. Rental costs are also an example, since the landlord fixes the rent independent of the renter's level of sales. These are the kinds of expenses that go into SG&A.

The cost of borrowing money, or interest, is an indirect expense: lenders insist on being paid regardless of how a company is performing, which is discussed further in Chapter 4. Interest (other than interest costs associated with a project under construction) appears in the income statement and can be thought of as the cost of renting "other people's money." It is the annual expense of borrowing principal, the amount of the loan. The one exception is interest costs related to a project under construction, which are not expensed in the current year but rather accumulated in an account called "Interest during construction" and added to the capital cost of the project.

It is important to note that principal repayments do not appear on the income statement, only on the balance sheet and statement of cash flow. There are two conventions for where interest on long-term debt other than interest during construction appears on the income statement. Some companies put interest charges on long-term debt in SG&A expense, while others put it as a negative entry in other income, which is discussed below. Interest charges are discussed further in Appendix 3.2.

The cost of selling most often goes into SG&A, especially if a single marketing and sales group sells more than one product line. However, in some companies, sales costs can be partitioned by product line because sales people are dedicated to a single line of the company's business. In these cases, particularly if sales costs are partially or highly variable (in that more sales cause higher selling costs on a near linear basis as would occur for sales compensation based solely on commission), the cost of selling might be included in COGS.

As a first approximation, SG&A costs would be **fixed**, i.e., invariable with changes in sales level. This is simply not true for major changes in revenue that have corresponding changes in the level of manufacturing (or service delivery) and sales. Companies that have very large sales growth almost always find that they need more staff to process functions such as purchasing and billing and often need more fixed assets (and hence incur more depreciation). If a company goes through a halving of its sales (as routinely occurs to some companies during an economic downturn), then management will see if sales and administrative staff and expenses can be **downsized** without damaging the future recovery of the company. This requires an analysis that is specific to a company: it is poor judgment to lay off staff that have a wealth of experience in the company and play a key role, while it is good judgment to prune staff and any other expenses that are not critical and can be replaced when sales increase.

Nevertheless, for small changes in revenue, it is useful to think of SG&A as fully fixed, just as it is useful to think of COGS as fully variable. Typically, if you can achieve a small but significant increase in sales, such as 5 to 15%, you might expect to support this change in sales level without an increase in SG&A. This is especially true if the number of customers does not increase, but the sales per customer increase, since there is then no increase in invoicing and accounting entries, simply bigger numbers per transaction.

Sample Problem 3.4.3 Assigning Costs to COGS versus SG&A

You recently started working as an accountant for a heavy vessel manufacturing company. The previous accountant did not separate expenses per job or by type, so the income statement had total expenses. The owner looked at the results and asked for cost tracking per job, where appropriate, to help analyze individual jobs in detail. You have been provided with the following list of expenses and asked to classify each expense as COGS or SG&A so that COGS can be tracked per job:

1. Steel used at the shop floor
2. Valves
3. Flanges
4. The purchase of specialist contract welding services
5. Corporate lawyer
6. Rags used in manufacturing area for cleanup
7. Receptionist salary
8. Cutting tool bits
9. Expenses paid for delivery of the vessel to the customer
10. Salary of the quality control manager
11. R&D expenditure (with the assumption that it is not capitalized)
12. Insulation material used
13. Fuel costs

Solution:

1	Steel used at the shop floor	COGS	Direct manufacturing cost
2	Valves	COGS	Direct manufacturing cost
3	Flanges	COGS	Direct manufacturing cost
4	The purchase of specialist contract welding services	COGS	Direct manufacturing cost
5	Corporate lawyer	SG&A	Indirect administrative cost
6	Rags used in manufacturing area for cleanup	SG&A	It is taken as part of SG&A even though it is a direct cost because it is a very small portion of the manufacturing cost and it is very difficult to keep track of its cost per job.
7	Receptionist salary	SG&A	Indirect administrative cost
8	Cutting tool bits	SG&A	It is taken as part of SG&A even though it is a direct cost because it is a very small portion of the manufacturing cost and it is very difficult to keep track of its cost per job.

9	Expenses paid for delivery of the vessel to the customer	COGS	Direct manufacturing cost
10	Salary of the quality control manager	SG&A	Indirect sales expense
11	R&D expenditure (with the assumption that it is not capitalized)	SG&A	Expensed as a general expense
12	Insulation material used	COGS	Direct manufacturing cost
13	Fuel costs	SG&A	Indirect general expense

3.4.3.1 Depreciation

Depreciation, also referred to as amortization, is an indirect expense that is included in SG&A that requires special attention because it is key to understanding the difference between cash (or funds) flow and income as reported on the income statement. It is also crucial to understanding the difference between income as reported in a financial statement and income reported for purposes of tax.

If a person puts $1 million in an interest-bearing bank account, at the end of a time period, she will get the original investment back plus the interest. If she were to put the $1 million into a business, she would want a return on her investment (which comes from profits), but she would also want to be sure that the value of the initial capital investment is recognized as well. Depreciation is best thought of as an accounting charge that insures that the value of assets that wear out is recovered by the business.

As will be discussed further when the balance sheet is reviewed, people put money into a business in order to acquire assets with which to run a business. Some assets are part of working capital, and by their nature, they do not wear out. Some assets are fixed, such as land, buildings, machinery, furniture, and computers. All of these assets, except land, will eventually wear out or become obsolete. If a business operates for 30 years, the computers it first purchased would have been obsolete many times over (at least six times based on the historical evolution of computer and systems technology), and the furniture would have been replaced at least once and perhaps as many as three times. The machinery might have been replaced once, the buildings might just be coming to the end of their useful life, and the land would still have the same functionality that it had 30 years earlier.

Depreciation is an expense charged against (subtracted from) revenue that recovers the cost of the original assets (including interest accumulated during construction) that are wearing out. It is usually treated by class. Thus, buildings would be lumped into one class and might be depreciated over 20 or 30 years. Computers would be in another class and might be depreciated over as little as 2 years.

The time period for depreciation depends on three factors: the durability of the item itself, the rate of change in the design of the item (will technology evolution make something obsolete before it is worn out?), and the nature of the business for which the item is being used. Thus, a computer and a pump can each operate for 20 years in near continuous service with proper maintenance, so they have the same durability. However, the evolution of office systems in the last 20 years has ensured that computers are obsolete long before they wear out. Personal computers have been discarded not because they are broken, but rather because they will not run the kinds of systems that people think they need to be efficient. Similarly, a pump in a petrochemical plant will likely last just as long as a pump in a petroleum refinery. However, people are more confident that there will be a market 20 years from now for refined petroleum products that the refinery can economically supply than they are that there will be a market for a specialty petrochemical. For this reason, one might depreciate the same pump faster if it is located in a petrochemical plant than in an oil refinery.

Depreciation is a way of expensing the cost of an asset over its estimated useful life. Long-term assets are items that a company buys that are expected to create value for a period of over one year. Instead of charging the cost of this item in one year (which would distort an income statement), the value of the asset is booked or recorded on the balance sheet and then the value is drawn down over the course of its useful life. In this sense, all assets that wear out show up initially at full value on the balance sheet (Chapter 4) but are depreciated and flow through the income statement as depreciation. By the time an asset is taken out of service, its entire cost will have been expensed through depreciation or an extraordinary write-down on disposal. If an asset is sold for more than its book value, the gain is put in income as an extraordinary item, i.e., in other income.

3.4.3.2 *Depreciation as a Non-Cash Expense and Other Non-Cash Expenses*

When a company buys raw material, pays an employee, or buys telecom services or stationery, cash flows out of the business. If not right away, then it is normally within 30 to 60 days when the invoice is paid or the employee's check clears the bank. These are cash expenses and must be covered by cash that the business receives from revenue.

Depreciation is different in that there is no cash impact on the company in the time period that depreciation is assigned to the income statement. In effect, depreciation is a paper reduction of operating income that is designed to reflect past cash expenditures for assets that are wearing out and for which the value cannot be recovered if the business is broken up and its assets sold. To state this another way, a portion of the money that a business generates is designated as equating to the value of fixed assets that are wearing out and, hence, is not value creation as measured by net income. In a non-inflationary world that has no or very slow evolution of technology, one could also think that depreciation represented cash that was being saved to replace assets in kind in the future as they wear out, allowing the business to go on forever. However, there is no requirement to segregate depreciation into a separate account to buy assets in the future, and companies do not typically do this. Some assets, like pipelines, will never need to be replaced. As will be discussed later when balance sheets are discussed, if depreciation were not charged against income and deducted from the value of assets, then a company's financial statements would overstate both the value of the assets and the amount of operating income (value creation) the company generated.

Since depreciation is a charge that reflects past or future expenditures, but not current expenditures, no cash flows out of a business to cover this expense. The important concept that needs to be understood is that operating or net income measures the profitability (value creation) of a business after including a recovery of past expenditures for assets that are wearing out; it does not measure cash (funds) flow. Operating or net income measures the creation of value, not the creation of cash. From a cash perspective, some of the revenue that comes into a company is attributed to depreciation rather than being named operating and net income, but that cash still belongs to the company. If the cash that is attributed to depreciation were instead attributed to operating and net income, the income statement would overstate the true value created by the business. The company would be fooling itself into thinking it was creating value when in fact it would be using up an asset that it had purchased in the past without the potential to replace it.

It is also important to recognize that cumulated depreciation is not a reserved pool of cash within a company. Management can use the cash that depreciation represents in many ways:

- It can be used to pay down short-term or long-term debt.
- It can be used to buy new assets.
- It can go toward a dividend to shareholders.
- It can be left in the bank as cash.

Cumulative depreciation has been recognized by not calling this cash income, but this cash has not been reserved. Management would strongly resist creating a pool of cash because it restricts flexibility and requires that cash sit idle in a bank account until used at some time in the future for a single purpose (replacement of a given asset). Most management teams can find better uses for cash than having it sit in an account. A second consideration is that the asset that is wearing out may not replaced in kind, either because technology changes, or in the case of a pipeline or mine, because the natural resource is depleted.

Depreciation rates are driven by management's judgment of the useful life of assets. One management team might think that its computers will be useful for four years, whereas another team thinks that they will be obsolete in two years. One management team might think that a given petrochemical plant will be too inefficient to continue to operate in five years, while another might pick 10 years. These decisions affect the value of assets as stated in a company's books and the value of net income that is reported. Because depreciation practices are affected by management's judgment, they are normally discussed in a footnote to financial statements, i.e., the assumed asset life can usually be found by class in the footnotes.

In this text, depreciation is used as the prime example of a non-cash charge against income, i.e., a non-cash expense. However, it is important to recognize that there can be other entries on income statements that are non-cash, such as charges for future reclamation or an entry called future taxes payable; these are discussed in the inset.

The income of a business represents value creation, measured in cash. However, a business also retains the cash that is represented by non-cash charges against income. Distinguishing cash flow from net or operating income is crucial to proper financial analysis, and it is discussed in detail later in the text.

Non-Cash Charges against Income

Depreciation is not a current cash expense; it is recognition of a prior expenditure for an asset. This is why it is called a non-cash charge against income. Depreciation says that some of the cash coming into a business is not reflecting the creation of value but rather reflects the recovery of past spending on long-term assets. The business has the cash; it just is not given the label "income," which measures value, not cash.

Note that a company is not required to save this cash to buy replacement assets. Management can use the cash represented by depreciation to buy assets, but can also use it to repay debt or pay a dividend to shareholders. Some businesses always need to replace assets. For example, think of a trucking firm with 100 trucks that on average last 10 years. For this case, depreciation would closely align with reinvestment, since the company would depreciate 10% of its assets every year and on average buy 10 new trucks a year. Compare this to a company that operates a pipeline from a gas field to a larger pipeline. The pipeline will usually last as long as the gas resource, and the company will never have to replace its initial asset. Depreciation is cash that is available to management but that does not represent the creation of value. How management uses that cash will vary from company to company. The statement of cash flow, discussed in Chapter 5, will tell you where management gets cash from and how it uses it.

There can be other non-cash charges against income. One example is an entry called future taxes payable. Depreciation for tax purposes, as mandated by government, is often at a faster rate than book depreciation in the early years of an asset. The higher initial depreciation for tax purposes lowers taxable income (since depreciation is an expense), which lowers taxes paid in the early years after an investment. Governments do this in an effort to stimulate further investment by businesses. However, accounting will calculate the taxes that would have been paid if the book depreciation had been used and track the difference in an account called future income taxes. In effect, the statement of value created is reduced in the early years of assets by saying that some of the cash a business has will be paid to government in future years. If a business had a single asset, it would typically have future taxes payable grow in the early years of the asset and then shrink in later years as book depreciation catches up with tax depreciation. In effect, a company is again reducing its claimed value creation during the time when taxes are low and increasing its claimed value creation later when taxes are high. Income tax is discussed in more detail in Appendix 3.1 and in Chapter 7.

Another example of a non-cash charge against income is an allowance for future reclamation. Consider a surface mining operation that knows it will have to ultimately reclaim the open pit, i.e., restore it and revegetate it. Rather than report overstated earnings and then have a large negative income at the end of the mine, the company would reduce its stated earnings by an annual amount that will, over the estimated life of the plant, equal an amount it estimates is required for reclamation. It is very important to note, however, that such a charge, like depreciation, is a non-cash charge. The company is not required to actually set aside the cash; it is just reducing its statement of value created (earnings). The cash represented by this is in the hands of the company and can be used by management for any purpose, such as buying new equipment, paying down debt, paying a dividend, or saving for future expenses. A reserve allowance is not the same as a reserve fund.

There have been cases of companies that have gone bankrupt in their last year of production, making them unable to reclaim their operation. In this case, the government will typically have to cover these costs. If a government wanted to be certain of reclamation, it would have to require a reserve fund, i.e., actual cash transfers from the operating company every year into a trust fund that can only be used for reclamation. This would ensure that funds were in place at the end of the operation. The statement of cash flow, discussed in Chapter 5, identifies all non-cash charges against income.

3.4.3.3 Calculating Depreciation: Straight Line and Other Methods

In theory, what causes an asset such as a machine to wear out is its use in manufacturing, and thus, depreciation should be variable, or directly tied to the number of units made and sold. This would be called "units of production" depreciation. In practice, this is extremely rare since depreciation is almost always calculated per unit of time, not per unit of production.

The simplest and by far the most commonly used means of calculating an annual or monthly depreciation charge is called **straight-line depreciation**. It is defined as follows:

$$\text{Depreciation} = \frac{\text{original cost minus expected salvage value}}{\text{useful life}}$$

For example, imagine that all the rolling equipment in a steel plant costs $17 million and is to be depreciated over a 10-year period. At the end of the 10 years, the equipment has no salvage value, meaning that its scrap value would equal the cost someone would charge to haul it away to a scrap yard. Then, monthly depreciation would be calculated as follows:

$$\text{Depreciation (monthly)} = \frac{\$17,000,000 - 0}{120 \text{ months}} = \$141,666.67/\text{month}$$

There are other methods of calculating depreciation. One example is government-mandated depreciation for the purpose of calculating tax, which uses an accelerated depreciation schedule that has high depreciation in the early years and steadily declining values over time. Canada uses the declining balance method; the United States uses the Modified Accelerated Cost Recovery System (MACRS) that drops rapidly. Both are very different from straight line. Concepts of tax are discussed in Appendix 3.1, and the declining balance method is discussed in detail in Chapter 7. All companies keep two sets of asset values: one that tells owners and lenders management's opinion of the remaining value of asset and a second set used solely for calculating taxes.

However, sometimes special depreciation calculations are used for certain types of assets for which straight-line depreciation does not accurately represent the loss in value. Consider a new car, which loses up to 30% of its resale value in its first day of operation as it goes from new to used. In the first few years of operation, a car loses a lot of its value, but the decrease in value in subsequent years is far slower. The same is true for movie DVDs. The sale value of a hit movie declines rapidly but does not go to zero for several years. One way of dealing with this kind of asset is to use **sum of the periods depreciation**, which is described in Appendix 3.1. Sum of the years depreciation would make sense for a car, and sum of the months depreciation is actually used by a major video rental company to calculate the value of its movie stock. Other methods not discussed in this text include units of production and units of time. By far, the most common method of depreciation of fixed assets is straight line.

Some loans are secured by assets, meaning that if the loan payments are not made, then the lender can seize the asset and sell it to get back the value of the loan. As will be discussed in detail in Chapter 4, lenders are very focused on preserving their capital, so they think carefully about the inherent remaining value in assets that are securing debt. A car depreciates quickly in its early years, while a house typically will hold its value for a very long time before declining rapidly in value. Lenders will apply their own thinking to the remaining value of assets regardless of what method of depreciation a company uses.

What if an asset lasts longer than its depreciation period? Then the book value of the asset is zero or equal to the estimated salvage value, since the accumulated depreciation equals the estimated loss in value of the asset. The asset is written off, i.e., all its value has been charged to income statements over time, and for the rest of its operating life, the annual depreciation is zero.

Sample Problem 3.4.4 Calculating Depreciation

A company buys machinery for $17 million and depreciates it on a straight-line basis. The expected life for the machinery is 16 years with salvage value of $500,000 at the end of year 16. Calculate the annual depreciation. Will the depreciation expense come under COGS, SG&A, or indirect expenses on the income statement? Is depreciation a cash or non-cash expense? If this machinery is the only depreciable asset owned by the company, how much higher is cash flow from operations than operating income?

You own a business and decide to buy some equipment for automating the manufacturing process. You purchase it at a price of $5 million. You expect it to last 10 years and have no value at the end of that period. After four years, you realize that there is new technology on the market that can reduce your manufacturing cost drastically; the new equipment costs $7 million, and you expect it to last 10 years and have no value at the end of that period. To stay competitive, you decide to sell the old equipment and buy the new one. The old equipment is sold for $1.4 million at the end of year 4. Calculate the amount of depreciation from this equipment for years 1 to 4 and for year 5 and thereafter. Calculate the amount of gain/loss at the end of year 4, and explain where it would appear on the income statement. If, in year 5, contribution margin and SG&A excluding depreciation are the same as in year 4, what is the change in operating income and cash flow from operations in year 5 versus year 4?

Solution:

Part I

$$\text{Depreciation} = \frac{\text{original cost} - \text{salvage value}}{\text{useful life}}$$
$$= \frac{17 - 0.50}{16}$$
$$= \$1.03125 \text{ million}$$

Depreciation is almost always treated as a general expense appearing in SG&A; exceptions are vanishingly rare. Depreciation is the loss in the value of the asset every year that is charged against revenue for the recovery of the original cost. Since there is no cash outflow every year for the loss in the value of the asset, depreciation is treated as a non-cash expense. Cash flow from operations adds back depreciation amount to the operating income. For this company, cash flow from operations is higher than net income by $1.03125 million.

Part II

$$\text{Depreciation} = \frac{\text{original cost} - \text{salvage value}}{\text{useful life}}$$
$$= \frac{\$(5 - 0) \text{ million}}{10}$$
$$= \$0.5 \text{ million}$$

Using the same approach, depreciation for the new equipment starting in year 5 is $0.7 million.

At the end of year 4:

Remaining value of equipment	= original value − accumulated depreciation
	= $5 million − $(4 × 0.5) million
	= $3 million
Sale price	= $1.4 million
Gain/loss on sale of equipment	= sale price − depreciated value of the asset
	= $(1.4 − 3) million
	= −1.6 million

Since loss on sale of equipment is only a one-time charge and not a regular expense, it would be charged to other income in the income statement.

If contribution margin and SG&A excluding depreciation is the same in year 5 as in year 4, then operating income would decrease by $0.2 million because depreciation increased from $0.5 to $0.7 million. However, cash flow from operations would be unchanged, since depreciation is a non-cash charge against income. The company has the cash represented by depreciation; it just does not call this cash income, since income means value creation, not cash generation.

3.4.3.4 Early Retirement of Depreciating Assets

Accountants and financial managers are by nature conservative, in part, because auditors, who assess the financial statements of large publicly traded companies, are conservative. The purpose of auditing for publicly traded companies is to give the public a sense of comfort that the accounting procedures followed are prudent and that the reported net income and asset values for the company are "conservative but reasonable." Hence, it is not unusual that the true asset life exceeds the depreciation period.

However, a gross understatement of the depreciation period hurts a business. It appears to depress a company's earning power in the early life of an asset (because depreciation, which is an expense that reduces income, is very high compared to the true rate at which the equipment is wearing out). Earnings are then higher than appropriate later in the life of the equipment (because the equipment has been fully depreciated long before the equipment has reached the end of its useful life). Variability in operating income does not make a business easy to sell, so the best test of a depreciation period is conservative but reasonable.

If an asset is sold for more than its remaining value (its original value minus the accumulated depreciation), then the company realizes a gain on the sale of assets, and the amount in excess of the remaining book value is taken into other income. As is discussed below, other income is not treated as operating income because the ordinary business of the company is to sell its products and services, not its equipment.

Sometimes, an asset is retired for a salvage value that is less than its remaining value (its original value minus the accumulated depreciation). In this case, a charge is made against income (a negative entry in other income) to bring the cumulative depreciation expense to the difference between the original purchase value and the salvage value. Thus, if an asset cost $17,000,000, had an accumulated depreciation of $12,000,000, and was retired and sold for $2,000,000, a terminal expense of $3,000,000 must be recognized as a negative entry in other income. Gain or loss on disposition of assets is discussed further in Section 3.6.2.

It is important to note that at the end of an asset's life, its net cost (original cost minus salvage value) is recovered as an expense and deducted from the revenue of the company's net income. In that way, a person looking at income statements over a period of years knows that the reported income is the value that the business generated after it had recovered the cost of all assets that have a limited life. Net income, also called profit or gain, is a measure of value creation, not cash retention.

3.4.3.5 Illustrating the Impact of Depreciation Period

Choosing a depreciation period for a company's financial statements is a matter of management judgment. There is no correct formula and no rigid rule. There is a rigid rule for calculating depreciation for tax purposes, as noted below, and it is worth noting that all companies in essence have two sets of statements: one for stakeholders and management based on management judgment of depreciation and one for tax calculations based on mandated depreciation of assets. The purpose of management's estimate of book depreciation is to conservatively estimate the useful life of assets; the purpose of tax depreciation is to achieve a goal of government, which is often to stimulate further investment. Hence, assets are frequently depreciated for tax purposes far faster than for book purposes.

To explore the impact of management judgment on depreciation, consider this example. Three different companies have the same single asset worth $5 million and with no estimated net salvage value. Each management does not know how long the asset will last, and the three firms pick 5, 10, and 20 years as the depreciation period. Hence, for the three firms, the annual depreciation is $1 million, $500,000, and $250,000, respectively. Each of the firms has income (revenue minus expenses) before depreciation of $1 million per year. In actual experience, the asset turns out to last 10 years, after which it is scrapped. What is the impact on reported income of the three different assumptions on the depreciation period?

As illustrated in Figure 3.1, picking a five-year depreciation period gives an unsteady income over 10 years. For five years, the income is zero, since income before depreciation is $1 million and depreciation is $1 million ($5 million asset value divided by five years). However, in year 6, the asset is fully depreciated, depreciation falls to zero, and the firm's income jumps to $1 million per year. The company that picks a 10-year depreciation period has a steady income over the 10-year period of $500,000 per year. The company that picks a 20-year depreciation period has an income of $750,000 per year, but at the end of the tenth year, the asset has a remaining book value. The undepreciated amount of $2.5 million must be written off, or charged as a negative amount in other income.

Figure 3.1: Net Income for Three Different Depreciation Periods

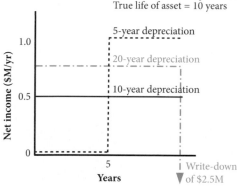

Figure 3.1 illustrates two very important points. First, the income reported per year is affected by the selection of the depreciation period for the asset. In year 1, net income ranges from zero to $750,000 per year, even though the three businesses are identical. Note, for example, that changing the depreciation from 10 to 20 years increases annual earnings by 50%. Second, total earnings over the 10-year period for the three businesses are identical: a total of $5 million in earnings (value creation) for all three businesses. Picking a different depreciation period changes when income is reported, but it does not create income. The 20-year depreciation period appears to increase income, but the increase, $250,000 per year for 10 years compared to the 10-year depreciation period, is exactly offset by the write-down on disposal of the asset of $2.5 million.

Picking the short depreciation period (5 years) would make the business hard to sell because a buyer in year 7, for example, would not trust the income. Income was zero for five years and then jumped up; unsteady income creates a sense of unease in buyers. The 20-year depreciation period overstates earnings and would increase the sale value of a business unless the buyer recognized that the depreciation of assets did not match their real life. If a company consistently picks too long a depreciation period, it will have a history of write-downs of assets on disposition, which in turn is a sign that operating income has been overstated. Companies with steady income and minor adjustments of income on disposition of assets are the easiest to sell because the buyer trusts that the stated income of the business truly reflects value creation.

Figure 3.1 illustrates that increasing the depreciation period and thereby reducing the annual depreciation would bump up reported earnings. In today's post-Enron climate of rigid auditing, it is unlikely that auditors would be comfortable with management increasing the depreciation period once an asset is in use. Reducing the depreciation period if management thinks an asset will not last as long as originally estimated would not be a problem.

Sample Problem 3.4.4 The Impact of Depreciation Period on Income

A company buys an asset with the original cost of $1.5 million. It turns out that the actual life of the piece of equipment is 15 years and salvage value is zero. The depreciation is calculated on a straight-line basis. The contribution margin is $400,000, and SG&A/indirect expenses excluding depreciation are $175,000. Calculate the annual income for the next 15 years if the company estimates salvage value to be zero and chooses the depreciation period to be 10, 15, or 20 years. Then, calculate the cumulative income over the 15-year period for all three cases. Assume the contribution margin and other SG&A expenses are the same for the next 15 years, and provide the income profile for all three cases. Explain in detail which is the best choice of depreciation period and why?

Solution:

Case I: Depreciation period = 10 years

Case II: Depreciation period = 15 years

Case III: Depreciation period = 20 years

Case I	Case II	Case III
$\text{Depreciation} = \dfrac{\$(1.5 - 0) \text{ million}}{10}$	$\text{Depreciation} = \dfrac{\$(1.5 - 0) \text{ million}}{15}$	$\text{Depreciation} = \dfrac{\$(1.5 - 0) \text{ million}}{20}$
= $0.15 million	= $0.1 million	= $0.075 million

Operating income = contribution margin – depreciation – other SG&A expenses

	Case I	Case II	Case III
Operating income =	$(0.4 – 0.15 – 0.175)	$(0.4 – 0.10 – 0.175)	$(0.4 – 0.075 – 0.175)
=	$0.075	$0.125	$0.15

In case I, the operating income would be $0.075 million for the next 10 years and $0.225 million for the next 5 years.

In case II, the operating income would be $0.125 for the next 15 years.

In case III, the operating income would be $0.15 million for the next 15 years and will have a write-down of $0.375 (1.5 – 15 × 0.075) million in that year.

In all three cases, the cumulative income over the 15-year period is $1.875 million. Altering depreciation changes when income is reported but does not change the total cumulative income.

The following figure shows the operating income profile for the three cases:

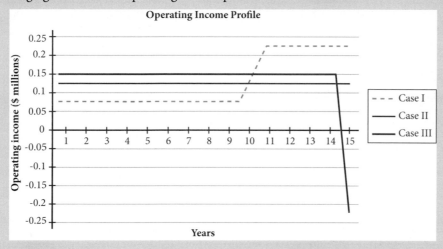

In case II, the depreciation period is equal to the life of the asset. This is the best choice because it provides a realistic figure of the depreciation and operating income every year. The other two cases give an unsteady income because of inaccurate depreciation. In case I, when the depreciation period is less than the expected life, the operating income is understated for the first 10 years and overstated for the next 5 years. Similarly, in case III, they have overstated income for the first 14 years and have a large negative income in year 15 because of the write-down.

Multiples of incomes are often used to estimate the sale value of a company. In case III, income has been overstated and will be corrected by a write-down on disposal of assets in year 15. This illustrates why anyone buying a company should carefully check that historical values for depreciation have not been understated.

3.5   Operating Income, Cash Flow from Operations, and the Concept of Breakeven

Net revenue minus COGS minus SG&A gives **operating income**, which is calculated before tax. This is not the total income of the company, but in terms of analyzing a business, it is the most important income, since it is the income the business is producing from its normal activities. Gain or loss on disposal of assets is typically of an intermittent nature. Another component of other income can be interest on long-term debt, which is often, but not always, put in other income as a negative entry (an expense). If operating income is calculated without the expense of interest on long-term debt, it can be thought of as the income of the ongoing business activity independent of financing, i.e., before charges for debt financing. A business can raise the funds it requires by debt or equity; this is discussed further in Chapters 4, 6, and 9. If operating income is calculated with the expense of interest on long-term debt, it can be thought of as the "all in" income of the ongoing business activity based on the financing of that business.

Remember that a business generates more cash than operating or net income, the difference being depreciation and any other non-cash charge against income. **Cash flow from operations** is the cash generated by normal business activities. Specifically, it is operating income plus depreciation and other non-cash charges against income. Like operating income, cash flow from operations is typically calculated before tax. This concept of cash flow from operations will be broadened in Chapter 5 when the statement of cash flow is discussed.

The purpose of a commercial activity is to create value, and the measure of value in commercial activities is income, realized as money. Thus, if a business has a positive operating income, it is creating value from its activities. If it has a negative value, it is not creating value and not sustainable in the long run. If a business generates cash but does not have a positive operating income, it can stay in business for the short to medium term, but not the long term. How a business can show a negative operating income and have a positive cash flow is discussed in Appendix 3.2; this concept is very important for understanding financial statements and how businesses operate through lean times.

If you own a business, you will likely want to sell it someday. One means of creating value in the eyes of a purchaser is to have a demonstrated long-term steady or steadily growing operating income. This is a sign that the business has a stable means of creating commercial value.

3.5.1 Breakeven

Breakeven is the name given to the sales level at which an accounting number is zero. The four accounting numbers for which breakeven is calculated are operating income, net income, cash flow from operations, and net cash flow.

Book breakeven, also called accounting breakeven, is the sales level at which operating income or net income goes from negative to positive. Breakeven for operating income occurs when the contribution margin matches the SG&A. Every sale above the break-even sales level will drive operating income more positive.

Should breakeven be calculated on operating or net income? If financing costs (interest on long-term debt) are included in SG&A, then operating income is usually close to net income and represents the "normal" income of the business. Breakeven of operating income has meaning. If financing costs are recorded as a negative entry in other income, then break-even net income will have more meaning.

One important concept is the difference between income from operations and cash flow from operations. Cash flow from operations is normally operating income plus the current year's non-cash charges against income, such as depreciation. Remember that depreciation reflects the recovery of money that was spent in the past on assets that are wearing out. Because the money was spent in the past, the cash represented by depreciation is available to the business, even though it is not a part of operating income.

Sometimes, a business will create a book reserve for some future activity; for example, a mine might have a charge against its current earnings to provide for future reclamation of a mine site. Unless required by law, this reserve is not a separate cash account; it is simply a book non cash charge against earnings that is, in effect, saying that "In order not to lead an investor into thinking that we are creating more value than we actually are doing, we must reduce our stated income to reflect money we will be required to spend in the future." Such book reserves are also non-cash charges against income. To calculate cash flow from operations, one would add back in the annual addition to a reserve, much as one adds back in annual depreciation charges. However, in the remainder of this text, the only non-cash charge against earnings that will be considered is depreciation.

Cash breakeven is the point at which operating income plus depreciation (cash flow from operations) becomes positive. The difference between cash and book break-even sales levels is the amount of sales required to generate contribution margin equal to depreciation, just as the difference between operating income and cash flow from operations is normally just depreciation.

Note that cash breakeven means that the operations of a business excluding any change in assets (for example, an increase in inventory or the purchase of a long-term asset) are generating cash; this is different from the overall business generating cash. If a business is slightly above cash breakeven, but its customers are slow in paying their bills, then overall operations may be cash negative, and the business may need some additional short-term borrowing. If a business is slightly above cash breakeven, but management buys a very expensive piece of equipment, the overall business will have a negative cash flow that might require more equity or long-term borrowings.

Even though the full analysis of cash flow in a business is more complicated, the simple test of cash breakeven is a quick check on the health of a business. In the vernacular of small businesses, breakeven is known as "**covering the nut**," and is a crucial target each month in any company. For the small business owner, the focus is often on cash breakeven: if the cash nut is covered, then the owner does not have to dip into his own cash reserves to keep the business going. For businesses that are part of larger publicly traded companies, covering the book nut is more important. The large company may not run out of cash in the aggregate, but the person managing a business unit that does not cover the book nut and generate earnings is going to attract the attention of someone in the head office. This is because the most widely followed measure of the performance of a stock is its **price to earnings (P/E) ratio**, the share price divided by a company's earnings per share.

Graphical representations of these concepts usually suffer from over-simplification but may help you to understand some key concepts. Figure 3.2 shows the idealized case in which fixed costs are fully fixed (independent of sales level) and contribution margin is constant for all sales levels.

Figure 3.2: Breakeven in an Idealized Case

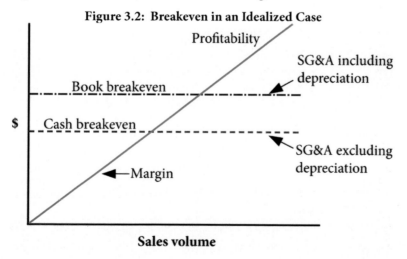

In Figure 3.2, margin is the cash the company receives from a sale minus the direct variable costs it spends to create the sale. The intersection of the margin line with the lower dashed line is the point at which cash breakeven is achieved. For lower sales, the company is losing cash, or in other words, below the lower dashed line, the company is consuming cash. In this region, the owners of the business must ensure there is a periodic cash injection. The intersection of the margin line with the upper dashed line is the point at which book breakeven is reached, i.e., the wearing out of assets represented by depreciation is being recovered. In the region between the two lines, the business is not creating value, but it is generating cash from operations. Above the upper dashed line, the business is creating value, i.e., it is covering all its cash and non-cash charges and has an excess value left over.

Start-up businesses lose cash until they build up sales. All start-up companies will be focused on forecasting the sales level that achieves first cash and then book breakeven, and this will also be the major focus of whoever advances funding to the start-up. The dream of every entrepreneur and every investor in a start-up company is to exceed book break-even sales level. This is why investors in start-up companies pay as much attention to a marketing plan as to the projected financial statements. Having a credible plan to reach breakeven is a key part of financing any start-up. Pricing strategy is part of any marketing plan. High prices during start-up recover more margin per sale but retard sales growth, whereas lower prices promote a larger market size but postpone the point of cost recovery. Striking the right balance requires good judgment; there is no magic formula to tell a manager how best to run a business. Figure 3.3 illustrates what an investor in a start-up company fears: a company that never achieves profitability.

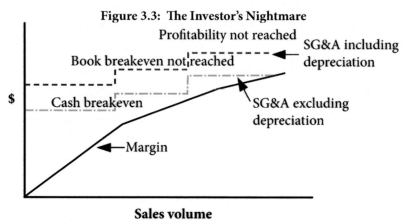

Figure 3.3: The Investor's Nightmare

Three problems are illustrated in Figure 3.3. First, margin drops as sales increase. This can occur for many reasons, including competitors that offer the same good or service at a lower price or finding that incremental customers do not get as high a benefit from a good or service as the initial purchasers and, therefore, are not willing to pay as much. The second problem is that SG&A other than depreciation is not fixed or constant with growing sales. An example of this would be a company discovering that it needed increases in marketing, accounting, and warehouse staff to support growing sales. The third problem is that depreciation increases because more assets, such as more warehouses and more manufacturing assets, are also needed to support growing sales.

Any entrepreneur trying to raise financing will need a convincing plan to achieve book breakeven sales without excessive cost increases.

Calculating Book and Cash Breakeven

If other income is minor, then at cash breakeven, contribution margin equals SG&A (fixed costs) excluding depreciation. At book breakeven, contribution margin equals SG&A including depreciation. (Note that if other income includes the financing cost on long-term debt, breakeven would include SG&A plus other income. The examples below are based on other income being minor one-time items and not including interest on long term debt.) For the simple case of constant contribution margin regardless of sales level and truly fixed SG&A, calculating cash and book breakeven is easy. Use the following equation if SG&A and the fractional contribution margin (CM) are known:

$$\text{Contribution margin} = \text{sales} \times [1 - \text{COGS (fraction)}] = \text{SG\&A}$$

You can solve this for sales at which either cash or book breakeven is achieved. For example, if a company has an SG&A excluding depreciation of $1 million, annual depreciation of $1 million, and a contribution margin per sales dollar of 0.5, then solve as follows:

$$\text{Cash breakeven sales} = \$1 \text{ million} \div 0.5 = \$2 \text{ million}$$

$$\text{Book breakeven sales} = \$2 \text{ million} \div 0.5 = \$4 \text{ million}$$

The assumption that SG&A is fixed is usually only valid for modest changes from current levels of sales; for large changes in sales level, increased selling and administrative costs are expected, such as more sales, accounting and warehouse staff. One approach to this is to estimate a growth in SG&A related to sales, but at a lower value than the COGS.

Consider the following problem: a company has $2.1 million of sales today, SG&A costs of $1.8 million excluding depreciation, annual depreciation of $0.9 million, and a COGS of 50% (and therefore a contribution margin of 50% or 0.5). Management estimates that SG&A will increase from current levels at a rate of 20% of sales if there is a large growth in sales, half due to increases in depreciation and half due to increases in staff.

To solve such a problem, one can work through the algebra, but by far the easiest and most versatile way to do this is to use a spreadsheet program with a goal seek function. Solving this problem is illustrated below: once the formulae are put in the appropriate cells, use a goal seek tool to make either operating cash flow or operating income equal to zero.

	Contribution margin (%)	50			
	Incremental increase in SG&A (%) (1/2 is depreciation)	20			

	Current Values ($000)	Cash Breakeven ($000)	Book Breakeven ($000)	Comment
Sales	2,100	3,975	7,600	Use goal seek to solve for B/E sales
COGS	1,050	1,988	3,800	Sales × [1 – CM (fraction)]
Contribution margin	1,050	1,988	3,800	Contribution margin = Sales – COGS
SG&A excluding depreciation	1,800	1,988	2,350	Increases at 10% of *incremental* sales
Depreciation	900	1,088	1,450	Increases at 10% of *incremental* sales
Operating income	–1,650	–1,088	0	OL = Contribution margin – SG&A including depreciation
Other income	0	0	0	
Net income	–1,650	–1,088	0	
Operational cash flow	–750	0	1,450	OCF = operating income + depreciation

Use the formula for SG&A to calculate the breakeven sales levels.

$$SG\&A = 1,800 + 0.1 \times (\text{breakeven sales} - \text{current sales})$$

A similar approach is taken for depreciation.

This company is losing $750,000 per year of cash at current levels of sales and has a book loss of $1,650,000. You can be sure the owners and managers are focused on getting to cash breakeven, and after that, to book breakeven.

Sample Problem 3.5.1 Calculating Cash and Book Breakeven

Control Corp., a company specializing in electrical controls, started business last year. Its year-end income statement for last year shows that its operating income and operating cash flow is negative. In preparing a presentation to possible investors, the owner of the business is interested in knowing the cash and book breakeven sales level for the following cases:

1. SG&A and fixed costs (including depreciation) do not change with the increasing sales level.
2. Depreciation stays the same, but the SG&A and fixed costs (excluding depreciation) increase at 10% of the incremental sales.
3. Both depreciation and SG&A (excluding depreciation) increase at 10% of the incremental sales, which means SG&A and fixed costs (including depreciation) increase at 20% of the sales level.

Provide the required analysis using the following information from last year's income statement:

Contribution margin (%)	60
Particulars	**Last Year ($000)**
Sales	4,500
COGS	1,800
Contribution margin	2,700
SG&A excluding depreciation	3,500
Depreciation	500
Operating income	−1,300
Other income	0
Net income	−1,300
Operating cash flow	−800

Solution:

This kind of calculation is critical to any start-up business. When operating cash flow is zero, the first focus is cash breakeven because a company below cash breakeven requires ongoing injections of cash from its owner(s). However, when net income is zero, book breakeven is also important because investors want to make a profit, i.e., create value that more than offsets the wearing out of assets. The easiest way to solve these problems is to set up a spreadsheet and use a goal seek function to set either operating cash flow or net income to zero.

Case 1

	Current Values ($000)	Cash Breakeven ($000)	Book Breakeven ($000)	Comments
Contribution margin (%)	60			
Sales	4,500	5,833	6,667	Use goal seek to find the B/E sales
COGS	1,800	2,333	2,667	Sales × (1 – CM)
Contribution margin	2,700	3,500	4,000	Sales – COGS
SG&A excluding depreciation	3,500	3,500	3,500	Stays constant
Depreciation	500	500	500	Stays constant
Operating income	–1,300	–500	0	Cont margin – SG&A excl. dep. – dep.
Other income	0	0	0	Stays constant
Net income	–1,300	–500	0	Operating income + other income
Operating cash flow	–800	0	500	Operating income + depreciation

Case 2

	Current Values ($000)	Cash Breakeven ($000)	Book Breakeven ($000)	Comments
Contribution margin (%)	60			
Sales	4,500	6,100	7,100	Use goal seek to find the B/E sales
COGS	1,800	2,440	2,840	Sales × (1 – CM)
Contribution margin	2,700	3,660	4,260	Sales – COGS
SG&A excluding depreciation	3,500	3,660	3,760	Increases at 10% of incremental sales
Depreciation	500	500	500	Stays constant
Operating income	–1,300	–500	0	Cont margin – SG&A excl. dep. – dep.
Other income	0	0	0	Stays constant
Net income	–1,300	–500	0	Operating income + other income
Operating cash flow	–800	0	500	Operating income + depreciation

Case 3

Contribution margin (%)	60			
	Current Values ($000)	**Cash Breakeven ($000)**	**Book Breakeven ($000)**	**Comments**
Sales	4,500	6,100	7,750	Use goal seek to find the B/E sales
COGS	1,800	2,440	3,100	Sales × (1 – CM)
Contribution margin	2,700	3,660	4,650	Sales – COGS
SG&A excluding depreciation	3,500	3,660	3,825	Increases at 10% of incremental sales
Depreciation	500	660	825	Increases at 10% of incremental sales
Operating income	–1,300	–600	0	Contribution margin – SG&A excl. dep. – dep.
Other income	0	0	0	Stays constant
Net income	–1,300	–660	0	Operating income + other income
Operating cash flow	–800	0	825	Operating income + depreciation

Note that in cases 2 and 3, the cash breakeven levels are the same. This is because the cash breakeven level has operating cash flow equal to zero and operating cash flow is not affected by a change in depreciation.

Sample Problem 3.5.2 Cash Flow from Operations and Net Cash Flow

You are a financial analyst of an investment bank. Your team is evaluating Sweetco, Bitterco, and Sourco as candidates for a possible merger. Your boss asks you to calculate cash flow from operations and net cash flow for all three companies and comment on the operational health of these companies.

($ millions)	Sweetco	Bitterco	Sourco
Revenue	442	319	552
COGS	265	239	386
Contribution margin	177	80	166
Depreciation	20	55	45
Other SG&A	82	103	130
Operating income	75	–78	–10
Other income	–18	–21	–11
Net income	56	–98	–20

Solution:

($ millions)	Sweetco	Bitterco	Sourco
Operating income	75	−78	−10
Add depreciation	20	55	45
= Cash flow from operations	95	−23	35
Add other income	−18	−21	−11
= Net cash flow	76	−43	24

Sweetco is in good shape, with positive operating income and net income. Any company with positive operating and net income will have positive cash flow from operations and net cash flow.

Bitterco has negative operating and net income. Even after adding back the depreciation amount, the cash flow from operations and net cash flow are negative. Bitterco is in terrible shape and would need some drastic changes operationally to survive even in the short run, since it is consuming cash every day that it is in operation.

Sourco has negative operating and net income, but after adding back depreciation, the cash flow from operations is more than $35 million. The cash flow figure still stays positive even after deducting the negative other income figure of $10.9 million. Sourco can likely survive in the short to medium term since it has healthy cash flow. In the long term, it is not generating enough income (value) to replace its assets, but unless it needs to replace its assets in the near term, it has time to make some adjustments.

A merger between Sweetco and Sourco might make sense if the management team can identify ways to improve the income of Sourco over time. A merger with Bitterco is a mistake unless some obvious very short-term fixes are identified, which is unlikely.

This analysis assumes that items in other income are cash income or expenses. Recall that a loss on disposition of an asset shows up as a negative entry in other income, but it is the same as depreciation, a non-cash charge. Therefore, in a real analysis of a company, you would identify non-cash items in other income as well as in operating income and add them back in to calculate cash flow. The statement of cash flow (Chapter 5) will do this.

Sample Problem 3.5.3 Using CFFO and NCF to Evaluate the Health of a Company

The income statements of three different companies in the mortgage industry are shown as follows:

($000)	Badco	Fairco	Goodco
Gross revenue	32,450	52,325	85,000
Bad debts	440	677	325
Net revenue	32,010	51,648	84,675
COGS	19,206	36,154	59,272
Contribution margin	12,804	15,494	25,403
Depreciation	5,400	7,235	9,226
Other SG&A	16,625	16,698	18,450
Operating income	−9,221	−8,439	−2,273
Other income	−3,940	7,900	−2,445
Net income	−13,161	−539	−4,718

Due to the current economic downturn in the industry, it has become very difficult for these companies to recover costs and make a profit: all have negative net income.

The federal government is worried about the current economic downturn and the impact of the failure of mortgage companies on new home buyers. You are working as an analyst with the government. Your boss asks you to analyze the financial health and survivability of these three companies by calculating the cash flow from operations (CFFO) and net cash flow (NCF)

Solution:

($000)	Badco	Fairco	Goodco
Operating income	−9,221	−8,439	−2,273
Add depreciation	5,400	7,235	9,226
= Cash flow from operations	−3,821	−1,204	6,953
Add other income	−3,940	7,900	−2,445
= Net cash flow	−7,761	6,696	4,508

All three companies have negative operating income and net income because of the downturn in the industry. The cash flow from operations and net cash flow for Badco is negative. This means that this company has a very poor chance of survival because this company is losing money monthly from its ongoing operations. Fairco has negative cash flow from operations, so like Badco, it is losing money from its ongoing operations. However, a significant positive other income, which is presumably a one-time event, has given it a positive cash flow. Fairco has some short-term breathing room because of the one-time other income item, but it is in very serious mid-term trouble unless it can get to a positive CFFO. Goodco, in spite of having negative income, has positive CFFO and NCF, which make its prospects of survival the highest because it is generating cash from its basic operations.

3.6   Other Income

As noted above, the category **other income** traditionally had two or three components. The first component is an unusual one-time cost or revenue that is not part of its core business activities or usual ongoing activities. The second is adjustments on disposition of assets. The third category is interest on long term debt, but this is not universally put into other income: some companies put interest on long-term debt into SG&A. More recently a fourth category has been added to other income: the calculated change in value of derivative instruments (for example, long-term purchase contracts) and assets held for resale.

3.6.1   Income from Non-Core Business Activities

Suppose a company makes a product and decides that it does not want to sell this gadget into Africa because it is too costly to open up in Africa relative to the perceived total market size. However, an African firm learns of the gadget and approaches the company to buy a one-time, fully paid-up license to make the item for resale only in Africa. This is a one-time **windfall** related to the company's business of making the product but not a direct consequence of the full manufacture and sale of the product. If the license revenue were reported in operating income, it would create a one-year distortion in margin that would confuse the managers, the investors, and any prospective buyer. Anyone tracking year-over-year performance would end up needing to take the "blip" out of the sales revenue in order to understand company performance.

Income from the sale of the license is helpful to the business and can be used for some valuable purpose such as paying a dividend to shareholders, retiring debt, or buying a new asset. The books would not balance if the income from the land or license sale did not show up somewhere, so the Solution: in each case is to put this kind of revenue from a one-time or non-normal activity into other income. Other income would frequently be the subject of a footnote to annual financial statements to explain the source of the revenue or expense.

3.6.2 Gain or Loss on Disposal of Assets and Extraordinary Write-downs

A **gain or loss on sale of assets**, which occurs when the salvage value of an asset is greater or less than the remaining undepreciated book value, is reflected as an entry to the income statement. One can think of this entry as a one-time correction to past depreciation or, in the case of land, a one-time recognition of a change in value. Typically, this is entered into other income as a gain on sale of assets or loss on sale of assets, although the words "on disposal of assets" or "on liquidation of assets" may also show up.

Note that on occasion, assets will be **written down**, which means that their book value is being reduced by a decision of management. One frequent reason for doing this is that a change in business has occurred so that in the judgment of management, the assets do not continue to retain value. For example, suppose you are in the trucking business and you buy land for a lay-down yard in a remote area to help service a shipping contract to a mine site. Three years later, the mine closes, and you believe it will not reopen. You find that you cannot sell the land. In this case, you would write the asset down to zero, since it will have no ongoing value to your business. Another example is the fixed manufacturing assets for a product that no longer has a market. Plants that made Freon, a refrigerant that was banned over concerns about ozone depletion, are an example; remaining book value would be written down to zero. Another frequent reason for a write-down is stale or obsolete inventory. As a company's product line evolves, it is normal that some raw materials and finished goods inventory become unusable; frequently, the only practical disposition of this material is as scrap. The correct procedure is to take a write-down representing the value of the inventory that is no longer usable. (It is particularly important when buying a company to determine the quality of the inventory as well as the fixed assets and ensure that if a write-down is necessary, it is taken prior to purchase.) In all of these cases, a write-down is entered as a loss in other income, the same as a loss on sale of assets.

If a gain or loss on sale of an asset is small compared to a company's net income, the difference is not material. If, however, there is a major gain or loss at the time of the sale/salvage of an asset, this means that the operating income reported in prior years has been misstated. If, for example, there is a large loss on the sale of an asset, then in hindsight, the depreciation for the asset should have been higher than was actually claimed. Because depreciation was too low in past years, the unrecovered cost for the asset that "wore out" has to be claimed in a one-time entry, as illustrated in Figure 3.1.

Technically, the loss is from operations, but to report it in the year the asset is retired distorts that year relative to previous years. It is also too much effort to go back and restate one's prior years' accounting statements, so the common Solution: is an entry in other income. However, a person using financial statements to critically evaluate the worth of a business should be careful. Consistent or even one-time significant entries in other income for loss on disposal of assets means that operating income should be adjusted in any pro forma projection of future results. Operating income has been overstated in the past if a company is consistently showing extraordinary losses due to a sale of assets or write-down of assets.

A negative entry in other income related to a write-down or an adjustment when an asset is disposed of is just like depreciation: it is a non-cash charge against income. Hence, in preparing a detailed analysis of cash flow, an accountant would take this into account.

Sample Problem 3.6.1 Disposition of Assets

Company Drill Fast Inc. buys assets worth $2 million. The estimated life of these assets is 20 years, and it would be depreciated on a straight-line basis. The salvage value at the end of 20 years is expected to be $200,000. Give the accounting treatment for the following three cases:

1. The asset is sold at the end of year 8 for $1.7 million.
2. It is sold for $50,000 at the end of its useful life.
3. It is sold for $350,000 at the end of its useful life.

Solution:

$$\text{Depreciation} = \frac{\text{original value} - \text{salvage value}}{\text{asset's useful life}}$$
$$= \frac{\$(2,000,000 - 200,000)}{20}$$
$$= \$90,000$$

Case I:

In case of early retirement of the asset in year 8, the depreciated value of the asset would be calculated; this is original value less the accumulated depreciation.

Accumulated depreciation	$= 8 \times \$90,000$
	$= \$720,000$
Asset value (at the end of year 8)	$= \$2,000,000 - \$720,000$
	$= \$1,280,000$
Sale price	$= \$1,700,000$

Gain/loss on sale of asset (at the end of year 8) $= \$(1,700,000 - 1,280,000)$
$$= \$420,000$$

At the end of year 8, a gain on sale of asset of $420,000 would appear under other income. In effect, Drill Fast's income for the last eight years was understated by more than $50,000 per year. Cash flow for the year would be increased by $1.7 million.

Case II:

Gain/loss on sale of asset (at the end of year 20) = sale price – estimated salvage value
$$= \$50,000 - \$200,000$$
$$= -\$150,000$$

In this case, loss on sale of asset would appear in other income as a negative value on the income statement in year 20. Drill Fast was wrong in its estimation of salvage value and, hence, its calculation of depreciation, but the difference per year by which income was overstated, approximately $7,000 per year, is small relative to the original asset value. Small discrepancies between estimated and actual salvage value are normal and not a source of concern.

The write-down of –$150,000 per year is a non-cash charge against income, so to calculate net cash flow, add –$150,000 back into net income.

Case III:

Gain/loss on sale of asset (at the end of year 20) = sale price – estimated salvage value

$$= \$350,000 - \$200,000$$

$$= \$150,000$$

The gain on sale of asset would appear on the income statement of year 20 under other income. This would increase the net income figure of year 20. As with case II, the difference is not significant relative to the original asset value. The $150,000 is a cash gain and would contribute to net cash flow.

3.6.3   Interest Expense as an Other Income Entry

Interest payable on long-term debt often shows up in other income as a negative entry, i.e., an expense. All businesses require some capital; even those with no fixed assets will require some **working capital**, as is discussed in Chapter 4. How the capital is sourced (debt versus equity) is a business judgment on the part of the owners. If the investment in a business comes in the form of equity, then the investors will eventually expect a return. This can be in the form of a dividend or through the increased value of the business, which is in effect reinvesting earnings that are kept in the company. The investor can benefit from the increased value of the business by selling his shares in the company. If the investment comes in the form of debt, then interest payments must be made on the debt. The underlying earning power of the commercial activities being conducted by the business can be thought of as independent of the source of financing. For example, the customer buying shoes at a certain price from a store is indifferent to whether the store is financed by equity or debt.

If long-term interest charges are put into other income, then the operating income represents the earning power of the commercial activity independent of the source of financing. In a sense, the operating income is the amount that is available from the commercial activity to reward the investors through interest or dividends. If the purpose of analyzing the income statement is to compare relative performance of shoe stores, for instance, then it helps to treat interest on long-term debt as other income. The efficiency of a store to other stores can be compared when the financing costs are separated from the operating costs. Earnings before interest and taxes (EBIT) is a common measure of the value of a business in that it looks at the raw earning power of a business before company-specific elements such as financing costs and tax treatment are factored into net income.

As with so many other aspects of financial statements, interest costs do not always appear in other income, and a person analyzing financial statements must read the statements and the notes to see where various cost elements are appearing.

Sample Problem 3.6.2 Interest on Long-term Debt in SG&A or in Other Income?

Buyerco, an international conglomerate, is looking at two companies (Oilco and Gasco) in the oil and gas industry for a possible takeover. The estimated price for the buyout is $20 million for Oilco and $14 million for Gasco. Buyerco plans to provide 50% of the purchase price in the form of cash raised by issuing new shares in Buyerco and 50% in the form of cash raised by additional debt within Oilco and Gasco at an interest rate of 10%. Both Oilco and Gasco have current interest on long-term debt of $100,000. Oilco treats it as a part of interest expense expenditure, and Gasco separates financing costs from operating income and includes it as other income. Prepare a pro-forma income statement after purchase for each of Oilco and Gasco, assuming that each continues the same accounting treatment of interest on long-term debt. What is the impact on operating and net income for the two companies assuming nothing else changes after the acquisition?

Oilco ($000)	
Revenue	14,700
COGS	8,820
Contribution margin	5,880
Interest on long-term debt	100
Other SG&A	3,240
Operating income	2,540
Other income	40
Net income	2,580

Gasco ($000)	
Revenue	13,230
COGS	9,261
Contribution margin	3,969
SG&A	2,440
Operating income	1,529
Other income	−100
Net income	1,429

Solution:

Oilco will have an increase in interest of $1 million per year (10% of half the purchase price); the extra interest is part of general SG&A and will reduce both operating income and net income. Gasco will have an increase in interest of $700,000 per year. The extra interest will show up as a negative entry in other income; therefore, operating income is unchanged, but net income decreases by the amount of extra interest.

Oilco ($000)		
	Before	**After**
Revenue	14,700	14,700
COGS	8,820	8,820
Contribution margin	5,880	5,880
Interest on long-term debt	100	1,100
Other SG&A	3,240	3,240
Operating income	2,540	1,540
Other income	40	40
Net income	2,580	1,580

Gasco ($000)		
	Before	**After**
Revenue	13,230	13,230
COGS	9,261	9,261
Contribution margin	3,969	3,969
SG&A	2,440	2,440
Operating income	1,529	1,529
Other income	−100	−800
Net income	1,429	729

Gasco's decision to put interest on long-term debt as a negative entry in other income means that operating income will be unchanged no matter how the purchase is financed.

3.6.4 Change in Value of Derivatives and Assets Held for Resale

In an effort to achieve full disclosure of a company's financial position, income statements now show the change in value of contractual obligations and investment portfolios. These are **marked to market**, meaning that the difference between the contracted purchase or sale price (or the original cost of an investment) and the current market price is calculated and shown as other income.

This is best illustrated by an example. A company enters into a long-term purchase contract to buy 20,000 MWh of power per year at a price of $70 per MWh. At the end of a financial reporting year, the market price of power is $60 per MWh. The company would show a loss on the derivative instrument (the contract to purchase power) of $200,000. The same company holds one million shares of a publicly traded company that it acquired for $14 per share. At year end, the share value is $22. The company would show a gain on the assets held for resale (the shares) of $8 million. Note that neither of these amounts represents a cash gain or loss; they are both notional changes in value. When the company entered into the long-term purchase contract for power, it chose to do so to reduce volatility. This is not taken into account when the notional loss of $200,000 is recorded. The company may intend to hold the one million shares for a long period of time, in which case, it does not see the benefit of the current stock price. However, current accounting standards want to reveal all changes in value within a company and require that these two sums be taken into account when reporting income.

A slightly different treatment occurs when a contract is considered to be a perfect hedge in which a company's future purchases are exactly offset by a purchase contract. In this case, the change in mark to market value is still calculated but is recorded as a temporary change in shareholder equity. This is a highly detailed element of accounting and is rare enough that its treatment is not included in this text.

3.7 Net Income and Net Cash Flow: Pre-Tax, Tax, and After-Tax

Net income (also called profit or net earnings) is the end point of all income statements; it is the sum over a given time period of the net gain or loss on all activities in the business. While this number is important in that it gets transferred to the sources and uses of funds statement, managers of most ongoing businesses are more focused on trends in operating income rather than net income because extraordinary or one-time items that show up in net income can distort the picture of what a business will do in the future.

Net income, earnings, and profit (or loss if negative) all mean the same thing: how much money did a business make or lose in a given time period? Again, this is important because it is a measure of commercial value creation.

Net income is normally calculated both pre and after tax; it is the after-tax figure that gets transferred to other financial statements. However, net income before tax and special measures of value creation, such as earnings before interest and taxes (EBIT) and earnings before interest, taxes, and depreciation (EBITD), are also sometimes shown in financial statements or calculated by analysts. EBIT and EBITD are discussed in Chapter 8.

Net cash flow from a business bears the same relationship to net income as cash flow from operations does to operating income. The difference is normally annual depreciation charges, although any other non-cash charges (for example, for a book reserve) would also be added back in determining net cash flow.

3.7.1 The Significance of Net Income and Net Cash Flow

Net income is the measure of the creation of value by an overall business. If a company has a negative net income indefinitely, it is not creating enough value to recover the value of the assets that are used in the business. As the assets wear out, there will likely not be enough money in the business to replace them. Net cash flow from a business is a much more urgent test of a company's performance and is a crucial test of a company's short-term viability. Managers of businesses that are losing cash very quickly should assess why they are in this business and why they should keep selling a good or service if the company cannot recover the cash cost of that sale.

In economic downturns, it is not unusual for companies in cyclical industries to have negative net income but positive cash flow. These businesses can survive a period of under-recovery of depreciation because they expect the cycle to turn and a period of high net income to occur. However, it is highly unusual for a company to operate with negative cash flow from operations other than during a start-up period. This is a critical concept for managers to understand.

Look at the three companies in this table:

($ millions)	Company A	Company B	Company C
Revenue	12.6	12.6	12.6
– COGS	8.1	8.1	8.1
= Contribution margin	4.5	4.5	4.5
– SG&A excl. depreciation	2.5	4.7	4.7
– Depreciation	3.0	0.6	0.6
= Operating income	−1.0	−0.8	−0.8
+ Other income	−0.5	0	1.8
= Net income	−1.5	−0.8	1.0
Cash flow from operations	2.0	−0.2	−0.2
Net cash flow	1.5	−0.2	1.6

Assuming that all three companies are mature and have been profitable at some point in the past, what are their prospects? On the basis of net income, it seems Company C is performing the best (it is the only one with positive income), and Company A the worst. However, a look at the operating cash flow and net cash flow helps give deeper insight.

Company B has the most serious problem of the three companies in that it is losing cash from its operation, $0.2 million per year. In effect, this company must have an injection of almost $20,000 per month just to stay in business because Company B is paying its customers to takes its goods or services. Owners of such a company usually shut it down quickly. When mature businesses have negative operating cash flow, they often are shut down within weeks or even days. If they continue to operate, suppliers are reluctant to ship goods on credit (discussed in Chapter 4). Company C is also in serious trouble because like Company B, it is losing cash on its normal operations. An item in other income, likely a one-time event, has given it $1.8 million in income (and cash) to offset its cash loss from its ordinary business of $0.2 million. However, what are Company C's prospects if it is losing cash in its normal course of business? Like Company B, it is paying its customers to takes its goods or services.

Now, consider Company A, which has a loss of $1.5 million, but a positive cash flow from operations of $2 million and a positive net cash flow of $1.5 million. This is because the loss is coming from depreciation. If Company A is not in need of new assets for a few years, it can continue to operate and try to solve its problem of negative income. Positive cash flow and negative income mean that a company is not creating enough value to offset the wearing out of its assets, but it still has cash after paying all cash expenses, so it does not need to raise money to stay in business.

This concept of thinking about cash flow separately from operating and net income is critical to understanding and managing companies. Chapter 5 will show a more sophisticated statement of cash flow to help you look even more deeply at this kind of issue.

Company A would not be shut down by its owners as long as it is generating cash. The owners may be disappointed that the income is less than that needed to recover the value of the assets, but "better some cash than none" would govern their thinking. Hence, short-term decisions about whether to continue operating a business or not are made on the basis of cash, not income. However, if Company A were trying to lure in new investors to expand the business, they would find this very difficult: why would anyone support buying new assets when the value of those in use are not being recovered? This illustrates that long-term investment decisions are made on the basis of income, not cash. Investing is focused on the creation of value, while survival is based on having cash. Hence, when one sees a negative income, the first issue to address is cash flow from operations. Companies with high asset values have high depreciation and may have significant cash flow from operations while experiencing negative income. Cyclical capital intense commodity businesses, for example, ammonia and methanol manufacture, often show this pattern. This type of company will not be in trouble when they report negative income. Contrast this to a company that has negligible assets, such as an engineering design firm. A negative income for such a company means negative cash flow because depreciation is negligible.

While short-term decisions about staying in business are based on cash flow, the importance of earnings, especially for publicly traded companies, cannot be overstated. Publicly traded companies try to maintain the value of their shares; most shareholders, in turn, buy based on the belief that the company can create value. Earnings are the most important determinant of share price for any mature company. Companies forecast earnings, as do financial analysts, and if a company revises its earnings forecast downward, a drop in stock price is typical. The most widely reported ratio for stocks is price earnings ratio, and if this ratio remains constant for a stock, then a change in earnings is directly reflected in a change in share price. Engineers who go to work for a publicly traded company will directly or indirectly be affected by the pressure on earnings performance.

3.8 *Statement of Retained Earnings*

Each year, the owners of the business have two choices: they can pay the money out of the business to themselves, or they can leave it in the business. If the money is left in the business, it is called **retained earnings**. The purpose of the statement of retained earnings is to record that this value has been retained in the business. The balance sheet will record cumulative retained earnings as one source of money for the business.

The statement of retained earnings is quite simple, as this example shows:

Sampleco
Statement of Retained Earnings for the Year Ended This Year ($000)

Retained earnings, December 31, last year	2,341
Net income for this year	389
Less dividends paid, this year	125
Retained earnings, December 31, this year	2,605

The statement of retained earnings must include the cumulative retained earnings (which will show up on the balance sheet), and it must indicate the current year's net income and how much of that net income is used for dividend payments.

What determines the dividend in a company? Basically, the shareholders (advised by management and the board of directors if the company is large and publicly traded) look at the opportunities for company growth from retaining earnings in the business versus the needs of the owners for a cash return on their equity investment. In practice, growth-oriented companies will often pay no dividend, while it is usual for large, stable utility companies to pay 65% of their earnings in dividends. A retired senior citizen trying to live on a stream of dividends will be drawn to utility type stocks, while a young person with a speculative approach to building wealth for a long-distant retirement would be relatively indifferent to dividends and much more focused on growth. In smaller companies, the needs of the owners sometimes vary, and this can pose problems for deciding between dividends and retaining earnings to finance future growth.

For owner-operated companies in Canada (those companies for which all owners play some role in the business), tax treatment favors taking money out of a company in a different manner. This is a special case discussed in Appendix 3.4.

Note that retained earnings can be negative and, in fact, frequently are for start-up companies, mineral exploration companies, and pharmaceutical research companies. For example, imagine a start-up company that will spend two years developing a software system. It has negligible revenue during these years, but certainly has expenses that are paid from the seed money (equity) put up by the owners of the business. In this case, for at least two years, the business will have a negative net income, and the retained earnings will typically be relabeled **cumulative deficit**, which can be thought of as negative retained earnings.

Retained earnings are real value that a company built up, but like depreciation, they are not kept as a separate cash reserve; it is simply money that is generated in a company and used to buy assets or inventory or to pay down short-term or long-term debt. This is discussed further when the balance sheet is considered.

The statement of retained earnings is so simple that it is often combined with the income statement or the balance sheet, but it is technically a separate financial statement.

3.9 *Working with Income Statements: Vertical and Horizontal Analysis*

By comparing income statements over a period of time, managers gain a powerful insight into the performance of a business. To extract meaningful management information from income statements, they perform vertical and horizontal analysis. **Vertical analysis** means that values are normalized in any given year most often by dividing the value by sales revenue. Hence, COGS and SG&A are expressed as a fraction or percentage of sales. This makes the values meaningful: a dollar value for COGS has less management value than COGS as a fraction of sales. Once vertical analysis is done, add **horizontal analysis** by calculating year-over-year changes in the numbers, often as a percentage increase or decrease. For example, a steady decline in sales year after year is a very bad indicator for a business, and a year-over-year increase in COGS as a fraction or percentage of sales is as well.

Spreadsheets make performing vertical and horizontal analysis easy. Imagine a friend is looking at purchasing one of two businesses, but is not skilled in using financial statements as management tools. You direct him to get a five-year history for the two companies, and he gives you the following data:

Company A

($000)	Year 1	Year 2	Year 3	Year 4	Year 5
Revenue	353	448	547	607	649
COGS	159	215	284	322	350
Contribution margin	194	233	263	285	299
SG&A	120	142	167	182	194
Operating income	74	91	96	103	105
Other income	0	0	0	0	0
Net income	74	91	96	103	105

Company B

($000)	Year 1	Year 2	Year 3	Year 4	Year 5
Revenue	512	572	644	731	811
COGS	248	275	316	362	393
Contribution margin	264	297	328	369	418
SG&A	162	166	169	177	180
Operating income	102	131	159	192	238
Other income	0	0	0	0	0
Net income	102	131	159	192	238

You then perform a vertical and horizontal analysis and return these calculations to her:

Company A

($000)	Year 1	Year 2	Year 3	Year 4	Year 5
Revenue	353	448	547	607	649
Revenue growth (%)		27.0	22.0	11.0	6.9
COGS	159	215	284	322	350
Contribution margin	194	233	263	285	299
CM (%)	55.0	52.0	48.0	47.0	46.0
SG&A	120	142	167	182	194
SG&A growth (%)		18.3	17.6	9.0	6.6
Operating income	74	91	96	103	105
Other income	0	0	0	0	0
Net income	74	91	96	103	105
Net income growth (%)		22.9	4.8	8.2	1.2

Company B

($000)	Year 1	Year 2	Year 3	Year 4	Year 5
Revenue	512	572	644	731	811
Revenue growth (%)		11.7	12.6	13.5	10.9
COGS	248	275	316	362	393
Contribution margin	264	297	328	369	418
CM (%)	51.5	52.0	51.0	50.5	51.5
SG&A	162	166	169	177	180
SG&A growth (%)		2.5	1.8	4.7	1.7
Operating income	102	131	159	192	238
Other income	0	0	0	0	0
Net income	102	131	159	192	238
Net income growth (%)		29.3	21.3	20.5	23.7

The vertical and horizontal analysis shows some serious problems with Company A despite its history of a steady growth in net income. For example, margin is dropping as a percentage of sales over the five-year period, while SG&A is increasing steadily and substantially over the five-year period. Sales growth was substantial in years one and two but more recently has slowed down. Finally, last year, it was only 6.9%, while in the same year, SG&A increased 6.6%. These are all serious problems, but this does not necessarily mean that your friend should not buy Company A. It would be important to discuss each of these issues with the current owner to see if they are the result of sloppy management or a more fundamental problem with the business. For example, did margin drop because the owners did not have the backbone to push through price increases, or did they drop because offshore competitors with lower costs were undercutting price? The former can be fixed by a new owner, while the latter cannot. Did SG&A go up because the owners hired their relatives to do make-work jobs? Again, this could be fixed by a new owner. The purpose of vertical and horizontal analysis is to help get the right questions on the table for discussion. Company A would require lots of discussion, including a detailed breakdown of the components of SG&A and cost of goods sold to see what specifically was causing the changes in these values.

Company B looks quite good from a vertical and horizontal analysis. Sales have grown steadily, margin has been steady, and SG&A growth has been well below sales growth. A buyer should ask for more details before buying this business, but the tone of the conversation would be different for this company compared to Company A.

Vertical and horizontal analysis is the basis of much internal management within companies. Managers report on their results by comparing them to budget and historical values. A good analysis of history usually leads to a good discussion of today's opportunities and problems.

Sample Problem 3.9.1 Using Vertical and Horizontal Analysis

Look at the five-year history portrayed in the income statements of Waterco and Heatco provided in the tables. Both companies have been missing their earnings expectations for each year, and their shares are trading at their lowest price in the companies' histories.

Waterco					
($ millions)	Year 1	Year 2	Year 3	Year 4	Year 5
Revenue	50.00	51.00	53.55	55.42	56.95
COGS	31.85	32.24	34.11	35.85	36.00
Contribution margin	18.15	18.76	19.44	19.57	20.95
SG&A	11.00	11.82	13.17	15.02	17.55
Operating income	7.15	6.94	6.27	4.55	3.40
Other income	0.00	0.00	0.00	0.00	0.00
Net income	7.15	6.94	6.27	4.55	3.40

Heatco					
($ millions)	Year 1	Year 2	Year 3	Year 4	Year 5
Revenue	200.00	210.00	235.20	275.18	316.46
COGS	127.40	135.83	159.04	196.87	235.70
Contribution margin	72.60	74.17	76.16	78.31	80.76
SG&A	14.00	14.80	15.94	17.41	18.95
Operating income	58.60	59.37	60.22	60.90	61.81
Other income	0.00	0.00	0.00	0.00	0.00
Net income	58.60	59.37	60.22	60.90	61.81

You are working as a financial analyst with an investment bank. You have been asked to carefully analyze both the companies by doing the horizontal and vertical analysis of the income statements. Give detailed reasons on why you think that Waterco and Heatco have dismal performances in spite of their steady or growing sales figures.

Solution:

Waterco					
($ millions)	Year 1	Year 2	Year 3	Year 4	Year 5
Revenue	50.00	51.00	53.55	55.42	56.95
Revenue growth (%)		2.00	5.00	3.49	2.76
COGS	31.85	32.24	34.11	35.85	36.00
Contribution margin	18.15	18.76	19.44	19.57	20.95
CM (%)	36.3	36.8	36.3	35.3	36.8
SG&A	11.00	11.82	13.17	15.02	17.55
SG&A growth (%)		7.45	11.42	14.05	16.84
Operating income	7.15	6.94	6.27	4.55	3.40
Other income	0.00	0.00	0.00	0.00	0.00
Net income	7.15	6.94	6.27	4.55	3.40
Net income growth (%)		−2.94	−9.65	−27.43	−25.27

Heatco					
($ millions)	Year 1	Year 2	Year 3	Year 4	Year 5
Revenue	200.00	210.00	235.20	275.18	316.46
Revenue growth (%)		5.00	12.00	17.00	15.00
COGS	127.40	135.83	159.04	196.87	235.70
Contribution margin	72.60	74.17	76.16	78.31	80.76
CM (%)	36.3	35.3	32.4	28.5	25.5
SG&A	14.00	14.80	15.94	17.41	18.95
SG&A growth (%)		5.71	7.70	9.22	8.85
Operating income	58.60	59.37	60.22	60.90	61.81
Other income	0.00	0.00	0.00	0.00	0.00
Net income	58.60	59.37	60.22	60.90	61.81
Net income growth (%)		1.31	1.43	1.13	1.49

Waterco's sales are relatively flat, growing slightly below inflation. Its net income is falling at a high rate. A vertical and horizontal analysis shows that its contribution margin is steady at around 35%, but its SG&A expenses are growing despite relatively flat sales. Waterco's key problem is a failure to control SG&A costs. Any company with a flat sales profile has to pay careful attention to control SG&A, since there is typically no increased contribution margin to offset increases in SG&A.

Heatco has a much higher growth rate in sales that is not reflected in the growth of net income, which is almost steady at around $60 million. The vertical and horizontal analysis shows that SG&A growth is significantly lower than growth in sales, but the contribution margin is falling as a percentage of sales. Either increases in direct costs are not being passed on to customers in the form of higher prices, or Heatco is discounting its price year over year.

Vertical and horizontal analysis is useful in quickly identifying where problems in net income arise; they help management focus on the right issues.

Appendix 3.1: Depreciation for Tax Purposes and the Calculation of Tax

In calculating tax, one starts with net revenue as per the income statement. Some minor adjustments are normally made to expenses; for example, a portion of certain meal or entertainment expenses are not allowed as deductions from income for tax purposes. However, depreciation is handled in a completely different matter for tax purposes.

Tax policy, set by governments, is meant to ensure revenue collection but is also designed to stimulate particular forms of economic activity. As noted above, there is a great deal of management judgment in determining an appropriate depreciation. Both to stimulate economic activity and reduce avoidance of taxes, governments have their own rules for depreciation. These rules outline how to deduct the cost of capital equipment from taxable income for purposes of calculating income tax. Two other features are common to both the US and Canada. First, an asset must be available for use, meaning that it must be completed and capable of operation before it can be depreciated for tax purposes. Second, the first year is subject to a half-year rule, which means that whatever depreciation for tax purposes is calculated, only half can be claimed in the first year. In effect, this is equivalent to an assumption that on average, assets become operational half-way through a company's financial year.

Individuals in Canada and the US file personal income taxes based on a calendar year. Companies can elect a year-end other than December 31 for financial statements and tax calculations.

A3.1.1 Tax Depreciation in Canada

In Canada, depreciation for tax purposes is called CCA, and it is calculated by class of equipment, i.e., all costs associated with a given equipment class have the same CCA rate applied to them. A declining balance method is used for most CCA classes so that a given percentage is multiplied times the residual **unclaimed capital cost allowance (UCC)**. UCC can be thought of as the remaining book value of an asset for tax calculations. With a declining balance, an asset is never fully depreciated for tax purposes. A full interpretive bulletin IT285R2 is available on Revenue Canada's web site. Details of calculating CCA are also discussed in Appendix 7.1.

A3.1.2 Tax Depreciation in the United States

The United States adopted the Modified Accelerated Cost Recovery System (MACRS) in 1986. Assets are assigned to a class, and a life is specified for total depreciation of the asset for tax purposes. Depreciation for tax purposes is by a predetermined schedule that incorporates the half-year rule and provides higher depreciation in the early years of the asset. A key difference between the declining balance method used in Canada and the MACRS method in the US is that the declining balance method never reaches a zero value for the asset.

Company Taxation: Look For Changes

Many countries around the world have decided to change their approach to the taxation of companies for these three reasons:

- A tax on business is generally a regressive tax; it burdens low-income people more than a graduated tax on personal income. Imagine taxes paid by companies producing food: who really pays these taxes? Customers do, and since low-income and high-income people eat similar amounts of food, the tax burden falls on both. Compare this to a graduated tax on personal income in which the first level of income bears no tax and tax rates go up on incremental earnings.

- Business taxes discourage investment if another jurisdiction is available that has a lower tax rate.
- Complicated business taxation systems force companies to hire skilled internal or external experts.

Taxation is very complex, and tax planning will continue to be a lively field as tax reform is expected to continue in countries around the world. In 2007, Canada announced a reduction in corporate tax rates by about one-third, from levels near 39% to about 25%, to be implemented by 2012. Reform of the complex rules of corporate taxation may emerge in the next few years.

A3.1.3 General Comments on Tax

The following steps must be taken to calculate income after tax:

- Make any minor adjustments in operating expenses that are required by law (for instance, a portion of certain meal expenses are not deductible as expenses for tax purposes).
- Add depreciation and any other non-cash charges against income, such as allowances for future reclamation or future taxes, back into operating income. This gives net taxable income plus depreciation and any other non-cash charges against income or net taxable cash flow from operations.
- Calculate depreciation for tax purposes using the appropriate mandated rates.
- Deduct the CCA from the net cash flow from operations, giving taxable income.
- Calculate income tax payable based on taxable income and the applicable tax rates. Note that tax rates can be different for small or large businesses and are sometimes specific to an industry.
- Deduct income tax from taxable income to get net income after tax.

Several points can be made about tax:

1. Depreciation for tax purposes is almost always faster than for book purposes. Since depreciation is an expense, this means that taxable income (in effect, net income for the purpose of calculating tax) is less than book net income. Governments are, in effect, rewarding firms that invest in the hope that they will continue to invest, i.e., depreciation for tax purposes is meant to stimulate economic activity.

2. Given the very conservative nature of accounting, companies track the difference between how much tax is actually paid and how much tax would have been paid if taxes were due on book net income rather than taxable income. This amount is referred to as future income tax, formerly called deferred taxes. Note that future income tax is not money that is actually due to the government; it is money that would have been due if the government did not have its own way of dealing with depreciation. It can be thought of as being due in the future, which is why it is labeled "future" or "deferred."

3. Incremental deferred taxes are shown in a company's annual income statement. Future taxes payable are like depreciation: they are a non-cash charge against income (they reduce book income, but the cash does not flow out of the company). In theory, one can think of future taxes payable as the taxable component of extra or faster depreciation for tax purposes. There are other components to future taxes payable, but these are usually minor compared to the impact of differences in timing of depreciation for tax versus book, and are ignored in the remainder of this text.

4. Cumulative future income tax (the sum of deferred taxes from the start-up of a company) is shown on the balance sheet as a liability. This is discussed in the next chapter. Like depreciation, the cash represented by deferred taxes is available to management to pay dividends, buy assets, or pay down debt. It does not sit as cash in a special reserve fund; rather, it is money that has come into a company that is not labeled income in order to ensure that income is not overstated by ignoring future potential tax costs.

5. Why do financial statements bother to show future taxes payable? Remember that accounting is conservative, and in the case where the depreciation for tax purposes is much higher than it is for book purposes, a lot of income is sheltered from tax by the high initial deduction of depreciation for tax purposes. A person trying to understand the future earning power of such a company might be warned that past earnings history will not continue if deferred taxes have been very high relative to net income. For example, some environmental projects in Canada at one point could be written off for tax purposes, i.e., the capital cost of the project could be charged as an expense for the purpose of calculating taxable income, at the rate of 25% in year 1, 50% in year 2, and 25% in year 3. The equipment itself might warrant a 10- or 20-year depreciation period for book purposes. However, such extreme examples are rare, and practically speaking, deferred tax is normally small compared to gross revenue and net income and does not warrant a lot of attention in financial analysis.

6. Tax calculations are always calculated on a whole-company basis. In Canada, each company is a separate "person" for legal purposes and must file a separate tax return. Hence, the losses in a wholly owned subsidiary cannot be offset against taxable income in a parent company in Canada; there is no consolidation for tax purposes. This leads to some interesting intercompany transactions to try to ensure that subsidiaries do not have a negative taxable income. If a company buys another firm in entirety and amalgamates the acquired company into the purchaser, the acquired company's historical cumulated tax losses can offset taxes payable by the acquiring company, but only if the two firms are in similar businesses. In the United States, the income from subsidiaries where the ownership is 80% or higher can be consolidated for tax purposes.

7. One consequence of the whole-company approach to preparing tax returns is that within a company, most divisional or product income statements are done on a pre-tax basis.

8. Despite the fact that pre-tax income is used in internal income statements, the marginal tax impact of a new investment must be considered to evaluate a new investment, as discussed in Chapter 7.

9. Tax returns for businesses, even small businesses, are almost always completed with professional help. Tax law and regulations are extremely complex, which is understandable given the huge impact that taxation matters have on both fiscal solvency of government and on economic activity by companies. Management should seek help from specialists in preparing tax forms and making decisions that affect the taxable position of the company.

The analysis of financial statements in this text does not consider income tax effects. For the income statement, this is equivalent to treating it as an internal divisional pre-tax income statement for a larger company. The principals of working with financial statements are not affected by ignoring tax, which would otherwise add so much complexity that the key points of financial analysis would be lost in the details. In practice, when running a small business, a manager relies on external help in dealing with tax matters, and when running a larger business, an internal accounting group will calculate tax based on rolled-up divisional income.

Future Taxes Payable

Future taxes payable, which may also go by the names future taxes recoverable and future income taxes, can be fairly complex in practice, but this item usually does not have a strong material impact when analyzing a company. Although future tax is most commonly a liability that arises from faster depreciation of assets for tax purposes than for book purposes, it can also be an asset.

Future taxes are most often a liability because depreciation for tax purposes is more rapid (and hence depreciation is higher) than depreciation for book purposes. Higher depreciation for tax calculation lowers the tax payable, since depreciation is treated as an expense, which reduces taxable income. Accounting tracks the tax a company would pay if it had used book depreciation instead of tax depreciation. Because eventually this tax is almost certain to be paid, accounting treats the difference as a non-cash charge against income, thereby reducing stated earnings. This amount is then booked as a liability on the balance sheet. As with depreciation, the company has the cash, but it just does not report it as earnings. If a company has a single asset, future income taxes will be a positive liability in the early years of the asset, and this liability will reduce as book depreciation catches up with tax depreciation.

Why does a tax authority require more rapid depreciation, which postpones its collection of tax revenue? Because it hopes that by leaving money in a company's hands, it will be reinvested, stimulating the economy.

How can future income taxes be an asset? Imagine the following situation: a company decides to close a plant that has $100 million of undepreciated value; it estimates that the assets, mainly land, can be sold for $10 million. In its books, the company will record a loss of $90 million, but it cannot take this loss into its tax calculations until the actual sale of the land occurs. For tax purposes, anticipated losses are not recognized (only actual losses when a transaction takes place). Hence, the company will save taxes by recording the loss for tax purposes, but not until the future. In this case, future income taxes are an asset.

Future income taxes are very often not a material factor in analyzing a company, and that by far, the most common situation is a liability recorded because of the more rapid depreciation of assets for tax purposes. Managers usually need not focus on any other aspect of future income taxes.

Appendix 3.2: Sum of the Periods Calculation of Depreciation versus Straight-Line Depreciation

Straight line is the most widely used means of calculating depreciation, but in relatively rare instances (as noted in Section 3.4.3.3), other methods may be more appropriate to calculate an accurate remaining value of an asset. The most frequently used alternate method is sum of the periods, most frequently referred to as sum of the years or sum of the years digits (SOYD) method.

To use the sum of the years digits method, use the following formula:

$$\text{Depreciation (SOYD)} = \text{original cost} - \text{expected salvage value} \times \left(\frac{N}{S}\right)$$

N is the number of years of depreciation remaining at the start of the year for which depreciation is being calculated. S is the cumulative sum of the total number of years of depreciation.

Hence, for a one-year depreciation period, S is 1, for two years, S is three (one plus two), for five years, S is 15 (1 + 2 + 3 + 4 + 5), etc.

For example, consider a $15,000,000 investment with no net salvage value being depreciated over five years. The following table shows the calculation of the depreciation of this asset by the SOYD method and compares it to straight-line depreciation.

Table A3.2.1: Sum of the Years versus Straight-Line Depreciation
Asset Value $15,000,000, No Salvage Value, Five-Year Depreciation Period

Year	N	S	$\left(\dfrac{N}{S}\right)$	Depreciation ($)	(SOYD) Cumulative (%)	Depreciation ($)	(Straight-Line) Cumulative (%)
1	5	15	0.33	5,000,000	33	3,000,000	20
2	4	15	0.27	4,000,000	60	3,000,000	40
3	3	15	0.20	3,000,000	80	3,000,000	60
4	2	15	0.13	2,000,000	93	3,000,000	80
5	1	15	0.07	1,000,000	100	3,000,000	100
				15,000,000		15,000,000	

Use a straight-line interpolation of the annual non-straight-line depreciation to determine the monthly value; therefore, monthly depreciation for SOYD is simply one-twelfth of the annual depreciation.

SOYD takes a higher depreciation in the early years of an asset and less in the later years. As noted before, a new car depreciates far more in the first hour of its use than in the last year of its use. While the SOYD approach has the elegance of weighting resale value, it puts a distortion into the smoothness of reported income. On balance, the straight-line method is used more often, which partly reflects the fact that the vast majority of businesses keep their assets throughout their depreciation period.

Sample Problem A3.2.1 Straight-Line versus SOYD Depreciation

Consider an asset that has an initial cost of $25,000,000 and expected life of 8 years. The salvage value is expected to be $1,000,000 at the end of that period. Calculate the depreciation for this same asset by straight-line and SOYD methods. Comment on which method would be more accurate if the asset is a fleet of vehicles or an expansion of an oil refinery.

Solution:
Straight-line method:

Under the straight-line method, the depreciation charged every year is equal. Therefore, for the given asset, charge 12.5% (100% ÷ 8) of original cost less salvage value for each year as depreciation.

$$\text{Depreciation} = \frac{\text{original value} - \text{salvage value}}{\text{life of asset}}$$

$$= \frac{\$25,000,000 - \$1,000,000}{8}$$

$$= \$3,000,000$$

Year	Depreciation ($)	Depreciation (%)	Cumulative Depreciation (%)
1	3,000,000	12.50	12.50
2	3,000,000	12.50	25.00
3	3,000,000	12.50	37.50
4	3,000,000	12.50	50.00
5	3,000,000	12.50	62.50
6	3,000,000	12.50	75.00
7	3,000,000	12.50	87.50
8	3,000,000	12.50	100.00

Under the SOYD method,

$$\text{Depreciation} = (\text{Original Cost} - \text{Salvage value}) \times N/S,$$

where N = number of years of life remaining
and S = sum of N.

The depreciation for each year is different under the SOYD method. It is front-loaded with more depreciation being charged in initial years.

Year	N	S	$\left(\dfrac{N}{S}\right)$	Depreciation ($)	Depreciation (%)	Cumulative Depreciation (%)
1	8	36	0.22	5,333,333.33	22.22	22.22
2	7	36	0.19	4,666,666.67	19.44	41.67
3	6	36	0.17	4,000,000.00	16.67	58.33
4	5	36	0.14	3,333,333.33	13.89	72.22
5	4	36	0.11	2,666,666.67	11.11	83.33
6	3	36	0.08	2,000,000.00	8.33	91.67
7	2	36	0.06	1,333,333.33	5.56	97.22
8	1	36	0.03	666,666.67	2.78	100.0

For a fleet of vehicles, SOYD makes more sense because much of the value of a vehicle is lost in the initial years. Vehicles are often not kept throughout the depreciation period; they get resold before the end of their life. The SOYD method is more accurate in estimating the resale value of the vehicle.

For an oil refinery, the straight-line method is more accurate. The realization of value from an oil refinery is steady over many years, and refineries are not typically sold partway through their useful life. Therefore, loss in the value of the oil refinery is best estimated to be the same each year by straight-line depreciation.

Sample Problem A3.2.2 Straight-Line versus SOMD Depreciation

Movieco is a successful movie rental store. A new DVD movie costs the store $25. Its expected life is 12 months, and its estimated salvage value is $5 at that time.

Calculate the depreciation by both the straight-line and sum-of-the-month's-digits method. Which method is a more appropriate choice?

Solution:

Straight-line method:

Month	Depreciation ($)	Depreciation (%)	Cumulative Depreciation (%)
1	1.67	8.33	8.33
2	1.67	8.33	16.67
3	1.67	8.33	25.00
4	1.67	8.33	33.33
5	1.67	8.33	41.67
6	1.67	8.33	50.00
7	1.67	8.33	58.33
8	1.67	8.33	66.67
9	1.67	8.3	75.00
10	1.67	8.33	83.33
11	1.67	8.33	91.67
12	1.67	8.33	100.00

$$\text{Depreciation} = \frac{\text{original cost} - \text{salvage value}}{\text{life of asset}}$$
$$= \frac{\$25 - \$5}{12}$$
$$= \$1.67$$

Under the straight-line method, the depreciation charged every period (month, in this case) is equal. Therefore, for the given asset, charge 8.33% (100% ÷ 12) of original cost less salvage value for each year as depreciation.

Sum of months digits (SOMD):

Month	N	S	$\left(\dfrac{N}{S}\right)$	Depreciation ($)	Depreciation (%)	Cumulative Depreciation (%)
1	12	78	0.15	3.08	15.38	15.38
2	11	78	0.14	2.82	14.10	29.49
3	10	78	0.13	2.56	12.82	42.31
4	9	78	0.12	2.31	11.54	53.85
5	8	78	0.10	2.05	10.26	64.10
6	7	78	0.09	1.79	8.97	73.08
7	6	78	0.08	1.54	7.69	80.77
8	5	78	0.06	1.28	6.41	87.18
9	4	78	0.05	1.03	5.13	92.31
10	3	78	0.04	0.77	3.85	96.15
11	2	78	0.03	0.51	2.56	98.72
12	1	78	0.01	0.26	1.28	100.00

Depreciation = (original cost – salvage value) $\times \left(\dfrac{N}{S}\right)$, where N = number of periods remaining and S = sum of N.

A DVD loses most of its value in the first few months since as the movie gets older, the number of rentals decreases drastically. Therefore, the sum of the months method is more accurate to calculate the monthly loss in the value of the DVD.

Appendix 3.3: Interest versus Principal Repayments

When people or companies borrow money from a lender, they accept that they must make payments to the lender. There are two components to these payments: interest and principal repayment (giving back to the lender the original amount of the loan). Interest and principal payments are treated quite differently in financial statements and for tax purposes. Interest is an expense to the payer and income to the lender; principal repayment is not treated as an expense to the borrower and does not create income for the lender.

The concepts of debt and interest are discussed in greater detail in chapters 5 and 7. However, in dealing with income statements and balance sheets, some basic concepts must be understood.

First, loans will have a payment due at a time period specified in the loan agreement. Most mortgages on residences have monthly payments, but many business loans have quarterly, semi-annual, or annual payments.

Second, a loan repayment is a single sum of money but can be thought of as having a component designated as interest and a component designated as principal repayment. The loan agreement will specify a basis for the repayment of principal; almost all loans require that interest on the outstanding balance (remaining principal) be paid on an ongoing basis. Only in very rare cases will a lender allow interest to compound by not being paid up as it becomes due.

If all payments have been made on a loan as per the loan agreement, the loan is current. If a payment has been missed, the loan is past due, overdue, or in arrears.

Third, principal can be repaid in a variety of ways. Three different methods of repayment of principal are shown in Table A3.3.1. Note that combinations of these methods can be used. For instance, a lender might specify no principal repayment for the first five years of a loan and then switch to straight-line principal repayment for the next five years.

Table A3.3.1

Methods of Principal Repayment			
Loan Type (Name)	Principal Repayment	Total Payment	Comments
1. Straight line	Constant in each period	Declines over the life of the loan, since the principal payment is the same in each period and the interest payment decreases as the principal is repaid.	This type of loan is very common for long-term loans to businesses that are secured by assets, since the remaining principal matches the depreciating value of the asset.

Methods of Principal Repayment			
Loan Type (Name)	**Principal Repayment**	**Total Payment**	**Comments**
2. Mortgage or levelized payment	Low in the initial period and increasing over the life of the asset	Constant in each period. This means that the sum of interest and principal is the same in each period. In the early stages of the loan, most of the payment is interest and principal repayment is low. In the late stages of the loan, interest is low and principal repayment is high.	This type of loan is very common for real property (land and buildings) since these tend to hold their market value and not depreciate in a straight line.
3. Balloon	Zero until the final period	Total payment is a constant for every period (interest on the total principal) except the final period. The final payment is interest plus the total principal amount.	This type of loan is typical for bonds.

Interest is treated as an operating expense of a company and shows up on the income statement. As noted above, interest can show up either in SG&A or as a negative entry in other income. Treating it as other income has the merit of distinguishing the financing cost of the business from the pure cost of operating the business independent of how it is financed. However, many companies put interest in SG&A because they reserve other income for non-recurring expenses.

Principal repayments are not treated as an operating cost and do not show up on the income statement. They are an important entry on the statement of cash flow, and they are reflected in the balance sheet. Principal payments are related to the financing of the business, not to the monthly, quarterly, and annual creation of value through the delivery of a good or a service. As will be clearer when the balance sheet is considered in Chapter 4, a company can raise equity (investment by owners) to pay down principal or can use retained earnings (value created by the company and not paid out to owners as dividends) to pay down principal. Alternatively, it can increase borrowings if it needs money for growth. Hence, changes in the principal amount of debt do not show up on the income statement.

As noted in Table A3.3.1, much business long-term debt is secured by assets and issued based on a fixed and constant schedule of the repayment of principal. For example, a company that borrows $1 million to finance new equipment might arrange a 10-year repayment schedule in which 10 annual principal repayments of $100,000 are made in addition to interest on the unpaid principal. This is referred to as a straight-line repayment of principal. If the company cannot meet its interest and principal repayment obligations, then the lender has the right to seize the assets and sell them to recover the outstanding portion of the debt. Because the assets are the security for the loan, the repayment schedule of principal should reflect the declining value of the assets, i.e., a bank that has a 10-year repayment schedule has at least some notion that the assets can be sold for 90% of original value after one year, 50% of original value after five years, etc.

As noted in Table A3.3.1, most real estate debt is also secured by assets, but is subject to a different form of financing in which payments are **levelized**, meaning the combined payment of principal and interest is constant. Principal retirement in the early years is low; most of the total payment in the early years goes to interest. Total interest payments over the course of the loan are higher, but the early year payments are lower. Lenders consider this for real estate because the loss in resale value of real estate in the early years is normally quite low, so the security for the debt retains its value. Levelized payments are the basis of almost all home mortgages and allow young couples to buy the largest possible home based on their current income. It is important to note that in the case of a levelized payment, the interest expense on the income statement varies each year.

The following table compares fixed principal (straight-line) repayment versus levelized payment for $1,000 of debt with an interest rate of 8% compounded annually, a term of 20 years, and one annual payment of principal and interest.

Table A3.3.2

	Straight Line				Level			
Year	Interest Paid ($)	Principal Paid ($)	Total Payment ($)	Remaining Balance ($)	Interest Paid ($)	Principal Paid ($)	Total Payment ($)	Remaining Balance ($)
1	80.00	50.00	130.00	950.00	80.00	21.85	101.85	978.15
2	76.00	50.00	126.00	900.00	78.25	23.60	101.85	954.55
3	72.00	50.00	122.00	850.00	76.36	25.49	101.85	929.06
4	68.00	50.00	118.00	800.00	74.32	27.53	101.85	901.53
5	64.00	50.00	114.00	750.00	72.12	29.73	101.85	871.80
6	60.00	50.00	110.00	700.00	69.74	32.11	101.85	839.69
7	56.00	50.00	106.00	650.00	67.18	34.68	101.85	805.02
8	52.00	50.00	102.00	600.00	64.40	37.45	101.85	767.57
9	48.00	50.00	98.00	550.00	61.41	40.45	101.85	727.12
10	44.00	50.00	94.00	500.00	58.17	43.68	101.85	683.44
11	40.00	50.00	90.00	450.00	54.67	47.18	101.85	636.26
12	36.00	50.00	86.00	400.00	50.90	50.95	101.85	585.31
13	32.00	50.00	82.00	350.00	46.82	55.03	101.85	530.28
14	28.00	50.00	78.00	300.00	42.42	59.43	101.85	470.85
15	24.00	50.00	74.00	250.00	37.67	64.18	101.85	406.67
16	20.00	50.00	70.00	200.00	32.53	69.32	101.85	337.35
17	16.00	50.00	66.00	150.00	26.99	74.86	101.85	262.48
18	12.00	50.00	62.00	100.00	21.00	80.85	101.85	181.63
19	8.00	50.00	58.00	50.00	14.53	87.32	101.85	94.31
20	4.00	50.00	54.00	0.00	7.54	94.31	101.85	0.00

What are the comparable values for a balloon repayment of $1,000? For years 1 through 19, the interest payment is $80 per year, the principal repayment is zero, and the remaining balance is $1,000. For year 20, the interest payment is $80, the principal repayment is $1,000, and the total payment is $1,080.

Note that in all cases of loan repayment, the remaining balance at the end of the loan period is zero, i.e., the principal amount is fully returned to the lender.

Appendix 3.4: Taking Money out of a Canadian Owner-Operated Business

If a company is operated by its owners, as many small companies are, then tax treatment makes it advantageous to "bonus out" money from the company rather than paying a dividend on shares. Initial earnings in small companies are taxed at a low rate, and it may make sense to dividend this amount out. However, once a company's marginal earnings move into a higher bracket, say 40%, then the effective tax on a dividend would be 40% within the company and about 30% by the individual receiving the dividend for a total net tax rate of about 58%. (For a dollar of earnings in the company, 40 cents of tax is paid in the company, and the owner receiving the dividend, assuming they are in a high tax bracket, would pay an additional 30% of the remaining 60 cents as tax). If the money is paid out as a bonus to the owner/managers, then the net tax rate, depending on the province, is 39 to 53% at the highest marginal tax rate. Hence, where the owners all work for a business, the common practice is to take money out of a business through a bonus that is treated as salary. This increases SG&A and reduces net income, reducing the tax paid by the company.

Such a company would always show low earnings because the bonuses are set to ensure this. If a person is purchasing a company like this, he or she should calculate notional earnings by adding back any management bonus above and beyond a normal compensation level to see what earnings would be in the absence of tax-effective bonusing of surplus earnings.

Sample Problem A3.4 Adjusting the Income Statement of an Owner-Operated Company

Acmeco is planning to buy a Canadian owner-operated business. Four years of income statements show that the business has earned a net profit of only $300,000 for the last four years. The operating and net incomes have been reduced by the salary and bonus that the owner has paid to himself each year.

Income Statements for Acmeco ($000)				
	Year 1	Year 2	Year 3	Year 4
Gross revenue	3,857	3,761	3,905	3,920
Other income	0	0	0	0
Returns and bad debts	0	0	0	0
Net revenue	3,857	3,761	3,905	3,920
COGS	1,542.8	1,504.4	1,562	1,568
Contribution margin	2,314.2	2,256.6	2,343	2,352
Manager's salary	180	180	180	180
Bonus	760	760	760	760
Other SG&A	1,062	1,050	1,020	1,108
Operating income	312.2	266.6	383	304
Net income	312.2	266.6	383	304

What adjustments would you make to the income statement to reflect how the company's income statements would look if Acmeco owned the business?

Solution:

The salary of $180,000 and the bonus of $760,000 each year have reduced the operating and net profit figure dramatically. If the same business were owned by Acmeco, then the managers would not pay the bonus that the previous owner took, which he did to minimize his overall tax. The compensation of $180,000 in the adjusted statement would cover salary plus bonus for the manager they appointed to run this business.

After adjustment, both the pre-tax operating and net income figures are almost $1,060,000 every year, as shown in the following table:

Adjusted Income Statements for Acmeco ($000)				
	Year 1	Year 2	Year 3	Year 4
Gross revenue	3,857	3,761	3,905	3,920
Other income	0	0	0	0
Returns and bad debts	0	0	0	0
Net revenue	3,857	3,761	3,905	3,920
COGS	1,542.8	1,504.4	1,562	1,568
Contribution margin	2,314.2	2,256.6	2,343	2,352
Manager's salary	180	180	180	180
Other SG&A	1,062	1,050	1,020	1,108
Operating income	1,072.2	1,026.6	1,143	1,064
Net income	1,072.2	1,026.6	1,143	1,064

For simplicity, the effect of taxes on the income statement has not been considered. By paying himself a large bonus, the previous owner would pay personal income tax on this amount. Since tax is calculated on an overall company basis, the net tax rate after purchase would depend on the tax position of the purchasing company.

Problems

3.1 Which of the following items would you classify in COGS?

1. Circuit boards that go into the manufactured item
2. Stationery
3. The pay of the receptionist in the sales office
4. The pay of the receptionist in the manufacturing plant
5. Miscellaneous screws and fittings
6. Telephone charges
7. Raw steel for structural members
8. The pay of a welder brought in on contract
9. The pay of a welder on salary
10. The pay of the floor sweeper in the manufacturing plant
11. The cost of contract cleaning in the manufacturing plant
12. The cost of the crew of a service vehicle
13. The maintenance charges of a service vehicle
14. The annual registration cost of a service vehicle
15. The cost of annual business permits
16. Welding consumables (i.e., welding rod)
17. The pay of the shipping department
18. Part or all of the company president's salary
19. Freight on inbound materials
20. Freight on outbound products (assuming FOB point is remote from the factory, i.e., the manufacturer pays the freight rather than the customer.)

3.2 Large rotating equipment (for example, air blowers or gas compressors used in oil refining operations) requires lubrication. Given the enormous capital cost of such equipment, the lubrication system must be highly instrumented, i.e., it must have equipment shutdown links in the event of low lube oil pressure, pump failure, etc. Typically, a separate skid containing the lube oil pump and holding tank is ordered separate from the compressor or air blower.

You work for a small company with a staff of 20 that manufactures these products as well as oil field gas compressor skids. The company does not code its labor to specific projects, since labor moves around the shop floor from job to job. Also, tracking the number of hours on each skid proved to be too inaccurate to be of value. However, component parts are tracked and coded to each product skid. Over the last five years, margin based on COGS of component parts has run at only 32%, i.e., COGS (component parts) has run at 68%.

A pipeline company that is building a major expansion has requested a budgetary quote (in essence, an indication price that will be used by the pipeline company to prepare its investment analysis, which may influence whether the company is asked to prepare a formal bid in the future). The requested quote is for one lube oil skid that is twice the capacity of any unit built before in the shop. The pipeline company indicates that they may require 20 such units (two at each of 10 compressor stations along the new pipeline). An engineer in the company has priced components at $356,000.

What do you give as a budgetary quote?

What reservations would you have about the accuracy of the quote? Is it at more risk of being too high or too low? Why? Can you think of questions you would ask the engineer?

3.3 Polymerco, a North American manufacturer of specialty polymers, has the following highly condensed income statement:

Polymerco Income Statement		
	This Year ($000)	Last Year ($000)
Gross sales	25,421	24,224
Bad debt	nil	nil
Net sales	25,421	24,224
COGS	22,243	21,341
Contribution margin	3,178	2,883
CM (%)	12.5	11.9
SG&A	2,122	2,067
Operating income	1,056	816
Other income and interest on long-term debt	−60	−50
Net income	996	766

Current sales are to North American customers only. The president casually mentions that it would be nice to have more offshore sales to diversify the company. What are your recommendations for the following situations?

- Polymerco's production is running at 84% of capacity.
- Polymerco's production is running at 100% of capacity.

3.4 A friend of yours decides to start a hotshot business. A hotshot business involves quick deliveries to operating facilities such as refineries or oil wells that have a high marginal cost of downtime. His entire proposed customer base is within a narrow area, so trip length is consistent. He intends to sell the business after one year in order to return to school and wants to keep monthly books in order to demonstrate the value of the business to a potential purchaser.

For each of the following scenarios, what expense items should he consider to be within COGS?

- He is the sole employee and, hence, responsible for selling, administration, and driving. He buys a pickup truck.
- He buys a pickup truck but decides to look after the office and selling. He pays a friend on a per-trip basis to do the driving.
- He pays a friend a per-trip fee to both supply a pickup truck and do the driving.

If the trip length was highly variable (for example, some trips of 15 km and some of 1,500 km) instead of consistent, what other information would you need?

Can you think of a kind of expense that could go into COGS that might create a timing problem within your friend's relevant time frame?

3.5 a) Your aunt graduated with a degree in chemistry in the late 1960s and started a small distribution company. Over the years, she has skillfully managed the business. She sees an opportunity to expand by buying a medium-sized local distribution company, Distco. She has asked you to help.

You sit down with the accountant for Distco and ask how she has determined COGS in the past. The accountant tells you that every year, there were changes in what went into COGS and what went into SG&A because Distco's owners could not come up with a scheme that met their needs. She says, however, that she has the information by raw account and will recast the financial data in a way that makes sense to you. Since your aunt is away for two weeks, you decide to analyze the data.

Distco has three warehouses. Permanent staffing is two people per warehouse: one to take orders and arrange shipping and one to package up orders. Extra help is brought in on a temporary basis if needed for busy times. In addition, the head office has a president, a receptionist, two bookkeepers, and a two-person sales team.

Classify the following accounts into COGS, SG&A, or asset:

Warehouse staff salaries	
Annual Christmas party	
Temporary staff salaries	
Purchase cost of chemicals and supplies	
Shipping costs from supplier to warehouse	
Shipping costs from warehouse to customer	
Phone costs	
Travel for sales staff	
Head office staff salaries	
Cost of benefits for permanent staff	
Cost of storage racks	
Utility bills	
New computer hardware and software to support integrated order, inventory, sale, and invoice system	
Membership in Chamber of Commerce	
Warehouse and office rental charges	
Snow removal and grounds upkeep costs	

b) After the accountant takes your advice, she returns with the following five-year income statement for Distco:

Distco Summary Income Statement					
($000)	Year 1	Year 2	Year 3	Year 4	Year 5
Gross sales	4,662	5,126	6,229	6,641	6,978
Bad debt	nil	nil	nil	nil	nil
Net sales	4,662	5,126	6,229	6,641	6,978
COGS	3,846	4,260	5,388	5,857	6,183
Contribution margin	816	866	841	784	795
SG&A	420	434	447	423	424
Operating income	396	432	394	361	371
Other income and interest on long-term debt	-60	-50	-40	-30	-20
Net income	336	382	354	331	351

What do you tell your aunt about the business? Why?

Be sure to look not only at aggregate net income from the business (which is slightly higher over the five-year period) but also at the margin.

c) What do you think creates the value in a distribution business? Think of what someone else would need to enter the business. What would you try to do to preserve value if you and your aunt decided to proceed to buy Distco?

3.6 You are the new Marketing VP for Watermetco, a company that sells two items: meters manufactured by a major supplier (an OEM, or Original Equipment Manufacturer) and meter servicing and calibration. These business lines are fairly independent in that you service all kinds of meters, not just the ones that you sell, and you sell meters to customers who do their own service. Hence, the two lines of business are not linked, i.e., you do not need to sell a meter to get the service work for the meter.

Your customers are water utilities. These utilities could buy the meters directly from the manufacturer, but they place orders through you for convenience. You have the summary shown in the following table for the current performance of the US region from your financial contact within the company.

Watermetco Financial Forecast US Regional Office

	Meter Sales	Meter Service	Total
Revenue			
Product sales	2,100,000		2,100,000
Service sales		672,000	672,000
Parts sales for service		39,000	39,000
Subtotal	2,100,000	711,000	2,811,000
Percent of total (%)	74.7	25.3	100
Direct Costs			
Cost of materials	1,942,000	36,500	1,978,500
Direct salaries and fringe per product	71,800	213,600	285,400
(includes sales costs)			
WCB and other direct employee costs	700	1,100	1,800
Government sealing fees		2,800	2,800
Freight		18,600	18,600
Direct sales costs (travel, etc.)	10,000	3,400	13,400
Small tools and supplies		9,500	9,500
Subtotal	2,024,500	285,500	2,310,000
Contribution margin	75,500	425,500	501,000
CM (%)	3.6	59.8	17.8
General and Admin Costs			
Travel and accommodation			62,000
Advertising and promotions			65,000
Vehicle lease			6,000
Business and property tax			20,700
Legal and professional fees			12,000
Office wages and salaries			96,000
Office fringe benefits			11,900
Lawn, snow, cleaning, and security			6,700
Utilities			13,000
Printing and stationery			7,000
Subscriptions			1,200
Telephone			12,800
Subtotal			314,300
Net income			186,700

The president of the company tells you that as part of the overall strategy of the company, you are to ensure an expansion of activity in the existing US region with the goal of generating more net income. As a result, you are going to hire a sales leader.

Based on the financial statement, explain in one or two paragraphs what you will tell the new sales person to emphasize and why. Make sure to include the following:

- What is the approximate cost of the extra staff person (the sales leader) in terms of salary and likely level of expense?

- What percentage increase in meter sales and in meter service would be necessary to recover the cost of this extra staff?

3.7 You are the president of a medium-sized manufacturing company, and you face the following situations:

- Margin is falling, and bad debt is rising, nearly dollar for dollar.
- Margin is falling, and bad debt is rising, but only at a fraction of the margin loss. Unit sales are rising.
- Margin is falling, sales are falling, and bad debt is rising.
- Margin is falling, and warranty claims are rising, nearly dollar for dollar.
- Margin is falling, and COGS is increasing, nearly dollar for dollar.

You have a Chief Financial Officer (CFO), a Vice President of Marketing, and a General Manager of Production reporting to you. With which one or two of your staff do you first discuss the issue, and what questions do you try to get answered (one or two sentences per case)?

3.8 The table shows the compressed income statement of a company.

	Past Year ($)	Next Year ($)
Revenue	18,232,000	18,232,000
Allowance for bad debt	182,000	182,000
Net revenue	18,050,000	18,050,000
Cost of goods sold	12,179,000	12,179,000
Contribution margin	5,871,000	5,871,000
Contribution margin (%)	32.2	32.2
Sales, General, and Administrative Expenses	2,796,000	2,796,000
All items except depreciation	2,430,000	
Depreciation	645,000	
Operating income	400,000	0
Other income	1,045,000	
Net income		
Operating cash flow		
Net cash flow		

What is the company's cash flow from operations in the past year and its net cash flow from operations in the past year?

In the next year, sales, contribution margin, and SG&A expenses each hold steady. There is no extraordinary income or expense in the company that is not related to the core business, i.e., other income is zero for the next year. However, an existing piece of equipment had an original cost of $14,000,000 (no salvage value was assumed at the time the original depreciation schedule was created), and an accumulated depreciation of $10,000,000 is retired for a salvage value of $4,000,000. A new piece of equipment is bought and installed early in the next year for $21,000,000. Management determines to use the same depreciation period of 7 years for the new piece of equipment that it had used for the old piece of equipment.

Complete the income statement for the next year, assuming that the depreciation for all items other than the new piece of equipment is unchanged. Using straight-line depreciation, answer the following questions:

- How long was the old piece of equipment in service? Is an extraordinary adjustment required at the time of its retirement?
- What is the cash flow from operations in the next year?
- What is the net cash flow from all items shown on the income statement for the next year?
- Just given the data for the two years, was the company sound in buying the piece of equipment? Why? (one or two sentences)
- If the salvage value of the old piece of equipment was $1,000,000 instead of $4,000,000, assume that you show the impact of the unrecovered depreciation on the old piece of equipment in other income. What is the value of other income next year in this case? Does cash flow from operations change?

3.9 Your friend decides to open a video rental outlet that specializes in classic films. Most of her stock is reissued DVDs, and she does not change her stock each year. She is not skilled in financial matters and asks you to help her understand her business. She hands you a shoebox full of her receipts and notes, from which you withdraw the following information:

Rent-a-Classic ($)	
Staff wages, Jan–Jun	24,782
Cash register and computer purchase	9,587
Cash receipts for the 3-month period Jan–Mar	24,478
Store fixtures (shelving and counter)	16,000
Cash receipts for the 3-month period Oct–Dec	51,266
WCB and vacation payments for the year	496
Purchase of video stock, used videos	39,000
Advertising (neighborhood drop of flyer)	266
Cash receipts for the 3-month period Apr–Jun	36,221
Promotion (support a neighborhood hockey team)	400
Office supplies (pens, paper, etc)	396
General manager (Aunt's) monthly pay	3,000
Building rental, annual charge (includes snow removal)	38,000
Cash receipts for the 3-month period Jul–Sept	42,875
Membership, South Side Business Association	400
Subscription, Video World Magazine	120
Staff Christmas party	475
Telephone, annual bill	692
Building cleaning service, annual charge	5,600
Natural gas, annual charge	3,678
Sold table and six chairs left in store by previous occupant	500
Advertising (ad in community paper)	400
Software for title and cash management	650
Annual business tax	425
Staff wages, Jul–Dec	26,822
Purchase of video stock, new releases	52,000
Annual fee for payroll preparation	480
Electricity and water, annual bill	1,896
Advertising (neighborhood drop of flyer)	298

Is your friend's business creating value? Is it generating cash? Should she be in this business?

Some hints to do this exercise:

- Is there cost of sales in a video rental business? If no, then ignore the variable cost component.
- Distinguish between assets and expenses. Remember that asset purchases do not go on an income statement, only depreciation.
- Make any reasonable assumption on depreciation by asset class, but be prepared to justify it. Do you think the depreciation period should be set by the life of the assets or the life of the overall business?
- Simplify the income statement by grouping some expenses (e.g., lump all advertising and promotional costs into one category).
- In addition to the income statement, think about cash flow from the business and the trend line of sales.

3.10 Answer the following questions about depreciation:

a) In one or two sentences, explain the purpose of putting depreciation into an income statement.

b) If an asset has a depreciation period of 12 years, an original value of $13.45 million, and an estimated salvage value of $250,000, what is its accumulated depreciation (straight line) at the end of the fifth year?

c) An asset has an original purchase value of $12 million, a depreciation period of 6 years, and an estimated salvage value of zero. What is the entry into other income if it is sold for a salvage value of $6 million after four years of operating the piece of equipment? If the salvage value is $4 million? If the salvage value is $2 million? If the salvage value is zero?

d) Assume an asset has an original value of $5 million, a depreciation period of five years, and no salvage value. If it is sold after three years for $1 million, then there is $1 million in non-depreciated value that must be reflected in the income statement as other income. Is this true or false? If true, is the entry in other income a loss or a gain? In hindsight, was the operating income for the business understated or overstated for the three-year period in which the piece of equipment was operated?

3.11 Oilpatchco is a stand-alone oil field supply and service firm that is 75% owned by a large publicly traded company. The company has three business lines: a pump product, a sucker rod product, and a service division that services the company's products. (Sucker rod is the name given to the metal shaft that connects an oil well's surface motor to the pump at the bottom of the well.) Assume that for the five-year period, activity in the oil patch has been steady or growing slightly. The pump product is a new design that is displacing other styles of pumps in specialized applications. Oilpatchco assembles pump components, so the labor content is low compared to the material. Oilpatchco manufactures sucker rods from raw steel, with capital-intensive equipment. Service is in the field to operating wells and offered through a fleet of vehicles.

This small business has a vice president of marketing (which includes sales), of finance and admin, of manufacturing (which includes research and new product development), and of service. The VP of Marketing is responsible for the pump business, the VP of Manufacturing is responsible for the rod business line, and the VP of Service is responsible for the service business line.

Look at the five-year history portrayed in the income statements in the following table.

Oilpatchco Income Statements

($000)	Year 1	Year 2	Year 3	Year 4	Year 5
Revenue					
Pumps					
Units sold	421	466	558	679	779
Revenue	2,515	2,759	3,175	3,782	4,300
Warranty and bad debt	35.2	42.8	59.7	75.3	103.2
Net revenue	2,480	2,716	3,115	3,707	4,197
Cost of goods sold	1,811	2,066	2,469	3,023	3,499
Contribution margin	669	650	646	684	698
Rod					
Km sold	312.0	327.6	334.2	357.5	379.0
Revenue	7,017	7,662	8,116	8,926	9,802
Warranty and bad debt	63.2	65.9	66.6	63.4	62.7
Net revenue	6,954	7,597	8,050	8,862	9,739
Cost of goods sold	3,298	3,563	3,717	4,034	4,342
Contribution margin	3,656	4,034	4,332	4,828	5,397
Service					
Revenue	4,272	4,656	5,255	5,511	5,853
Warranty and bad debt	51.3	51.2	47.3	44.1	41.0
Net revenue	4,221	4,605	5,207	5,467	5,812
Cost of goods sold	1,837	1,979	2,207	2,287	2,400
Contribution margin	2,384	2,626	3,000	3,180	3,412
Total gross revenue	13,804	15,078	16,546	18,219	19,955
Total warranty and bad debt	149.6	159.9	173.5	182.7	206.9
Total net revenue	13,655	14,918	16,372	18,036	19,748
Total cost of goods sold	6,946	7,608	8,393	9,344	10,240
Total contribution margin	6,709	7,310	7,979	8,692	9,507
SG&A Expense					
All expenses less depreciation	2,457	2,555	2,657	2,764	2,874
Depreciation	3,125	3,301	3,456	3,701	3,812
Total SG&A	5,582	5,856	6,113	6,464	6,687
Operating income	1,126	1,454	1,866	2,227	2,821

Answer the following questions by making a table of key numbers or ratios you have extracted from the income statements through vertical and horizontal analysis:

- Does the business have a problem? If yes, what is the problem?
- If it has a problem, what do you think are possible causes of the problem? Is one possible cause more likely than others?
- Assume you work for the large publicly traded company. If you agreed to a transfer to become the president of this business, what would you focus on in the first six months?
- With which direct report(s) would you spend the most time in the first month? Why?

- Provide a marked-up income statement for Oilpatchco with any supplemental calculations you have done to help in your analysis of the business.

Following are some hints on doing this problem:

- If the income statement has units sold as well as revenue, you should look at price per unit. If a product line is changing rapidly, this may not have meaning, but it can be a measure of price history for a stable product line.
- In analyzing a business over many years, always look at price history and annual growth rate for sales (units and $), and calculate the bad debt/warranty cost, COGS, and contribution margin as a percentage of sales, preferably by product line.
- Think of yourself as a business manager whose job security depends on your ability to analyze this business and identify any problems you see. Use critical judgment.

3.12 An abbreviated income statement for Startupco is as follows:

Income Statement for Startupco		
	($000)	Percentage of Sales (%)
Sales	1,231	100
Less allowance for bad debt/warranty	18	1.5
Net revenue	1,213	98.5
Cost of goods sold	486	
Contribution margin	727	59.1
SG&A excluding depreciation	1,109	
	420	
Depreciation		
Operating income	−802	−65.2
Other income	0	
Net income	−802	−65.2

Assuming SG&A excluding depreciation is fixed, what is the break-even sales level at which Startupco covers the nut?

Assuming SG&A excluding depreciation increases at 30% of sales, i.e., each $1 increase in sales increases SG&A excluding depreciation by $0.30 above its current level, what is the break-even sales level at which Startupco covers the nut?

In each case, assume that depreciation is fully fixed and COGS is fully variable. Answer each of the two cases for book and cash.

The Balance Sheet

Key Concepts

- The balance sheet records at a point in time what a company has (assets) at the price of acquisition, and where the funds came from (liabilities and shareholder equity). Because all transactions are recorded at cost, assets are balanced by liabilities and equity.

- Liabilities and equity are records of the historical source of funds. Those funds no longer exist as such as they were used to acquire the assets.

- Liabilities are other peoples' money that a company has a legal obligation to repay. Lenders to a company have powerful rights to force collection of money owed or cause the bankruptcy of a company if payment cannot be made.

- Shareholder equity consists of share capital (proceeds from the sale of shares) and retained earnings. Shareholders elect company directors but have no legal right as shareholders to force a dividend payment or to trigger bankruptcy.

- Lenders get a modest return on their funds, so their focus is on security of repayment. Equity investors typically focus on dividends and growth in a company. Based on long-term averages, stocks are more volatile than bonds but have a higher return.

- Long-term lenders are usually secured by a claim on specific assets, such as a mortgage on land and buildings. In the event of non-payment, the long-term lender has the right to seize these assets and force their sale.

- Short-term lenders are usually unsecured, so they look to current assets for security of payment. Current assets such as inventory and receivables minus current liabilities such as money owed to suppliers and the short-term lender is called working capital. The ratio of current assets to current liabilities is called the working capital ratio. The primary cause of business failure is inadequate working capital.

- Fixing a working capital deficiency requires funds from non-current sources, either long-term debt or shareholder equity. Company growth almost always requires an increase in working capital.

- Company financial management decisions determine the ratio of liabilities to total assets, known as the leverage or debt ratio. High leverage increases return on equity in good times and places a company at significantly higher risk of insolvency (bankruptcy) in bad times.
- Preferred shares are a hybrid form of financing with some elements that mimic debt and some that mimic equity. Common shareholders think of preferred shares as debt, while lenders think of them as equity.

Chapter 4: The Balance Sheet

The balance sheet is probably the financial statement that managers least understand, but it is the most critical statement to a business in the short term. In the long term, companies that do not create value have problems, but in the short term, it is the balance sheet that illustrates those problems. Thus, one can say that companies fail because of balance sheet problems, recognizing that those problems may have arisen from a long history of negative earnings on the income statement. This chapter will first discuss the mechanics of the balance sheet, i.e., what each component measures. Then, the difference between debt and equity, two different types of money that companies use, will be explained. Next, you will see why the balance sheet is so important by looking at the different expectations that debt and equity have. Finally, you will learn about a hybrid form of financing: preferred shares that combine some of the features of debt and equity.

4.1   The Purpose of the Balance Sheet

The **balance sheet** shows what assets a business has at a given point in time and where the money came from to acquire those assets. Information in the balance sheet is organized in a manner that makes it easy to extract very helpful information.

The following is a simple equation that governs balance sheets:

$$\text{Assets} = \text{Liabilities} + \text{Shareholders' equity (capital)}$$

This can be thought of as a simple conservation equation. Money that goes into an enterprise is one of the following:

- Someone else's money, a **liability**, which in a broad sense is debt (money legally owed to others).
- The shareholders' direct investment (share capital) and the earnings made by the business and left in the business (retained earnings). The combination of share capital and retained earnings is called equity or **shareholders' equity**.

Cash from liabilities and equity is used to acquire **assets**, which the enterprise uses to create value. Note that some assets are material things, such as a machine, and some may be non-material. A patent (rights to use a technology) or receivables (money your customers owe you for goods you have shipped but they have not yet issued a cheque for) are examples of non-material assets.

As material assets wear out (depreciate) or become useless (are written off), they create a reduction in income. Remember that depreciation and write-downs show up on the income statement, and they reduce net income. Appropriate entries, such as accumulated depreciation, remove this value from the balance sheet so that at any point in time there is agreement between the remaining value of assets and the historical entries on previous income statements. This is discussed further below.

Balance sheets are calculated at a point in time because what a company has is constantly changing. A business will have current assets such as cash, receivables, inventory, and payables that will change on an hour-by-hour or day-by-day basis. This is no different than an individual's situation. Your bank and credit card balances are changing as you deposit your income and spend it. The balance sheet is therefore different than the income statement, which is calculated over a period of time. The income statement is a rate value (dollars per month or dollars per year), while the balance sheet is a point value (dollars).

4.2   *The Form and Components of the Balance Sheet*

Many balance sheets show assets on the left side and liabilities and shareholders' equity on the right side. An alternate presentation shows assets at the top of the balance sheet and liabilities and equity at the bottom. Assets are shown in decreasing order of liquidity, where **liquidity** measures the length of time it typically takes to convert something into cash. The assets at the top of the sheet are the most available assets, which means they are the quickest to be realized as cash. Similarly, liabilities and equity are shown in increasing order of when they must be paid. The most pressing liabilities are at the top of the list, while the liabilities that extend the farthest into the future are at the bottom, followed by shareholder's equity. A company has no legal obligation to return equity to its shareholders, so shareholders' equity is below even the most long-term liability. Short-term debt is at the top of the list of liabilities because it is a **demand loan** that under certain circumstances can become due at once.

As with income statements, there are some differences in terminology and practice between various companies. The important standard is consistency from period to period.

The distinction between current and long term is typically a one-year test. The space between current assets and long-term assets (and current liabilities and long-term debt and equity) is called the **current line**. The values of assets above this line are expected to be realized (to become cash) in less than a year. Inventory is almost always turned into product and sold within a year, and receivables are either collected within a year or written off as bad debt. The value of liabilities above this line is expected to become due and payable as cash in less than a year. For example, a company's suppliers typically deliver goods and invoice for payment in terms of net 30 days, meaning they want payment for the value of the goods within 30 days.

A typical balance sheet is shown below.

Assets	Liabilities
Current Assets	**Current Liabilities**
Cash	Short-term credit line
Receivables	Accounts payable
Short-term investments	Accrued expenses
Inventory	Taxes payable
Prepaid expenses	Current portion of long-term debt
Non-Current Assets	**Non-Current Liabilities**
Land, buildings, and equipment at cost	Repayable grants
Less accumulated depreciation	Long-term debt
Long-term investments	**Shareholders'/Owners' Equity**
	Capital shares
Goodwill and intangible assets	Retained earnings
Total assets	**Total liabilities and equity**

Assets are Present Tense; Liabilities and Equity are Past Tense

The assets of a company exist and have value at the time the balance sheet is calculated. They are intended to represent a conservative statement of the true value.

Assets in the balance sheet are recorded at the lesser of cost minus accumulated depreciation or market value. If an asset, such as land and a building, goes up in value, its value on the balance sheet is never increased. However, if the long-term market value of the land and building is lower than the purchase price and is permanently impaired, i.e., expected to remain lower for an indefinite period of time, the value of the asset is written down and reported as a loss in other income, which is a comparable entry to depreciation. This means the original cost of assets from the balance sheet can always be reconstructed by taking its book value less accumulated depreciation including any write-down.

Shareholder's equity records the value of money that owners invested in a company. This entry can be thought of as history in that the money is not sitting somewhere in the company: it has been used to acquire the assets. The same is true for liabilities: the money represented by liabilities has been used to acquire the assets in the company. Therefore, the liability and asset side of a balance sheet can be thought of as a historical record of how the company got the resources to acquire its assets. Liabilities and equity are history; assets are "here and now."

Remember that a liability is the term used when a company has a legal obligation to pay. While the money represented by liabilities has been used, making it "history," the obligation is "here and now." Companies must cover their liabilities as these become due.

Liquidity

Liquidity measures the length of time it typically takes to convert something into cash. Consider two assets: a car and a house. You can typically sell a car to a used car dealer and get the cash within a day or two. You can also sell a house in a day or two if the price is favorable enough, but it typically takes one to three months for all the legal documentation and financial arrangements to be finalized. If you want the best price for your house, it usually takes longer than a few days to sell. Hence, a car is a more liquid asset than a house.

Liquidity is a significant factor in the value placed on certain investments. Imagine two people, one of whom owns a 25% interest in a privately held business, with a value of $1 million, and another who owns a portfolio of stocks and bonds worth $1 million. The stocks and bonds are highly liquid; every business day there is a market in which people can sell stocks and bonds, and the cash from this is deposited into the account of the seller three days later. Selling a minority interest in a privately held business is extremely difficult. Usually, the other owners of the business have a right of approval of a new buyer (who will become their partner if the sale is approved) or even a right of first refusal (the right to match an offer of any buyer and buy the interest themselves). Rights of first refusal decrease the interest that buyers would otherwise have because they know that their "due diligence" in evaluating the minority interest may be wasted if the other existing owners exercise their right and buy up the minority interest. All of these factors combine to make a minority interest in a privately held company very difficult to sell and very difficult to realize full value.

Stock and bond markets are always concerned about liquidity. They take many steps to ensure that the market functions smoothly, that at any point in time, willing buyers and sellers can transact, and that funds are transferred promptly and reliably thereafter. Even long term investment vehicles, for example, 30-year bonds, can be sold at any time, although the price will be that day's price and not the face value of the bond, as discussed in Chapter 7. Liquidity makes ordinary investors more willing to buy stocks and bonds because they know that if their personal situation changes (for example, they have a family crisis of some sort), they are not kept from accessing their wealth.

When a business goes from being privately held to publicly traded on a stock exchange through a process called an initial public offering (IPO), all that is changing is liquidity and breadth of ownership. It is not unusual for the value of a company to more than double when it goes public, which is a sign of the high value of liquidity.

4.3 Assets

4.3.1 Current Assets

Assets that a company holds at a point in time that are expected to be converted into cash in less than one year are called **current assets.** They are important because they have the potential to be turned into cash in the near term, which is important to short-term creditors (those represented by current liabilities). The most liquid asset is **cash** itself, although it is normally a minor fraction of a company's assets. **Receivables** are the money owed to the company, typically from customers for goods already shipped. These can be counted on to generate cash quickly and are the second most liquid asset a company has. **Short-term investments** such as 30- or 90-day bonds rank ahead of **inventory** because in theory, one could borrow on them, whereas inventory cannot always be sold quickly for cash when a company is in distress. Note, however, that most companies have no short-term investments; the few that do are usually in a cyclical business where cash accumulates at certain times of the year. For example, a ski hill might have a large amount of cash in May that it will want to access by October. It will get a better interest rate if it invests this money in locked-in four-month deposits. Finally, most companies have some **prepaid expenses.** An example is an insurance bill that is paid in April for a full year's period. If the company keeps monthly financial statements, it does not want to charge the full annual amount in one lump sum; to do so would distort that month's earnings and make month-to-month comparisons of values meaningless. Hence, it stores the future value of this expense as an asset. At the end of April, 1/12 of the bill is expensed and 11/12 is carried in prepaid expenses. The following month, another 1/12 of the bill is expensed, and 10/12 is carried in prepaid expenses, and so on. For minor, non-material annual payments, this need not be done, but for more major expenses, this approach allows month-to-month consistency. Unless the 11/12 is initially carried as an asset, it would have to be fully expensed to get the books to balance.

Receivables and inventory are both typically related to sales and will increase as sales grow. Receivables are typically measured in equivalent days of sales, or the total amount of money owed as receivables is divided by monthly sales, and the resulting fraction is multiplied by 30. This number is a measure of the average time that a business takes to collect money from customers after a sale is booked (accrued), and it is typically 30 to 60 days for most businesses. Large companies are usually very reliable payers (the bad debt allowance or expense is low), but are slow to process an invoice because the paper related to the sale must be circulated within the large company. On average, small companies are less reliable but quicker payers. Since customers will not be quicker to pay a large invoice than a small invoice, as sales or sales per customer grow, the receivables measured in days is often unchanged, meaning the receivables measured in dollars is increasing.

Similarly, inventory is often measured as days of sales. As sales grow, it is usual to expect more inventory to be on hand to ensure that manufacturing is not delayed. Receivables and inventory are related to days by dividing by sales, i.e., the total dollar value of receivables or inventory is equated to days of sales revenue. Some inventory in a company is raw materials, while some is finished products, so when inventory is 30 days, it means it is worth the same amount of money as 30 days of sales. If most of the inventory is carried as raw materials and these are a small fraction of the total value of a sale, then in fact 30 days of inventory might support many months of production. This convention is a useful way of measuring trends in inventory, but it does not relate to the number of production days that can be supported from inventory. Payables follow a different convention, as discussed below.

Cash is often a small number or zero because a business puts all its spare cash into paying back short-term debt. It is normal for a business to arrange a short-term credit line with a bank and then "float" on this line. The amount of short-term debt varies day by day as payments from customers are deposited or payments to suppliers are cashed.

4.3.2 Fixed Assets

A company's hard assets are called **fixed assets**; they are part of non-current assets because their value will be realized over a period longer than a year. Examples are land, buildings, machinery, and vehicles. Some of these assets depreciate, but land does not, as discussed in Chapter 3. It is normal to show the full original purchase price of fixed assets and then to show accumulated depreciation as a reduction. Accumulated depreciation in this case would include all write-downs and losses from other income as well as accumulated depreciation that was included in the previous year's income statements. Small companies will show these three values on the main balance sheet: fixed assets at initial cost, accumulated depreciation, and the remaining net or book value of fixed assets. Large companies with lots of assets will usually just put the net value on the balance sheet and refer to a note about the financial statements, where the assets at cost and accumulated depreciation are documented. (Financial statements are accompanied by notes, and the notes form a part of the financial statements.) Depreciation on the balance sheet is accumulated and increases from year to year. The annual increase is what appears on the income statement.

Depreciation is the only negative value on the asset side of the balance sheet, so you can think of a negative asset entry as being the same in nature as a positive entry on the liability and equity side. Recall that liabilities and equity record where money came into the company and depreciation is a source of cash. Accumulated depreciation on the balance sheet is a record of cash kept in the business that exactly offsets the loss of value of the assets compared to their original cost.

If an asset is in service, its initial cost and accumulated depreciation are shown on the balance sheet or in a note to the balance sheet. This is true even if an asset is fully depreciated. Suppose a pump had an initial cost of $10,000 and was fully depreciated (no assumed salvage value) over 20 years but is still in service after 25 years. The $10,000 would be included in the assets at cost and in accumulated depreciation. Only when the pump is taken out of service is the $10,000 value removed from the two entries.

One advantage of seeing the initial value and accumulated depreciation is that it gives some indication of the age of assets. If Company A has assets with a cost of $5 million and accumulated depreciation of $4 million and Company B in the same industry has assets with a cost of $5 million and accumulated depreciation of $1 million, you can infer that Company A's assets are older than Company B's. However, be cautious in linking past asset value to current replacement value. Where firms have very long-lasting assets, some will have been built many years ago. In the last 40 years, cumulative inflation has reduced the purchasing value of a dollar by more than five times. Hence, old assets will have a low initial value relative to their replacement value in today's currency.

Technically, the label non-current assets would apply to fixed assets, long-term investments, and goodwill and intangible assets. In practice, all of these groups are sometimes labeled fixed assets, and both are used in this chapter.

4.3.3   Long-Term Investments

Sometimes, companies will have long-term financial investments such as bonds. This might be common in some industries like financial services. For example, insurance companies are obligated to have reserves to fund a higher than normal level of claims and might well invest these reserves. However, it is very rare in manufacturing and technology companies to have money tied up in long-term investments.

4.3.4   Goodwill and Intangible Assets

If a company buys another company for more than its book value, the surplus is considered by accounting rules to be **goodwill,** which is not treated as a fixed asset. This is a very conservative approach that ensures that the value of fixed assets will never exceed their original cost. Other intangible assets would include trademarks, patents, or franchise fees. These are of value, but they are not a fixed asset (an object). In the 1990s, goodwill and intangible assets could be depreciated over time just like fixed assets. Some spectacular cases of dot-com companies paying extraordinary amounts for acquisitions, followed in some cases by spectacular write-downs, led to a different standard. Goodwill and intangible assets can still be depreciated over time but need not be. Each year, management and the board of directors of a company must attest that the stated value of goodwill and intangible assets is truly representative of real value that will benefit the company in the future. The balance sheet shows the original purchase price and accumulated depreciation of goodwill, the same as for fixed assets.

4.3.5   Total Assets

The sum of current and non-current assets is total assets. This will always exactly equal total liabilities and equity. Often, people who are starting up a business think of the equity requirements as coming from hard assets, such as land, buildings, and equipment. In fact, a significant part of the assets of some businesses is tied up in receivables and inventory, which are not hard assets but simply the natural consequence of a business cycle. Both increase with sales, and the fact of business is that when sales grow, money is required to fund receivables (the value of product shipped to customers for which they have not yet paid) and higher levels of inventory. This money comes in part from increased payables, the money suppliers lend to help people buy their product. However, in almost all cases, the increase in payables is less than the increase in receivables because what a company sells is worth more than what it buys and its customers take as long to pay the company as the company does to pay its suppliers. The key message here is that growth in sales almost always requires money to fund the increase in receivables and inventory, only partly offset by payables. As discussed later, a shortage of what is known as "working capital," defined as the difference between current assets and current liabilities, has caused the downfall of companies when their sales suddenly increased. There are rare exceptions where an increase in sales generates cash.

4.4   Liabilities

4.4.1   Current Liabilities

Current liabilities can be thought of as obligations that are due in less than one year. A **short-term credit line** can usually be called at any time (it is a demand loan) and in any event will turn over many times in a year. A short-term lender almost always puts conditions, also known as **covenants**, on the credit line, which are conditions that the business must meet in order to maintain the credit line. Understanding why these covenants exist and knowing how to predict whether they will be met in the future as a business goes through periods of growth or decline is a key part of financial analysis.

Payables are money owed to suppliers, and **accrued expenses** are money owing for services, usually wages owed to the workforce but not yet paid (payroll often runs two weeks or even a month behind the work, and this is an obligation that must be paid). **Taxes payable** are another form of accrued expenses, and sometimes, these two categories are lumped together.

Like receivables and inventory, payables are converted to an equivalent days measure, but by convention they are related to days of COGS, not sales. The formula is as follows:

$$\text{Days payables} = \left(\frac{\text{payables (\$)}}{\text{(monthly sales} \times (1 - \text{contribution margin))}} \right) \times 30$$

As with inventory and receivables, payables and accrued expenses will usually be related to sales level. If sales go up, the need for materials goes up. The purchase on credit of material from suppliers creates payables. In effect, a company's suppliers help to finance growth by providing short-term (normally 30 days) credit. On occasion, a start-up company that has a chance of landing a major sale will approach its suppliers for longer terms on payables as a means of financing a single big sale, since the total time between buying raw materials and receiving money from the customer for the finished goods is longer than 30 days and can be as long as 180 days depending on the nature of the business. This is illustrated in Appendix 4.1.

Many companies have some form of long-term debt, which they use in addition to a short-term credit line in order to lock in an interest rate and payment schedule. However, the principal portion of long-term debt that is due in the next 12 months, known as the **current portion of long-term debt**, should be shown in the current liabilities area because it is due within a year and a default on it would jeopardize the company. Recall that only principal amounts associated with debt show up on the balance sheet. Interest can be thought of as the rental cost of money, and it will show up as an expense on the income statement. (Note, however, that interest owed but not yet paid might show up as an accrued expense until it is paid, at which point it shows up as an expense on the income statement.)

Current liabilities are in effect obligations to pay that must be honored in a year or less. Where will the company get the money from to pay these obligations? Recall that current assets are those that will turn into cash in less than a year. Hence, there is a natural relationship between current assets and current liabilities.

4.4.2 Long-Term (Non-Current) Liabilities

Money due for payment past one year goes into the long-term liabilities category. Sometimes, there is only a single entry: **long-term debt**. Small companies will often have one source of long-term debt, while large companies will have many different forms of it: secured loans, mortgages on properties, equipment leases, and bonds. In such cases, a single entry in the balance sheet is detailed in a related note that provides more detail. Typically provided or guaranteed by government, **repayable grants** are a form of debt that is repayable only if a company is successful in some project. For example, a project in a distressed area might be supported by a government grant for which repayment is contingent on the profitability of that project, not the overall company.

Long-term debt is often secured by a specific claim on assets. An example of this is a mortgage loan in which the lender is secured by a claim on the land and buildings. Many homebuyers need a mortgage to buy a home. Failure to repay the principal and interest gives the lender the right to go to court and force the sale of the property and to apply the proceeds to recover the outstanding amount of the loan. Debt and the differences between short- and long-term debt are discussed further in Section 4.8.

4.5   Shareholders'/Owners' Equity

4.5.1   Capital Shares

Capital shares are the money put into a business by the sale of shares in the company. (Note that in a partnership, there are no shares, so the entry would be relabeled partners' equity; the impact is the same.) This is the money that comes into the company from the company selling shares. After the shares are issued, the shareholder may sell them to a third party at a price that is different than their original sale price by the issuing company. This has no direct impact on the company itself.

This is an important concept to reflect on, especially in understanding publicly traded companies (those whose shares trade on a stock exchange). Such companies issue shares at one or more times, bringing money into the company. Sometimes, new shares are issued in Company A, who then uses them instead of cash to acquire Company B, but even in this case, an equivalent dollar value will be assigned to the issued shares. Once the shares are issued, they are usually free to be traded (sold to others). Investors in such companies hope that the market value of the shares goes up, i.e., some buyer will value them more in the future. However, this does not put any more money into the hands of the issuing company, but rather into the hands of the shareholder who sells the shares.

Companies do care about their share value but not because there is a direct effect on the financial health of the company. Management and the board of directors of a company have a legal and ethical duty to act in the best interests of the shareholders. One of the main criteria by which shareholders judge management is their ability to give a return on investment to shareholders through both dividends and increased share value. If a stock value plummets, there is often a call for a change in management of a company.

Sometimes, there are different classes of common shares. Some family-run businesses have attempted to retain effective control of a company, even as they raise equity from investors, by issuing non-voting shares. In theory, these shares are equal to voting common shares, but they cannot elect directors or vote on issues such as a takeover bid. Non-voting shares have come under a great deal of valid criticism.

The majority of capital shares are **common shares**, but there is another type of share, the **preferred share**, that has different properties. Some but not all companies issue preferred shares; these are discussed in Section 4.10.

4.5.2   Retained Earnings, Shareholders' Equity, and Market versus Book Value

As noted in Section 3.8, when a company creates value (net income), it can transfer that value out of the company as a dividend paid to owners (shareholders), or it can retain some or all of it in the business. **Retained earnings** on the balance sheet are the cumulative amount of value retained in the company rather than paid out to shareholders. The statement of retained earnings reports the incremental (or the annual) change, as well as the cumulative amount. Only the cumulative amount shows up on the balance sheet. Capital shares record the money that shareholders injected into a business. Retained earnings record the earnings that shareholders left in a business. **Shareholders' equity,** the amount of money that shareholders have in a business, is the sum of these two. In a partnership, which has no shares, this value is called owners' equity. Recall that retained earnings can be negative if a company either has negative income or pays a dividend larger than its net earnings. A start-up company that never has net earnings would show a steadily increasing negative value for retained earnings until the original share capital is used up, i.e., until shareholders' equity is zero. A zero value of shareholders' equity is one definition of a bankrupt company.

The book value of shareholders' equity is the direct original value of capital shares and retained earnings. If a business has a long period of negative net income, the market value of the shares in the company will be less than the book value, i.e., a prospective new investor will not be willing to pay as much for the shares as the original value minus the accumulated losses. Also, when a company has extraordinary success (for example, an exploratory oil well finds enormous reserves far higher than expected), the market value of the shares soars because the company is worth far more than the shareholders' equity (in essence, a large current market value has been created in anticipation of future earnings). This concept of the difference between market and book value of shareholders' equity is discussed further in Chapter 6.

4.5.3 *Shareholder Debt versus Shareholders' Equity*

Large publicly traded companies issue shares to shareholders. From the shareholders' perspective, the ability to buy and sell these shares is key to the willingness to invest in large companies. Modern enterprises have enormous capital requirements that are met by a wide variety of investors. Individuals invest in companies in two ways: directly (by share purchase in their own name) and indirectly through participation in mutual funds or pension plans. People have differing needs for their investments, the most important being that they need to get their money back when the purpose for which they are saving, such as for retirement or a home purchase, crystallizes. It is the existence of a liquid, regulated, and fair stock exchange system that makes people willing to invest in large companies.

A small company cannot afford to be publicly traded, in part because the reporting requirements for stock exchanges are too onerous and costly to be justifiable to a very small enterprise. These companies can sell shares to individual purchasers, but these shares are typically **illiquid**. This means that they are hard to sell to a third party because there is neither a public market in which to trade them nor a body of public information about them.

Sometimes, individual investors in a company choose to put their investment in the company in the form of debt rather than share equity. There are still shares in the company, but they may have a nominal value attached to them, even as low as $1. The significant investment in the company is a loan from the shareholder. This kind of debt is called **shareholder debt**, and it typically ranks below all other debt. This means it is paid out last. Shareholder debt is shown as a liability, but lenders will typically treat it as if it were equity when doing various ratio tests on a business. Lenders will also usually put covenants in place that forbid a company from retiring shareholder debt unless certain tests are met. Hence, shareholder debt is a special form of financing a company that, in practice, is closer to shareholders' equity than it is to third party long-term financing.

Sample Problem 4.5.1 Calculating Entries on the Balance Sheet

It is helpful to know how to estimate items on the balance sheet. Here are some examples, with all dollar values in ($000).

1. A company has $500 of sales per month. Its customers take an average of 38 days to pay their invoices. What is the value of receivables?

   The average time to pay is called either days of receivables or days sales outstanding. Use one of the following equations:

   $$\text{Receivables} = \text{sales per month} \times \frac{\text{days of receivables}}{30} = \$500 \times \left(\frac{38}{30}\right) = \$633$$

   $$\text{Receivables} = \text{sales per year} \times \frac{\text{days of receivables}}{365}$$

   These two calculations give slightly different values because 12 times 30 is not 365, but the difference is not material, i.e., it is too small to worry about.

2. The same company reports its inventory as 52 days of sales. The company has a single product with a COGS of 50%, and only material cost is included in COGS. What is the value of inventory?

   Using the same type of calculation as above:

   $$\text{Inventory} = \$500 \times \frac{52}{30} = \$867$$

   Note that when inventory is reported as days, it is typically reported as equivalent days of sales revenue. In the case of this company, the inventory represents 104 days of manufacturing, since COGS is exactly one-half of the final sale price. Most companies have many products with different values of COGS, often have labor costs included in COGS, and have both raw material and finished goods inventory. For these companies, it would be impossible to relate inventory reported in equivalent days of sales revenue to manufacturing days. Relating inventory to equivalent sales revenue is a convenient ratio that works for all companies.

3. A publicly traded company issued 1 million shares two years ago at $20 per share and increased the entry capital shares on its balance sheet by $20 million. The company has done very well, and the shares are now trading at $40 per share. Does it change the entry on its balance sheet?

   No. The fact that a share increases in value is a benefit to the owner of the share, but not the company that issued the shares. The balance sheet only shows the value of the money the company originally received for the shares.

4. A company pays an annual insurance premium of $120,000 but wants to track its costs accurately month by month. What balance sheet entry should they make to achieve this?

   The insurance premium will be charged on the monthly income statement at $10,000 per month. In the first month, the remainder of the payment ($110,000) is shown as a prepaid expense on the balance sheet. Each succeeding month, the prepaid expense is reduced by $10,000, which is the amount claimed that month as an expense on the income statement. This approach spreads the one-time payment evenly over 12 months.

5. A company takes out long-term debt of $10 million with a straight-line principal repayment over 10 years. What entries change on the balance sheet?

    Since a principal repayment of $1 million is due within one year, the current portion of the long-term debt would increase by $1 million, and the long-term debt entry below the current line would increase by $9 million. The loan would either increase cash by $10 million, decrease the short-term credit line by $10 million, or some combination of the two.

6. A company expects to have $1 million in net earnings and has $2 million in depreciation. It is contemplating three possible dividend strategies: no dividend, a dividend equal to earnings, and a dividend equal to net cash flow. What would the change in retained earnings be at year-end for each of the three contemplated dividends?

    Net earnings are either paid out in dividends, or they increase retained earnings. Note that if net earnings are negative or the dividend is larger than the earnings, then retained earnings will decrease. Also note that retained earnings cannot be negative. If the company pays no dividend, its retained earnings will increase by $1 million. If the dividend equals earnings ($1 million), then there will be no change in retained earnings. If the dividend equals net cash flow ($3 million), then retained earnings will decrease by $2 million.

In rare cases, a company can consistently pay a dividend higher than earnings. Most companies need to replace their assets over time. For example, a company operating a fleet of 100 trucks that have an average useful life of 10 years will replace, on average, 10 trucks per year at a cost that is close to each year's depreciation. However, consider a pipeline gathering system that brings gas from individual wells to a central point. The pipeline will never have to be rebuilt because the gas will be gone before the asset wears out. A pension company might buy these kinds of assets just to get the net cash flow and never intend to replace the existing assets or develop new gas fields.

4.6   Balance Sheet versus Income Statement

Several comments can be made about a balance sheet versus an income statement:

*   The income statement measures a rate: how much income do I make in a given period of time. The balance sheet measures wealth: how much do I have at this moment, and how much do I owe at this moment.

*   The income statement covers a period of time, and that period must be long enough to be meaningful. Typical periods for income statements are monthly, quarterly, and annually. Balance sheets are at a moment in time. It makes sense to do a balance sheet at the end of the period of time of an income statement. Hence, if an annual income statement covers a company's fiscal year of November 1 to October 31, then a balance sheet would be attached stating the company's assets and liabilities as of October 31 last year and this year.

*   To understand a business, both statements are needed. If, for example, an income statement shows a significant book and cash loss, you know the business is losing money. However, if the balance sheet shows substantial cash reserves, then the company may have enough time to be able to improve its performance. Contrast that to a company losing the same amount of money that has no cash and minimal equity. It will run into trouble very quickly. Anyone trying to understand a company's position must look at both the income statement and the balance sheet.

- If you are buying the assets of a company, then the balance sheet is of little interest other than to record the original purchase price of the fixed assets, but the income statement is of high interest. The income statement will tell you how much value the current owner has created by using the assets. It is not of particular relevance whether the current owner financed the assets or bought them with equity, since you are not assuming those obligations when you buy the assets.
- If you are buying a company, then the balance sheet is of just as much importance as the income statement because you are assuming the obligations of the company, i.e., the liabilities of the company become yours once you own the company. The balance sheet tells you what you are getting when you buy a company: both assets and fixed obligations to repay (liabilities).

4.7   Debt versus Equity

The balance sheet is a critical financial statement because of the key difference between the two major kinds of money in a company: debt and equity.

Money is a representation of value and can be converted into goods and services. People typically accumulate money over the course of their life, in large part reflecting the fact that people, on average, live longer than they work, and the stored value of savings is what they use to have an income during retirement. Some people do this directly, while others do it indirectly by participating in pension plans. In cases of extraordinary accumulation of wealth, the surplus can remain within a family for generations.

Money has a time value, a concept developed in detail in Chapter 7. Those with money for which they do not have an immediate use can move it to others who need to use it at this time. Those who want to use money are willing to pay a premium for this, and those who have money want to receive that premium. With very rare exception, those with money want it to grow in value, and pension plans, for example, rely on the growing value of savings in order to meet their obligations to pay retirees. Even money given to charities is often invested so that a charity can do good work over a long period of time based on the earning power of its money.

There are two major ways for someone with money to earn more: lend it (debt) or invest it (equity). An equity investor is an owner, who is subject to the full risk and benefit of ownership. Imagine that an oil well is being drilled, and you have a chance to buy an equity investment for $10,000. If the well is a dry hole, you have lost your money. If the well is a gusher, you might be able to sell your share for $100,000. Equity gets the full benefit and absorbs the full risk. If the well is a dry hole and your share is worth nothing, you have no recourse: you cannot sue the company because you are one of its owners. On the other hand, as an owner, you have a say in how the company is run. In a company, you vote for directors who in turn have a moral obligation to look after your interests. Shareholders meet once a year to elect directors, appoint an auditor, and vote on special resolutions.

Now, consider that you lend an oil company $10,000 at 6% for 10 years, with the full principal to be repaid at the end of 10 years (this pattern of payment is typical for a bond). The oil company then drills the well. Whether the well is a dry hole or a gusher, the company is obligated to pay you $600 per year for nine years and $10,600 at the end of the tenth year. If the company does not make a payment, you demand payment. If it is not forthcoming, you can go to court and have a receiver appointed who will take over the affairs of the company. The first obligation of a receiver is to see if the company can survive and pay all its creditors (lenders). If not, the receiver sells the company in whole or in parts and uses the proceeds to pay the creditors. In such a case, the shareholders will get nothing unless and until the obligation of the company to every one of its lenders is satisfied. On the other hand, if the oil company is highly successful, you still only get the $600 annual interest payment and the return of your principal; you have no share in the company's success. You have no power to vote for directors of the company; you are at "arm's length" from the company and simply have a contract with it requiring them to repay your loan.

This illustrates the enormous difference between debt and equity. Debt is more secure, meaning it has less risk. It also has a capped return (the interest rate on the loan). Debt has powerful legal rights enshrined in law. Equity has more risk and ownership rights. In the long term, equity gets a higher average return (growth in value) than debt. For the 80-year period from 1926 to 2005, inflation as measured by the consumer price index averaged 3.1%. The average return on long-term bonds was 6.2%, and Canadian common stocks returned an average of 10.0%. However, this was little comfort to an investor who bought shares in 1929, only to watch 90% of the value of shares evaporate during the Great Depression. Long-term average performance does not create a guarantee of a reliable, shorter-term return.

As people approach retirement age, they typically have higher savings and a lower tolerance for risk. A person who at 30 risks all his or her savings to start up a company and fails has many years ahead to recoup the loss. Henry Ford is reputed to have gone bankrupt more than once before becoming a highly successful and very rich man. However, a person at 60 who risks all his or her savings in an investment that fails is in a very difficult circumstance. In developed countries, wealth and entrepreneurial spirit often do not align. Both debt and equity are mechanisms by which money can be transferred from those that have it (and want it to grow in value) to those that need it (and have both ideas and energy to create value). Developed economies are successful in creating growing wealth per capita over long periods of time because they have systems that help move capital to those that can use it.

Debt versus Equity: Two Examples

Michael Dell attended the University of Texas and made a great deal of money in helping people get their computer systems to work in the era before "plug and play." He decided to drop out to go into the computer business and became enormously successful. Along the way, in part to provide the money needed by a growing business, he decided to issue shares in Dell through an initial public offering. A person that bought those shares on the first day and held them for 13 years had a return of 40,000%! An initial share purchase of $10,000 would be worth $4 million 13 years later, equivalent to a compound average return of 59%. Dell also borrowed money, and the lenders got the going rate of interest, perhaps 7%. This might lead you to ask why anyone with money would lend rather than invest in Dell.

Consider Nortel, which was once considered a blue-chip company (a reliable and safe equity investment). Some bought Nortel shares for $125 per share, their peak price in the dot-com stock boom. Nortel shares have gone through a 10 to 1 consolidation (10 shares became one share) and have traded at about $0.10 per share, equivalent to one cent per share before the consolidation. This again illustrates the risk and opportunity in equity: compared to $125 per share, 99.99% of the value has been lost. Some people joked that had they bought $1,000 worth of beer instead of Nortel shares, the empty beer bottles would have had a higher value than the Nortel shares. However, the lender to Nortel got the going rate of interest, perhaps 7%. If Nortel fails to pay its lenders, it will be pushed into receivership

Debt and equity are two forms of company financing that are vastly different in risk and benefit. It is critical for anyone managing a business to realize how conservative lenders are and how much they focus on preservation of capital.

4.8   *How Debt Works*

Lenders want to preserve capital. Debt gets a low return, and if a borrower totally defaults (cannot repay any portion of a loan), it takes many years of many other loans to offset this loss. Hence, lenders focus on security: what ensures them that they will be repaid.

Do Banks Like to Lend Money?

Banks make a business out of renting money from those that have it (savers) and then re-renting it out to others at a higher rental (interest) rate to those that want it (borrowers). Bank officers can lose their jobs either by not lending money or by lending it to people who do not repay it. Developed economies have lots of accumulated savings, and people with this wealth are constantly searching for ways to increase its value. Banks are therefore always looking for good projects to lend money to. To meet the criteria of a "good project," there must be a very high likelihood of being able to repay the debt. A business that consistently creates value is a good prospect, provided they have not borrowed too much and that they have some physical assets to secure the loan.

Banks report non-performing loans as a special category, where a non-performing loan is defined as one for which interest payments are not being made. An unexpectedly high level of **non-performing loans** will impact the stock price of a bank: it is seen as a danger sign. One can see the bank's concern about keeping loans **current**, another word for performing, in how they structure personal credit lines. A personal credit line gives a person the right to borrow any amount up to a pre-arranged limit, with interest due only on the amount drawn. These kinds of loans are often secured by a claim against a person's home. For this kind of loan, the bank has the right to take the monthly interest payment from the person's regular checking account, the account into which employment income is deposited. This means that as long as the person has money in the regular checking account, the loan cannot go into the non-performing category.

On a more general level, engineers who are thinking of starting a business often think that no one will want to invest. This is not the case: there are usually lots of investors looking for good opportunities, and good management is more often the limiting item, i.e., there are fewer good ideas backed by sound managers than there is investment money. A competent person with a credible business plan that includes both a believable marketing plan and financial pro forma statements (forecasts) can usually find investment money.

4.8.1   Secured Lenders and Long-Term Debt

Some debt is for the purchase of hard assets such as cars, homes, and manufacturing plants. Usually, such debt is long term (to be repaid over a period of more than one year). The main way a lender has security in this case is to place a lien or mortgage on the property. This legal provision means that the lender can seize the asset and dispose of it if the loan is not repaid. Lenders will almost always appraise, or assess, the value of the asset before setting the loan amount. Where there is a risk that the asset will not cover the value of the loan, lenders sometimes ask for further security such as a personal guarantee or the guarantee of a co-signer.

Secured loans often come with some terms on them. The first is that the money be used for the purpose that was identified when the loan was negotiated. For example, a bank that is lending a homebuyer money to buy a house does not give the money to the buyer; it gives it to a trustee who holds the bank's money and the buyer's down payment and only releases it when the title is transferred. Funds held in trust can only be used by the trustee for a specified use. In this way, an unscrupulous person cannot take the bank's money and run away with it. Lending agreements will often specify that the asset securing the loan cannot be pledged to another lender, or if so, the other lender's claim must rank behind the first lender. The concept of ranking is important in loans, and it is illustrated by first versus second mortgages. A first mortgage will have the first claim to the proceeds of sale of a property, and the second mortgage only gets repaid from what is then left over. This means that the second mortgage lender has higher risk than the first mortgage lender of not being repaid, so second mortgages are at a higher interest rate than a first mortgage.

A common form of mortgage financing requires annual payments toward principal so that the remaining balance of the loan goes to zero over time. However, bond lending in which the principal is repaid in one payment at the end of the loan is popular with pension funds because the fund can then count on a long-term constant stream of interest payments from which they can in turn pay retirees. But consider a pension fund lending to a pipeline company via 30-year bonds: how does the pension fund manager know that the pipeline company will be able to repay the principal? Sometimes, the lender will require the borrower to place funds in trust every year so that there is sure to be enough money to repay the principal; this is called a **sinking fund**.

Secured lenders have a sense of safety about loan repayment. They do not need to keep too close a watch over a borrower because they are secured. Hence, the mortgage lender does not ask the borrower to report every month whether they still have a job because the property is security for the loan. This is different for unsecured lenders.

Personal Guarantees

When a small business gets financing from a bank, the bank usually requires the owner or owners to provide a personal guarantee of the loan. This means that if the business fails and cannot repay the loan, all of the personal assets of the owners can be claimed by the bank to repay the loan in full.

When individuals trying to start up a business first talk to a bank loans officer about a line of credit or long-term debt, they are sometimes shocked by the assurance from the bank officer that if the business fails, every possession of the individuals will be seized under the terms of the personal guarantee, including savings, house, furniture, and car. But this practice reflects the risk and reward in the transaction. Individuals who are successful in starting a company often become rich. The money they borrowed typically comes from people who are either saving for their retirement or already retired. Their reward is small, just the interest on their savings. Because the reward is so small, the request for security to ensure the recovery of the original loan amount is reasonable.

4.8.2 Unsecured Lenders and the Short-Term Credit Line

Think of a supplier to a company that delivers goods and then sends an invoice requesting payment within 30 days. In effect, the supplier is lending the value of the goods to the company. However, it typically has no specific security: if it is not paid, it has a general claim against the company. The same is true of workers to whom wages are owed. Finally, the short-term lender to a company is sometimes in this position: the bank that provides the day-to-day credit line typically has no claim against any non-current asset such as land, buildings, equipment, and intangibles like patents. Sometimes, short-term lenders will have a "first claim" on receivables and inventory, in which case they are secured relative to suppliers, but not as much as lenders secured by physical assets.

Short-term credit is lent subject to conditions. If those conditions are not met, the loan can be immediately called, meaning it becomes due and payable in full. This is known as a **demand loan**. The short-term lender is therefore concerned that a company has the resources to cover its loan in the event it is called. Recall that banks rent money at a cost and then re-rent it to borrowers at a higher interest rate. The spread is not very big, so the bank is not getting very much from each dollar that it lends. How then does a bank feel comfortable with a short-term credit line or a supplier when shipping goods?

Look at the following balance sheets of two companies, and think like a banker. How do you know you can be paid? Look in particular at the total amount of current assets and current liabilities.

Company A ($000)

Assets		Liabilities	
Current Assets		**Current Liabilities**	
Cash	—	Short-term credit line	82
Receivables	635	Accounts payable	192
Short-term investments	—	Accrued expenses	44
Inventory	408	Taxes payable	—
Prepaid expenses	—	Current portion of long-term debt	200
	1,043		518

Non-Current Assets

Land, building, and equipment at cost		**Long-Term Debt**	
		Repayable grants	—
Less accumulated depreciation		Long-term debt	1,800
	3,600		
		Shareholders' Equity	
Long-term investments	—	Capital shares	1,825
Goodwill	—	Retained earnings	500
Total assets	4,643	Total liability and equity	4,643
		Working capital	525
		Working capital ratio	2.01

Company B ($000)

Assets		**Liabilities**	
Current Assets		**Current Liabilities**	
Cash	—	Short-term credit line	807
Receivables	635	Accounts payable	192
Short-term investments	—	Accrued expenses	44
Inventory	408	Taxes payable	—
Prepaid expenses	—	Current portion of long-term debt	100
	1,043		1,143

Non-Current Assets		**Long-Term Debt**	
Land, building, and equipment at cost	4,500	Repayable grants	—
Less accumulated depreciation	900	Long-term debt	900
	3,600		
		Shareholders' Equity	
Long-term investments	—	Capital shares	2,100
Goodwill	—	Retained earnings	500
Total assets	4,643	Total liability and equity	4,643
		Working capital	−100
		Working capital ratio	0.91

Current assets are what will become cash in less than a year, and current liabilities are what require cash in less than a year. The long-term assets usually are security for long-term debt, so the short-term lender does not count on them. Hence, the short-term lender and suppliers only feel comfortable if current assets are larger than current liabilities. The difference between short-term assets and liabilities is called **working capital**.

Working capital = current assets – current liabilities

Working capital ratio = current assets ÷ current liabilities

For example, Company A has a significant surplus of current assets relative to current liabilities, so it will have many sources of cash with which to meet its short-term obligations. This is not true for Company B, which has a negative working capital: it does not have enough sources of short-term cash to meet its short-term obligations. In reality, a banker would have pulled the credit line on Company B, i.e., demanded immediate repayment of the short-term loan, and would have gone to court to have a receiver appointed if the company could not repay the loan.

The short-term lender provides a line of credit to a company. This means the company can borrow as needed up to the limit of the line. There are typically four conditions, called covenants, for keeping the short-term credit line:

1. The company will file monthly financial reports with the short-term credit lender.
2. The company will not pay a dividend to the owners without the consent of the lender (this covenant might apply to small business only).
3. The company will maintain an agreed level of working capital, determined in dollars.
4. The company will maintain an agreed level of working capital ratio.

The first covenant means the bank is informed, the second means the owners can not legally strip money from the company (and would be guilty of fraud and breach of contract if they did so), and the third and fourth covenants ensure that there is enough near-term cash in the business to meet near-term obligations. Suppose the bank covenants for companies A and B are a working capital level of $250,000 and a working capital ratio of 1.5. Company A has a satisfactory level of working capital and working capital ratio, but Company B has negative working capital and a ratio less than 1 and would be in violation of covenants 3 and 4.

What is the Right Level of Working Capital?

The right level for working capital and the working capital ratio are specific to each business. Remember that banks need to lend money, so they are always keen to find good businesses to lend to. They are also keen to be repaid, so banks are thoughtful in setting an appropriate level for working capital and a working capital ratio. Most companies keep very low levels of cash (or none), so most of the value of current assets is represented by inventory and receivables. A bank will carefully consider the quality of each of these when setting the working capital covenants for a short-term credit line.

Think of two businesses: one a regional wholesale distributor of lumber that sells to retail outlets and the other a firm that makes proprietary software embedded in a chip that performs a special function of encryption. Which inventory would be easier to sell if the business failed? The lumber could be sold quite readily: it is a standardized and stamped product sold by many companies and could probably be moved (resold to another company) for as much as 90 cents per dollar of inventory value. For the other company, who would buy a chip that used special proprietary software if the company that developed the software was no longer in operation?

Receivables work the same way. If a company's customers are very large corporations, they can be counted on to pay their invoices even if a supplier goes into receivership. However, if customers are numerous small businesses, it is more likely that some of those customers will try to get away with not paying the invoice of a failed company.

Banks are quite shrewd about setting covenants, and they also try to balance their loan portfolio to spread risk among industries. A bank that had a large number of loans to oil service companies might be reluctant to lend to another firm in this industry, whereas a bank with little exposure to the industry might be willing to lend to such a company. For this reason, business managers trying to find a short- or long-term credit facility should talk to more than one bank.

Banks also require companies to **age receivables**, i.e., track the dollar value of receivables that are less than 30 days old, 30 to 60 days old, 60 to 90 days old, and over 90 days old. Bank covenants on short-term debt typically require that in calculating current assets, a company not include receivables older than 90 days because the bank is concerned that this is bad debt, an expense, and not of real value to the company.

A Test That Stopped Working

The test that working capital as measured by current assets minus current liabilities had to be positive used to be applied to any company, large or small. However, some years ago, this test began to break down for large companies with sophisticated financing. Some financing for large companies is of a type that is expected to be paid back over the long term, but that in special circumstances could **accelerate**, or become due in the short term. The expectation of the lender and the company is that these circumstances will never occur, so both think of the financing as long term. However, the acceleration clause is put into the lending agreement to protect the lender should the company get into trouble. Accountants looked at these loans and, particularly in this current era of very strict application of accounting rules, declared that the financing had to go in the balance sheet as a current liability. The lenders and companies argued, unsuccessfully, that it should be classified as long-term debt; the accountants replied that as long as the acceleration clause was even a possibility, then the financing had to be considered short term and, hence, a current liability.

Small companies do not have multiple and complex types of financing, so the simple working capital test can be applied to them: current assets must exceed current liabilities by an agreed amount, and the ratio must exceed an agreed target. For large companies, the concept is still valid, but the test cannot be applied to the financial statements without knowing what fraction of the current liabilities is long-term financing with an acceleration clause. Of course, the lenders and the companies know this information, so the working capital test is still being applied; it just is not being done with the formal financial statement values of current assets and current liabilities.

For an example of this, visit the website of the TransCanada Corporation, a publicly traded pipeline and power generation company, and find their financial statements. Current liabilities exceed current assets for the reasons outlined above.

4.8.3 *The Impact of Growth on Working Capital*

A growth in sales in a company requires resources to fund inventory and receivables. Let's illustrate this by looking at the impact on Company A of doubling its sales, assuming that it can do this without any additional investment in fixed assets, i.e., it could add an additional shift to its current manufacturing operation. On the balance sheet, receivables will double, since customers do not pay their bills any quicker just because their order size is larger. Inventory will double because it is the buffer that both manufacturing and marketing need to ensure efficient operation of the assembly line and reliable fulfillment of sales orders; more inventory is needed to avoid shutdowns of the assembly line and also to avoid frustrated customers. Payables and accrued expenses will double because the company is buying twice as much raw material and has twice the labor force. Note, however, that for Company A, receivables and inventory are much larger than payables and accrued expenses. This is true for almost all companies, since payment terms are the same for their customers and their suppliers (net 30 days) and what they sell is worth more than what they buy. Initially, this imbalance is made up by an increase in the short-term credit line.

Company A with Doubled Sales ($000)

Assets		Liabilities	
Current Assets		**Current Liabilities**	
Cash	—	Short-term credit line	890
Receivables	1,270	Accounts payable	384
Short-term investments	—	Accrued expenses	88
Inventory	817	Taxes payable	—
Prepaid expenses	—	Current portion of long-term debt	200
	2,087		1,562
Fixed Assets		**Long-Term Debt**	
Land, building, and equipment at cost	4,500	Repayable grants	—
Less accumulated depreciation	900	Long-term debt	1,800
	3,600		
		Shareholders' Equity	
Long-term investments	—	Capital shares	1,825
Goodwill	—	Retained earnings	500
Total assets	5,687	Total liability and equity	5,687
		Working capital	525
		Working capital ratio	1.34

Company A is now in violation of its covenants on its short-term credit line. The absolute value of working capital stays the same (at $525,000), but the ratio drops because of the increase in current assets and current liabilities. The lender sees the working capital, but the low ratio is a concern because there are many demands for the current assets. If Company A fails, the suppliers and workers will be demanding payment along with the short-term credit line, and if the inventory does not fetch full value and the receivables are hard to collect, then there will not be enough cash to satisfy all the unsecured creditors. Company A has had a doubling in sales that has created a working capital crisis. Unless it acts, it will be shut down by its short-term lender. The primary mode of failure of a company is inadequate working capital. When people say that a company has run out of cash, it actually means the company has run out of working capital.

A further example of the impact of growth in sales is illustrated in Appendix 4.1.

The Exception to Working Capital: Dell and Wal-Mart

As Dell Corporation grew, it built a business based on the direct selling of computers to end users. Rather than having warehouses full of finished goods inventory that is sold to retail outlets and then resold to the end user, Dell makes a computer when it has an order. As it became a very large manufacturer, it got market power. Suppliers located close to Dell assembly plants and would carry inventory and ship it to Dell on a "just in time" basis.

This allowed Dell to develop an astonishing business model: it buys components from suppliers on a net 30-day basis. It does not maintain much raw materials inventory; its suppliers do that. It turns parts into a computer in about five days. Finally, it does not extend credit to many of its customers, who are often single individuals, so it frequently collects payment when the computer is shipped. This means that Dell is paid about 25 days sooner than it has to pay its suppliers. If you visit Dell's website and pull up their balance sheet, you can see that payables are far larger than inventory and larger than receivables as well. To maintain a positive working capital, Dell keeps a lot of cash on hand, which it gets from its customers well in advance of needing it to pay suppliers. Dell has no short-term credit line and does not create a working capital problem as sales grow. The Dell model has other advantages: there is minimal risk to Dell of write-down of stale inventory and low risk of bad debt, and the cost of warehousing and the markup by a retailer are avoided.

This is an intriguing model that works when a customer knows what they want and does not need to see the product in a retail outlet, and when the customer does not need the product today, but can wait for it to be shipped. This model might apply in the future to vehicle sales. Many buyers know what they want, including options, and will wait for the right car to be made rather than buy something on a dealer's lot. A great deal of inventory and receivable cost plus the cost of retailing could be taken out of vehicle purchase for those buyers who know what they want and are willing to wait for it to be made. Vehicles could be delivered from the point of shipment, usually by rail, to their home or place of business.

Most businesses, however, including Dell's suppliers, do maintain inventory and do allow customers to pay on terms of net 30 days. For these companies, a growth in sales creates a need for working capital.

Wal-Mart has a history of working closely with suppliers in an effort to minimize costs and pass savings on to its customers. Like Dell, it can frequently sell goods to cash-paying customers before it has to pay its suppliers and has a surplus of cash and no short-term credit line.

Sample Problem 4.8.1 The Impact of Sales Growth on Working Capital

The company XYZ Inc. manufactures fasteners. Its traditional market was eastern Canada, but it has recently identified two major customers: one in the US and one in Mexico. The marketingmanager thinks that sales will go up by a factor of three. No new fixed assets will be required, but the company will go from one shift per day to three shifts per day, tripling its manufacturing workforce.

The company's most recent balance sheet is as follows:

Company XYZ ($000)

Assets			Liabilities	
Current Assets			**Current Liabilities**	
Cash		—	Short-term credit line	150
Receivables		864	Accounts payable	591
Short-term investment		—	Accrued expenses	139
Inventory		576	Taxes payable	60
			Current portion of long-term debt	100
		1,440		1,040
Fixed Assets			**Long-Term Debt**	
Building and equipment at cost	4,200		Long-term debt	1,200
Less accumulated depreciation	1,200	3,000		
			Shareholders' Equity	
Long-term investment		—	Capital shares	1,500
			Retained earnings	700
Total assets		4,440	Total liabilities and equity	4,440
			Working capital	400
			Working capital ratio	1.38

The main component of accrued expenses is wages due to the manufacturing workforce. Estimate the company's balance sheet if sales triple, ignoring any change in retained earnings.

Solution:

Ignoring retained earnings since you do not know how profitable the new sales will be, you can expect these five things to change on the balance sheet in the short term:

- Receivables
- Inventory
- Payables
- Accrued expenses
- Short-term credit line

The first four of these should all go up by a factor of three. Receivables will triple because customers do not pay faster as their volume of purchases increases; the same logic applies to payables, the money XYZ owes its suppliers. If inventory was tightly managed at the current sales level, it can be expected to triple because it is the material needed to ensure that manufacturing is efficient and customers' orders are not delayed. Accrued expenses will triple because the manufacturing workforce will triple. This leads to the following pro forma (forecast) balance sheet:

Company XYZ ($000) after Sales Triple (Pro Forma)

Assets			Liabilities	
Current Assets			**Current Liabilities**	
Cash		—	Short-term credit line	1,570.00
Receivables		2,592	Accounts payable	1,773.00
Short-term investment		—	Accrued expenses	417.00
Inventory		1,728	Taxes payable	60.00
			Current portion of long-term debt	100.00
		4,320		3,920.00
Fixed Assets			**Long-Term Debt**	
Building and equipment at cost	4,200		Long-term debt	1,200
Less accumulated depreciation	1,200	3,000		
			Shareholders' Equity	
Long-term investment		—	Capital shares	1,500
Goodwill		—	Retained earnings	700
Total assets		7,320	Total liability and equity	7,320
			Working capital	400
			Working capital ratio	1.10

Note that all changes to the balance sheet occur above the current line, so current assets and current liabilities increase equally, with the short-term credit line increasing to make up the difference in the increases in receivables plus inventory minus payables and accrued expenses. However, XYZ would be in trouble with its short-term lender, since a working capital ratio of 1.1 is below any reasonable covenant on a short-term credit line. XYZ cannot survive a tripling in sales unless it arranges more long-term debt or raises equity by selling additional shares. Very high growth in sales usually requires a long-term source of funds, since receivables plus inventory is higher than payables plus accrued expenses for most companies.

4.8.4 Fixing Working Capital Problems

You have now seen two balance sheets for companies that are in serious trouble. It is critical for a manager of a company to know how to fix a working capital deficiency. Imagine that the bank manager for Company B gives it 45 days to get adequate working capital or have its credit line pulled. Many managers in this situation proceed to take the wrong corrective action because they do not understand balance sheets.

Imagine that the president of Company B, after talking to the bank, focuses on increasing the working capital above $250,000 from its current level of –$100,000. She notes that there is a high value in inventory and receivables, and also in payables. She first meets with her Chief Financial Officer (CFO) and tells him to focus on collecting receivables more quickly by having clerks phone all customers to ask for more rapid payment of invoices. Collecting some of the receivables will reduce short-term borrowing. She also tells the CFO to slow down payment of suppliers, changing from paying in 25 days, the current average, to paying in 50 days. This will also reduce short-term borrowing because, in effect, the suppliers end up lending more money to the company. The suppliers will not like being paid in 50 days, but they will likely tolerate it. Finally, she meets with the VPs of marketing and sales and tells them to find a way to live with half the inventory they now have. Both protest, but she explains the crisis the company is in. She then goes back to her office and looks forward to next month's balance sheet, which she will take to the bank. The following sheet shows what she gets from halving inventory and receivables and doubling payables:

Company B with Half the Inventory and Receivables and Twice the Payables ($000)

Assets		Liabilities	
Current Assets		**Current Liabilities**	
Cash	—	Short-term credit line	94
Receivables	318	Accounts payable	384
Short-term investments	—	Accrued expenses	44
Inventory	204	Taxes payable	—
Prepaid expenses	—	Current portion of long-term debt	100
	522		622
Fixed Assets		**Long-Term Debt**	
Land, building, and equipment at cost	4,500	Repayable grants	—
Less accumulated depreciation	900	Long-term debt	900
	3,600		
		Shareholders' Equity	
Long-term investments	—	Capital shares	2,100
Goodwill	—	Retained earnings	500
Total assets	4,122	Total liability and equity	4,122
		Working capital	−100
		Working capital ratio	0.84

The short-term borrowing has dropped dramatically, from over $800,000 to $94,000, but the working capital is still negative! All the hard work of nagging customers, running with low inventory, and failing to pay suppliers has not helped at all. To understand why this is so, think of what happens when a dollar of receivables is collected. Short-term debt goes down when the dollar is deposited, reducing current liabilities, but short-term assets also go down by a dollar. Since working capital is the difference between current assets and current liabilities, there is no change in working capital. The bank is owed less, but it still has no comfort that the company can repay that debt. The bank will still pull the credit line. Think of a dollar of increased payables. All that occurs when payables increase is that the bank is owed less and a supplier is owed more. Since suppliers or banks can push a company into receivership (since a payable is a court-recognized obligation to pay, which is the same as a short-term credit line), the bank is no more secure that it will be repaid. Again, the bank will still pull the credit line.

Company B can be saved either by putting in more shareholder equity or arranging for more long-term debt. The following example uses long-term debt for illustration purposes, but the same outcome would arise from an increase in capital shares. Look at Company B's assets, which have a book value of $3.6 million. Its long-term debt is only $1 million ($900,000 below the current line and $100,000 above the current line, i.e., due within one year). Company B might be able to go to its long-term lender and borrow more money, particularly if it has been profitable and has had stable or growing sales. If instead of hounding customers to collect receivables, cutting inventory, and stretching payables, it arranges an increase of $750,000 in its long-term debt, it will have the following balance sheet as compared to its original balance sheet in Section 4.8.2. Assume a 10-year repayment schedule with equal principal repayments, so $675,000 of the new long-term debt goes below the current line, and $75,000 goes above the current line, since it will have to be paid 365 days from the time the loan is increased.

Company B with a $750,000 Increase in Long-Term Debt ($000)

Assets			Liabilities	
Current Assets			**Current Liabilities**	
Cash	—		Short-term credit line	57
Receivables	635		Accounts payable	192
Short-term investments	—		Accrued expenses	44
Inventory	408		Taxes payable	—
Prepaid expenses	—		Current portion of long-term debt	175
		1,043		468
Fixed Assets			**Long-Term Debt**	
Land, building, and equipment at cost	4,500		Repayable grants	—
Less accumulated depreciation	900		Long-term debt	1,575
		3,600		
			Shareholders' Equity	
Long-term investments	—		Capital shares	2,100
Goodwill	—		Retained earnings	500
Total assets		4,643	Total liability and equity	4,643
			Working capital	575
			Working capital ratio	2.23

Company B's problem is now solved. By bringing in a source of money that does not require repayment in less than a year ($675,000 of the loan amount), it has reduced its short-term borrowing and now has adequate working capital. This illustrates a general rule: a working capital problem cannot be fixed by any action "above the line." Sometimes, it is also stated as "You can't fix an above-the-line problem above the line." This means that actions taken above the current line do not increase the amount of working capital. They change the working capital ratio, but not the absolute level of working capital because the difference between current assets and current liabilities is not changed. To get more working capital, a company needs to either increase share capital or increase long-term debt, both of which are below-the-line solutions. This situation is often featured in the media: when a company gets in trouble, reporters talk about the solution involving either refinancing, meaning more long-term debt, or equity injection, meaning more share capital.

Note also that one way of increasing shareholder equity in a company is to retain all earnings within the company by not paying any dividend. Start-up companies with high growth rates rarely pay dividends for exactly this reason: they need the value to stay in the company as equity in order to finance the growth in sales.

Managers can still focus on operating with low inventory, on promptly collecting receivables, and on taking advantage of supplier credit up to a realistic level that does not aggravate the supplier into a price increase; all of these will reduce short-term borrowing, which will save interest expense. These actions will not, however, solve a working capital deficiency.

After its sales double, Company A does not have a working capital deficiency, but it does have an inadequate working capital ratio. If Company A took extraordinary efforts to collect receivables, operate with low inventory, and stretch its payables by paying its bills later, it could improve its working capital ratio. However, customers do not like to be hounded to pay bills early, inventory is needed for efficient operation of manufacturing and effective fulfillment of sales orders, and suppliers who are "stretched" too much sometimes retaliate with a price increase. Company A's best strategy to support a doubling of sales is again to arrange for more share capital or more long-term debt, so it can focus on growing sales rather than making extraordinary efforts to reduce short-term borrowing.

The Perils of Ignorance

Many engineers manage companies but do not have a good background in financial statements, especially the balance sheet. There are cases of managers working diligently to reduce inventory, collect receivables, and maximize the use of supplier credit who have no idea why the short-term credit line is pulled and the business put into receivership, with a receiver placing a padlock on the door of the business to ensure the change in management.

People trained in first aid are taught to first check for breathing because the component of human function with the shortest critical time is the need for air. In a business, working capital is "breath," and every good manager will know how to measure it and how to fix a working capital problem below the line.

Sample Problem 4.8.2 Impact of Debt and Equity on Working Capital

Norton Switchgear is a manufacturing company. The balance sheet for the company is as follows:

Norton Switchgear ($000)

Assets			Liabilities	
Current Assets			**Current Liabilities**	
Cash		—	Short-term credit line	123
Receivables		864	Accounts payable	140
Short-term investment		—	Accrued expenses	123
Inventory		531	Taxes payable	60
Prepaid expenses		31	Current portion of long-term debt	100
		1,426		546
Fixed Assets			**Long-Term Debt**	
Building and equipment at cost	2,366		Long-term debt	876
Less accumulated depreciation	656	1,710		
			Shareholders' Equity	
Long-term investment		—	Capital shares	1,400
Goodwill		—	Retained earnings	314
Total assets		3,136	**Total liabilities and equity**	3,136
			Working capital	880
			Working capital ratio	2.6

To finance an expansion, the company wants to raise $500,000 and is in negotiations with both a long-term lender and a potential new shareholder. The lender is proposing a five-year loan with straight-line principal repayment. Estimate the balance sheet, including working capital and a working capital ratio, for the two cases.

Solution:

Option 1: Equity Capital

If a new shareholder buys shares for $500,000, all the funds come in below the current line. The company's short-term debt goes to zero, and it has cash on hand of $377. Note that although the short-term credit line is zero, the company would still have a credit line in place so that it could borrow up to the limits of its covenants in the future.

Norton Switchgear ($000): Pro Forma Balance Sheet with Increased Equity

Assets			Liabilities	
Current Assets			**Current Liabilities**	
Cash		377	Short-term credit line	0
Receivables		864	Accounts payable	140
Short-term investment		—	Accrued expenses	123
Inventory		531	Taxes payable	60
Prepaid expenses		31	Current portion of long-term debt	100
		1,803		423
Fixed Assets			**Long-Term Debt**	
Building and equipment at cost	2,366		Long-term debt	876
Less accumulated depreciation	656	1,710		
			Shareholders' Equity	
Long-term investment		—	Capital shares	1,900
Goodwill		—	Retained earnings	314
Total assets		3,513	Total liability and equity	3,513
			Working capital	1,380
			Working capital ratio	4.3

Option 2: Long-Term Debt

If $500,000 is raised as debt with a five-year straight-line repayment, then only $400,000 of the debt is recorded below the current line of the balance sheet. The $100,000 principal repayment due after one year is shown in the current portion of the long-term debt. Therefore, the working capital and working capital ratio is different for raising long-term debt versus equity.

Norton Switchgear($000): Pro Forma Balance Sheet with Increased Long-Term Debt

Assets			Liabilities	
Current Assets			**Current Liabilities**	
Cash		377	Short-term credit line	0
Receivables		864	Accounts payable	140
Short-term investment		—	Accrued expenses	123
Inventory		531	Taxes payable	60
Prepaid expenses		31	Current portion of long-term debt	200
		1,803		523
Fixed Assets			**Long-Term Debt**	
Building and equipment at cost	2,366		Long-term debt	1,276
Less accumulated depreciation	656	1,710		
			Shareholder's Equity	
Long-term investment		—	Capital shares	1,400
Goodwill		—	Retained earnings	314
Total assets		3,513	Total liability and equity	3,513
			Working capital	1,280
			Working capital ratio	3.4

4.9 The Concept of Leverage

Companies strive to create value, measured by net or operating income, and require assets to do this. One key measure of a business is the amount of value it creates from its assets. The ratio of net income or operating income to assets is a critical ratio, and it represents the earning power of a business. If a person had a choice of investing $10 million to own a business that had a net income of $2 million, it would be the better choice compared to investing the same $10 million to own a business that has a net income of $0.5 million.

However, assets are funded by two sources of money: debt (liabilities) and equity. Debt has a fixed cost, its interest rate, and the equity investors get all the benefit of net income once the interest costs on debt and any required principal repayments have been paid. The equity investors are, therefore, most concerned not with the earning power of the business (return on assets), but rather with how much is left for them after paying for debt costs.

The management of a company has the ability to increase or decrease debt versus equity. In Section 4.8.4, Company B could fix its working capital problem by bringing equity into the company (issuing shares) or increasing its long-term debt. In general, the management of any company can increase borrowing and buy back some of its own shares or issue additional shares and pay down debt. This is a financial management decision that is independent of the operational management of the company. At the operational level, nothing is changed when debt increases or decreases relative to equity: the need to manufacture, sell, and service a product is unchanged. However, there are significant financial implications of the ratio of liabilities to assets. For example, what fraction of a company's assets was funded by other people's money? This is called the **leverage ratio**. A lever is a device that multiplies the force or distance of a motion. Leverage in finance multiplies the upside and downside return on equity because the equity takes a higher level of risk than debt and all the risk avoided by debt is the responsibility of the equity investors.

Consider three companies (Lodebtco, Medebtco, and Hidebtco) with an identical income from operations (before interest) and an identical asset base. Therefore, the return on assets based on operating income will be the same in each case. The only difference is in the liabilities and shareholders' equity portion of the balance sheets. Lodebto's bank debt is 10% of its assets, and its debt ratio (which includes all liabilities) is 18.2%. Medebtco's bank debt is 40% of its assets, and its debt ratio is 48.2%. Hidebtco's bank debt is 70% of its assets, and its debt ratio is 78.2%. Lodebtco has relied on owner's equity, while Hidebtco has used other people's money (debt) to build the same business.

For simplicity, assume the interest rate on all debt is 10% (in the real world, Hidebtco might expect to pay a higher interest rate than Lodebtco because of the higher risk to the lender of such a high level of debt). The tables show the income statements, balance sheets, and key ratios, including the return on equity for a good year and a bad year. Note that in a good year, the earning power of the business (the return on assets) is higher than the cost of debt, but in a bad year, the earning power of the business is below the cost of debt. In particular, note the return on assets and the return on equity for the three cases.

Leverage in a Good Year

	Lodebtco ($000)	Medebtco ($000)	Hidebtco ($000)
Income Statement			
Sales	10,000	10,000	10,000
COGS	5,000	5,000	5,000
Contribution margin	5,000	5,000	5,000
Margin (%)	50	50	50
SG&A	3,000	3,000	3,000
Operating income	2,000	2,000	2,000
Interest charges (10% of long-term debt)	97	388	679
Net income from operations	1,903	1,612	1,321

Balance Sheet (end of year)

Assets

Current Assets

Cash	100	100	100
Receivables	1,000	1,000	1,000
Inventory	500	500	500
Prepaid expenses	100	100	100
	1,700	1,700	1,700

Fixed Assets

Land, building, and equipment at cost	10,000	10,000	10,000
Less accumulated depreciation	−2,000	−2,000	−2,000
Goodwill	—	—	—
Total assets	9,700	9,700	9,700

Liabilities

Current Liabilities

Short-term credit line	—	—	—
Accounts payable	500	500	500
Accrued expenses	150	150	150
Taxes payable	150	150	150
Current portion of long-term debt	97	388	679
	897	1,188	1,479
Long-term debt	873	3,492	6,111

Shareholders' Equity

Capital shares	6,930	4,020	1,110
Retained earnings	1,000	1,000	1,000
Total liability and equity	9,700	9,700	9,700

Key Ratios

Working capital ratio	1.90	1.43	1.15
Bank debt/assets (%)	10.0	40.0	70.0
Debt ratio (liabilities/assets) (%)	18.2	48.2	78.2
Return on assets (operation inc./assets) (%)	20.6	20.6	20.6
Return on equity (net inc./equity) (%)	24.0	32.1	62.6

Leverage in a Bad Year

	Lodebtco ($000)	Medebtco ($000)	Hidebtco ($000)
Income Statement			
Sales	7,000	7,000	7,000
COGS	3,500	3,500	3,500
Contribution margin	3,500	3,500	3,500
Margin (%)	50	50	50
SG&A	3,000	3,000	3,000
Operating income	500	500	500
Interest charges (10% of long-term debt)	97	388	679
Net income from operations	403	112	−179

Balance Sheet (end of year)

Assets

Current Assets

Cash	100	100	100
Receivables	1,000	1,000	1,000
Inventory	500	500	500
Prepaid expenses	100	100	100
	1,700	1,700	1,700

Fixed Assets

Land, building, and equipment at cost	10,000	10,000	10,000
Less accumulated depreciation	−2,000	−2,000	−2,000
Goodwill	—	—	—
Total assets	9,700	9,700	9,700

Liabilities

Current Liabilities

Short-term credit line	—	—	—
Accounts payable	500	500	500
Accrued expenses	150	150	150
Taxes payable	150	150	150
Current portion of long-term debt	97	388	679
	897	1,188	1,479
Long-term debt	873	3,492	6,111

Shareholders' Equity

Capital shares	6,930	4,020	1,110
Retained earnings	1,000	1,000	1,000
Total liabilities and equity	9,700	9,700	9,700

Key Ratios

Working capital ratio	1.90	1.43	1.15
Bank debt/assets (%)	10.0	40.0	70.0
Debt ratio (liabilities/assets) (%)	18.2	48.2	78.2
Return on assets (operating inc./assets) (%)	5.2	5.2	5.2
Return on equity (net inc./equity) (%)	5.1	2.2	−8.5

Notice how much more volatile (subject to change) the net income and return on equity is for Hidebtco compared to Lodebtco, even though the base business operating income and return on assets (based on operating income) is identical (the only difference is financing). Although return on assets from operating income is the same for all three companies, the return on equity is far higher in a good year for Hidebtco. Investors in this company would see a high return for their smaller equity stake, a case of "less is more." But look at the bad year's performance: Hidebtco shows a loss, and shareholder's equity drops because net income is negative, whereas the investor in Lodebtco or Medebtco continues to see a small but positive return on equity. The "bad year" is a 30% drop in sales; unless Hidebtco has cash reserves, it will likely be unable to pay the principal payment on its debt. Highly leveraged companies are vulnerable to business downturns, and one acquisition strategy is for low leverage companies to acquire, at a distressed price, highly leveraged competitors during economic downturns.

The reason return on equity is so volatile as debt increases is that all of the change in the income of the company concentrates on the equity, and as debt increases, the equity portion is reduced. In other words, debt comes into the company at a fixed return (in this case, 10%), and the variation in real return is spread over a smaller amount of equity. In a good year, this is excellent for investors: a smaller initial investment gives a much higher return. In a bad year, however, the effect is reversed: the investor in Lodebtco has a modest return, but the investor in Hidebtco faces a loss because interest payments exceed operating income. This is not just theoretical. Business history is full of over-leveraged companies that cannot operate sustainably as debt costs exceed operating income.

Several points can be made about leverage:

- Leverage is measured by debt ratio, but this means the ratio of total liabilities to total assets. Averages vary by industry, and there is no correct amount. Very stable companies with reliable levels of sales, such as utility companies, will have very high levels of debt and still have low overall risk. In commodity industries, such as oil or fertilizers, a blue-chip company will strive to have more equity than liabilities and, in some cases, will aim for at least twice as much equity as liabilities (a debt ratio of 33%).
- Volatility, or the variability in company (and stock) performance, increases with increasing leverage. Highly leveraged companies are at a much higher risk of going out of business in a downturn.
- Volatility is created by the different risk and return levels that exist between debt and equity. Debt has lower risk and lower return; lenders accept a lower return because debt has a higher claim (ranks higher) than equity when a company gets into trouble. Equity carries the risk that debt avoids.
- Leverage helps equity investors in a good year and hurts them in a bad year. The saying "Leverage up equals leverage down" tries to match the opportunity and the peril of leverage. Risk-averse investors will likely avoid highly leveraged companies, but some investors like the risk and the higher performance that can be realized in good times. Many investors are not interested in publicly traded companies with very low leverage because there is insufficient opportunity for a gain in value relative to more leveraged stocks.
- Lenders like the right amount of leverage. If all firms had no leverage, there would be no lenders. If all firms were over-leveraged, default levels on debt would be at unacceptable levels.

Leverage can be illustrated graphically as well. First, consider a company that has 50% leverage in good times: the earning power of assets is higher than the cost of debt. As shown in the figure below, the earning power of the investment (return on assets) is higher than the cost of debt. Since debt only gets its fixed cost (the interest rate), the portion of earnings A can be transferred to the equity owners, and this increases (levers up) the return on equity.

50% Leverage in Good Times

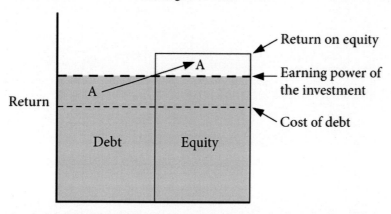

The earning power of the debt portion in excess of the cost of debt
is transferred to equity and increases the return on equity.

Next, look at the impact of higher leverage in good times. At 80% leverage, the size of A is larger, and it is being given to a smaller base of equity. Hence, the leverage (the increase in return on equity over the earning power of the investment) is higher as the leverage (the ratio of liabilities to total assets) increases.

80% Leverage in Good Times

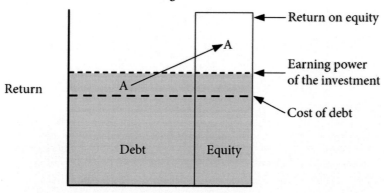

More earning power of the debt portion in excess of the cost of debt
is transferred to less equity and increases the return on equity.

Now, look at the impact of bad times, when the fixed cost of debt is higher than the earning power of the investment. Since debt must be paid, the equity owners now earn less than the earning power of the investment. They now transfer A to the holder of debt. Notice that the holder of debt is insulated from the impact of bad times; their return (interest) is unchanged. However, the equity owner has seen his return drop sharply.

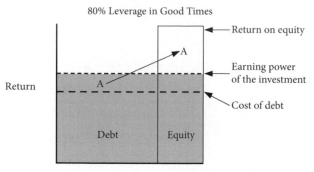

80% Leverage in Good Times

More earning power of the debt portion in excess of the cost of debt
is transferred to less equity and increases the return on equity.

For the highly levered equity owners, the situation is more serious because in transferring A to service debt, they have more than exhausted their own earnings. They must find additional cash to pay the interest charges. They might be able to do this from depreciation, but they will also have to make a principal repayment as well. Hence, it is not unusual for highly leveraged companies to fail to cover debt payments and be taken over by the lenders or broken up in order to pay back the lenders.

80% Leverage in Bad Times

So much cash must be transferred to service debt that the return
on equity is below zero; interest and principal can't be covered.

Sample Problem 4.9.1 Impact of Leverage During Good and Bad Times

Manufacturing firms A, B, and C have the balance sheets shown below. The main difference in these firms is the leverage ratio. All three firms started four years ago and arranged long-term debt with a 20-year term and straight-line repayment of principal. Company A borrowed $1 million at an interest rate of 5.5%, Company B borrowed $4 million at an interest rate of 6.0%, and Company C borrowed $7 million at an interest rate of 6.5%. Note that as leverage increases, the credit rating of a company decreases, making the cost of borrowing increase.

Each company is depreciating its fixed assets over a 20-year period on a straight-line basis with no assumed salvage value, and each company has set up its accounting so that operating income is calculated before interest on long-term debt, i.e., interest on long-term debt shows up as a negative entry in other income.

For the three companies, calculate net income, return on assets, return on equity, net cash flow before principal repayment, and net cash flow after principal repayment for these two cases: good times in which operating income is $1 million and bad times in which operating income is $200,000.

Balance Sheet (end of the 4th year)

	A ($)	B ($)	C ($)
Assets			
Current Assets			
Cash	30,000	10,000	30,000
Receivables	2,220,000	2,500,000	1,920,000
Inventory	1,600,000	1,450,000	1,300,000
	3,850,000	3,960,000	3,250,000
Fixed Assets			
Building and equipment at cost	9,000,000	9,400,000	9,500,000
Less accumulated depreciation	1,800,000	1,880,000	1,900,000
	7,200,000	7,520,000	7,600,000
Goodwill	—	—	—
Total assets	11,050,000	11,480,000	10,850,000
Liabilities and Equity			
Current Liabilities			
Short-term credit line	676,000	876,000	626,000
Accounts payable	942,000	1,222,000	892,000
Taxes payable	432,000	382,000	332,000
Current portion of long-term debt	50,000	200,000	350,000
	2,100,000	2,680,000	2,200,000
Long-term debt	750,000	3,000,000	5,250,000
Shareholders' Equity			
Capital	6,400,000	3,400,000	400,000
Retained earnings	1,800,000	2,400,000	3,000,000
Total liability and equity	11,050,000	11,480,000	10,850,000

Solution:

Interest on long-term debt is the remaining long-term debt (both the current and the non-current portion) times the interest rate.

For Company A, $800,000 × 5.5%.

For Company B, $3.2 million × 6%.

For Company C, $5.6 million × 6.5%.

Good Times—5th year

	A ($)	B ($)	C ($)
a. Operating income	1,000,000	1,000,000	1,000,000
b. Long-term interest charges	44,000	192,000	364,000
c. Net income from operations (a. – b.)	956,000	808,000	636,000
d. Return on assets (operating income/total assets) (%)	9.05	8.71	9.22
e. Return on equity (net income/equity) (%)	11.66	13.93	18.71
f. Depreciation (1/20 × fixed assets at cost)	450,000	470,000	475,000
g. Net cash flow (c. + f.)	1,406,000	1,278,000	1,111,000
h. Principal repayment (1/20 × original loan amount)	50,000	200,000	350,000
i. Cash flow after principal repayment (g. – h.)	1,356,000	1,078,000	761,000

Bad Times—5th year

	A ($)	B ($)	C ($)
a. Operating income	200,000	200,000	200,000
b. Long-term interest charges	44,000	192,000	364,000
c. Net income from operations (a. – b.)	156,000	8,000	−164,000
d. Return on assets (operating income/total assets) (%)	1.81	1.74	1.84
e. Return on equity (net income/equity) (%)	1.90	0.14	−4.82
f. Depreciation (1/20 × fixed assets at cost)	450,000	470,000	475,000
g. Net cash flow (c. + f.)	606,000	478,000	311,000
h. Principal repayment (1/20 × original loan amount)	50,000	200,000	350,000
i. Cash flow after principal repayment (g. – h.)	556,000	278,000	−39,000

In good times, Company C has the highest rate of return on equity. In bad times, Company C does not have enough cash from the business to make the annual principal repayment that is due at the end of the year. It would be very hard for Company C to borrow more money to get the cash to make the principal payment, since it is already highly leveraged and has negative net income. This example illustrates the maxim that "leverage up equals leverage down." A higher return in good times comes at the cost of higher risk in bad times.

Sample Problem 4.9.2 *Leverage*

Provided below is the balance sheet of Partsco, a very successful supplier to the auto industry. Its major source of financing during its rapid growth has consisted of long-term debt from the venture capital firm that supported the company during its start-up. The venture capital firm owns half of the share capital of Partsco in addition to holding $1.9 million in long-term debt.

Partsco Ltd. Balance Sheet, Year-End Last Year ($000)

Assets			Liabilities	
Current Assets			**Current Liabilities**	
Cash		10	Short-term credit line	50
Receivables		286	Accounts payable	308
Short-term investment		0	Accrued expenses	181
Inventory		150	Taxes payable	209
Prepaid expenses		75	Current portion of long-term debt	100
		511		848
Non-Current Assets			**Long-Term Debt**	
Building and equipment at cost	3,127		Long-term debt	1,900
Less accumulated depreciation	400	2,727		
			Shareholders' Equity	
Long-term investment		0	Capital shares	400
Goodwill		0	Retained earnings	100
Total assets		3,248	**Total liabilities and equity**	3,248

As part of its exit strategy, the venture capital firm wants Partsco to reduce its long-term borrowing by issuing shares, in essence converting debt to equity. After taking that step, the plan is to refinance the remaining long-term debt from a traditional lender such as a bank. What is Partsco's current leverage ratio, and what will that ratio be if it sells shares with a value of $1,000,000, assuming no other changes on the balance sheet?

Solution:

$$\text{Leverage} = \frac{\text{total liabilities} \times 100}{\text{total assets}}$$

$$\text{Total liabilities} = \$848,000 + \$1,900,000$$
$$= \$2,748,000$$

$$\text{Leverage} = \frac{\$2,748,000 \times 100}{\$3,248,000}$$
$$= 84.6\%$$

A leverage ratio of 84.6% is very high and would not typically be supported by traditional long-term lenders such as banks since such a highly leveraged company has too much risk of inability to service debt during an economic downturn. Very high leverage can occur in companies such as Partsco, where venture capital has been put into the company in the form of debt as well as equity.

After selling $1 million in shares and using the funds to repay debt, the new leverage ratio is

$$= \frac{(\$(1,900,000 - 1,000,000) + \$848,000) \times 100}{\$3,248,000}$$
$$= 53.8\%$$

With a leverage ratio of 54%, Partsco could look to traditional lending institutions as the source of its long-term debt.

4.10 Preferred Shares

A preferred share has some of the features of debt and some of the features of equity. Preferred shares are issued by a company with a prescribed dividend rate. This dividend is paid in preference to common shares, i.e., no dividend would be paid to common shareholders unless all dividends due to preferred shareholders had been paid. Like debt, a preferred share has a return that is a fixed and specified percentage. Technically, this return is paid as a dividend, so it comes from after-tax dollars of a company (dividends are not an expense of a company for income tax purposes, while interest is). In many jurisdictions including Canada, a dividend is taxed at a lower effective tax rate than interest income in order to encourage people to invest in companies. Hence, the dividend from a preferred share with a rate of 6% would give a greater after-tax benefit than a bond paying 6% interest.

Preferred shares only get the specified dividend, so they do not participate in any upside growth in the value of a company. In this, they are like debt. From the perspective of the common shareholder, who is concerned to get a leveraged return from the profitability of a company, preferred shares do not reduce the leverage. Therefore, the common shareholder views preferred shares as a form of debt when calculating leverage.

However, preferred shares lack some of the rights of debt. If a company's board of directors decides it cannot pay the dividend due to preferred shareholders, the preferred shareholders cannot petition the company into bankruptcy to force the payment of the dividend or the repayment of the shares. They rank behind debt, i.e., all obligations to lenders are satisfied in preference to preferred shares, so the "preferred" status is only in relation to common shares. Since the primary concern of a lender is the security of repayment, they tend to see preferred shares as ranking behind and not representing a legally binding obligation on the company, so when calculating debt ratios, lenders treat preferred shares as equity.

Preferred shares thus have the remarkable feature of being seen as equity by lenders and debt by common shareholders. Frequent features of preferred shares are that they are redeemable. This means they can be repurchased at the option of the company (sometimes after a specified period of time), and they are cumulative, i.e., any dividend missed is still due and must be paid in the future before any dividend is paid to common shareholders.

Why do companies issue preferred shares instead of debt? Typically, they are trying to maintain a good credit rating on their debt. Credit rating agencies, such as Moody's, Dominion Bond Rating Service (DBRS), and Standard and Poor's, assign a rating to debt based on its risk. Each uses a different scale for defining the risk of bonds, but typically, a rating of A is good, and B, C, and D down the line indicates lower quality of debt (more risk). Credit rating agencies carefully assess companies, and lenders rely on them to buy bonds. A lower credit rating means that a company will have to pay a higher interest rate for debt, since the market is less willing to purchase these bonds unless the higher interest rate offsets the higher risk. Credit rating agencies consider both the times interest earned ratio (discussed in Chapter 6) and the debt ratio in assessing a rating. When a company gets close to a limit that it is comfortable with for a credit rating, it will issue preferred shares rather than debt if it needs to raise funds that it can repay (as opposed to common shares).

Companies issue preferred shares instead of common shares because they may feel the market is undervaluing their shares, and hence, selling common shares in a low market will bring in too little money compared to the dilution of ownership. In some cases, companies try to avoid any dilution of ownership and will only issue common shares as a last resort.

Desperation Financing

Companies that are desperately in need of debt or equity, as might occur in a period of sustained bad times, will find an unsympathetic market. If a company is forced to sell shares to cover a period of losses, the share price is usually quite low, and the existing shareholders experience a significant dilution in their holdings. Another tough form of financing is a convertible debenture, which is the name given to debt that has the right, but not the obligation, to be converted to equity. If the company continues to do poorly and eventually goes into receivership, the holder of the convertible debenture keeps it as a debt instrument and then ranks ahead of equity in any payout of the proceeds from the breakup of the company. However, if the company turns around and becomes successful, the debt can be converted to common shares at the conversion price agreed at the time of the financing, usually a relatively low price. Money is serious business, and anyone thinking the bank will be sympathetic is likely to be disappointed.

The reason short-term lenders do not look to long-term assets for repayment is that long-term lenders have a first claim on these assets. When a company breaks up, it will sell them quickly, provided the sale price covers the amount of the long-term debt. A long-term lender will not spend a great deal of time and effort to spruce up an asset for sale in order to generate a surplus of funds to pay other unsecured creditors. An example of this is when a bank seizes a home for non-payment of a mortgage. If the homeowner were selling the house, he would cut the grass, sweep the walk, and tidy up the house during the sale process to get the highest possible offer, but once the bank has seized the house, it will be more inclined to take the first serious offer above the remaining balance of the mortgage.

4.11 Operational and Financial Management of a Company

To be successful in business, management must be efficient and effective in delivering a good or a service. The first test of this comes from the income statement: can management provide a good or a service at a low enough direct cost (COGS) to create a large enough margin to more than cover the fixed costs (SG&A) of the business, or in other words, create a profit? However, some concepts of operational effectiveness are contained in the balance sheet as well.

Imagine two competitive companies delivering the same good or service with the same level of sales (gross revenue), but one has twice the inventory and receivables that the other company has. Sloppy management requires more inventory, while good, tight management strives for "just in time" approaches that reduce inventory. Sloppy management allows receivables to build up (in effect, lending money to customers, usually with no interest since customers often do not pay it even if it is entered on a subsequent invoice). Good, tight management prompts customers to pay in a timely manner. Inventory and receivables are real costs to a business; they consume money. Good managers pay attention to such items. These concepts are developed further in chapters 6 and 9.

Balance sheets also illustrate two critical elements of financial management. The first is the ability of management to maintain enough current assets to cover current liabilities. The other element of financial management is setting the right balance between liabilities and equity. Firms with high liabilities (other people's money) relative to equity are more at risk if there is a downturn in business, since debt repayment is a legal obligation, while dividends are not.

A successful business requires good operational and financial management, and a good senior manager will be competent in both areas.

Appendix 4.1 Surviving the First Big Sale

Here is another example of the impact on working capital and the working capital ratio of an increase in sales.

Imagine a start-up company, Dataco, in which a recent graduate took a $500,000 loan from her rich uncle to start a company. It is based on developing proprietary software on a chip for compressing and encrypting files before they are transmitted over telephone company (telco) data transmission lines. The data is unencrypted and restored at the receiving end. The company has spent two years and $400,000 developing the software; this expense was capitalized (treated on the books as a long-term asset) and has been depreciating at the rate of $4,000 per month for 10 months. Losses to date are $95,000. The company is selling $25,000 per month of boxes to large telcos, who are testing the product. The company's sales strategy is a contribution margin of 50%. Cost of goods sold (COGS) is 90% materials and 10% labor, which is hired on a short-term contract basis as needed. The bank is happy enough to give them a short-term credit line, as there is good coverage via working capital. The receivables are from good solid customers, and are much higher than the bank debt. One day, they get an order for $1,000,000 worth of product. Can they survive this order?

To answer this question, first think like a banker, and then think like a manager to see if you can save the company. The company's starting balance sheet is shown as follows:

Dataco's Balance Sheet When It Gets the $1 Million Order ($000)

Assets		Liabilities	
Current Assets		**Current Liabilities**	
Cash	0	Short-term credit	15
Receivables	50	Accounts payable	30
Inventory	40	Accrued expenses	0
Prepaids	0	Taxes payable	0
Total current	90	Current portion of long-term debt	0
		Total current	45
Fixed Assets			
Cost	400		
Less depreciation	40	Long-term debt	0
Net	360		
		Shareholders' Equity	
Total assets	450	Capital shares	500
		Retained earnings	–95
		Total liabilities plus equity	450
		Working capital	45
		Working capital ratio	2.00

The balance sheet indicates that the initial investment of the uncle's money is $500,000 in capital shares. The losses to date are $95,000 (a negative entry in retained earnings), and the capitalized software development costs are $400,000 less $40,000 of cumulative depreciation.

Once the order comes in (time zero), management has a party and then gets to work. The next day, $450,000 of material is ordered (90% of 50% of the $1 million order), which arrives 30 days later. Terms of payment are net 30 days. In month 2, the contract labor force builds the product, which is shipped at the start of month 3, with payment terms of net 30 days. However, because it is the first large order, the customer takes longer than usual to do quality assurance tests and does not pay until 59 days after receiving the goods, or just before the end of month 5.

If Dataco proceeds to fill the order as planned, here is what its balance sheets will look like for the next five months:

Dataco's Balance Sheets over the Next Five Months ($000)

	Month 0	Month 1	Month 2	Month 3	Month 4	Month 5
Assets						
Current Assets						
Cash	0	0	0	0	0	505
Receivables	50	50	50	1,050	1,050	50
Inventory	40	490	540	40	40	40
Prepaids	0	0	0	0	0	0
Total current	90	540	590	1,090	1,090	595
Fixed Assets						
Cost	400	400	400	400	400	400
Less depreciation	40	44	48	52	56	60
Net	360	356	352	348	344	340
Total assets	450	896	942	1,438	1,434	935
Liabilities						
Current Liabilities						
Short-term credit	15	11	507	503	499	0
Accounts payable	30	480	30	30	30	30
Accrued expenses	0	0	0	0	0	0
Taxes payable	0	0	0	0	0	0
Current portion of long-term debt	0	0	0	0	0	0
Total current	45	491	537	533	529	30
Long-term debt	0	0	0	0	0	0
Shareholders' Equity						
Capital shares	500	500	500	500	500	500
Retained earnings	−95	−95	−95	405	405	405
Total liabilities plus equity	450	896	942	1,438	1,434	935
Working capital	45	49	53	557	561	565
Working capital ratio	2.00	1.10	1.10	2.05	2.06	19.83

First, look at month 5. If this order can be filled, this single sale gives the company over $500,000 in cash, which is more than the initial investment by the uncle. However, the company would fail in month 1 because the bank would pull the short-term credit line. Even if the small amount of bank debt ($11,000) could be paid off, there is no money to pay the supplier at the end of month 2.

To save this company and harvest the benefit of the $1 million order, management could do one of the following:

- Present its case to the bank and ask for leniency.
- Try to borrow long-term debt.
- Try to raise equity, say, from a venture capital firm.
- Ask the customer to prepay (to advance 50% of the sale price at time of order).
- Bootstrap the order (ship a tiny amount, retain the earnings, buy more material, ship again, retain the earnings, etc.).
- Make a special arrangement with the supplier.

If management asks for leniency, the bank is very unlikely to be the credit for this sale. Their gain is three months of interest on a half million dollars, perhaps $10,000. Their risk is enormous: what if the shipped product does not work, or what if management is killed in a car crash and the order is never filled? Why should the bank, which is using other people's savings, risk it to help the new graduate get rich?

It would be virtually impossible to borrow long-term debt because the only long-term asset in Dataco is a software program, which is likely worthless if the company fails. One of the problems with software companies is that lenders do not think of software as an adequate security for a long-term loan.

A venture capital firm would likely gladly put the needed $0.5 million into Dataco but would almost certainly ask for more than 50% ownership in exchange. This may seem harsh, but desperation financing has harsh terms. The venture capital company would argue, as the bank would, that it is not certain the product will work.

Customers would be very reluctant to advance $0.5 million to a start-up company prior to goods being shipped. A person would have to go quite high in a telco, perhaps as high as the chief financial officer, to get authority to prepay $0.5 million. People in the telco buying this product would be reluctant to risk their own career to push this extraordinary payment through the telco's bureaucracy.

Customers would likely be frightened off by a request to spread a $1 million order over many months, with a tiny shipment at the start. A $1 million order seems big to Dataco, but it is not big to the telco, who is not likely to feel comfortable being reminded of how shaky a company Dataco is.

The one solution most likely to work is to request extended credit terms, say payment in 180 days, from the material supplier. Provided the material supplier thinks it has a longer-term relationship with Dataco, a strategic alliance, it is the one party whose interests clearly align with Dataco: if Dataco succeeds, the supplier will have many more sales. If the short-term credit lender is unsecured, i.e., does not have a first claim on the receivables and inventory, then in addition to extended terms from the supplier, it would be necessary to get a letter from the supplier noting that it ranks behind the bank in a claim on unsecured assets. Taking these steps means that the bank's position is relatively unchanged from month 0. Taking this step avoids the need to fix the working capital problem below the line because, in effect, the supplier is providing the needed credit.

There are two key lessons from this example. First, growth in sales must be financed. Second, management can sometimes look to a strategic alliance with a supplier to solve a short-term credit problem.

Problems

4.1 The test to differentiate current from long-term assets and liabilities is whether the payment is due within one year. Some loans have what is called a balloon payment. For the term of the loan, only interest is paid, and at the end of the loan term, the entire principal is repaid (the balloon payment). This kind of financing is rare because it does not reflect the depreciation of assets, but it sometimes occurs if there is an excess of assets to secure the loan. Imagine that a company has a loan for $25 million. What is the current liability of the loan in year one for three different loan types: a five-year term with straight-line repayment of principal, a loan with principal recovered by a full balloon payment at the end of year five, and a loan with a levelized (mortgage) type annual repayment with a 20-year term and 8% interest? An 8% 20-year term mortgage is illustrated in Appendix 3.3.

4.2 You are considering buying Exampleco, a manufacturing company. The president and CFO are traveling and will not be back for two weeks, and the financial statements cannot be released until then. However, you have talked to the daughter of the owner and have written down the following comments. Try to construct a balance sheet for the company, making reasonable assumptions where necessary.

- *[Capital/Shares]* "We started Exampleco two years ago with $3.3 million that dad had inherited."
- *[Receivables]* "Our sales have done well, and if we can keep them at last month's performance, we would reach $4.2 million a year. We hope to do even better than that."
- *[Equip Dep]* "We bought four and half million dollars of equipment at an auction. It was used equipment but had been completely rebuilt, so dad decided on a 10-year depreciation period."
- "We just rent the space we are in."
- *[CASH]* "We never have any cash or notes in the bank. Dad set up a credit line, and we float on that. The bank didn't want to give us long-term financing until we were in operation for two years. We are trying to decide right now whether to take out some long-term financing and really expand the business or sell it to you and stay on as operators."
- *[?]* "At first, our draw on our credit line was over 3 million, and the only way we could get it was to have a personal guarantee from my uncle. Lucky for us, the business has gone well, and the draw from the bank has dropped over the two years we have been in business. Dad thinks we can get the requirement for a personal guarantee lifted."
- *[?]* "When we set up the business, we decided to leave the depreciation in the business. We also decided to set up an objective of leaving a quarter million dollars of net income per year in the company and treating ourselves to a dividend on everything else. So far we have met our objective."
- *[Inventory]* "We play it safe on inventory. It is running 35 days of sales, which is a lot considering our materials' cost is only 50% of sales. We could probably bring it down, but we have just been too busy filling orders."
- *[Payables]* "We have been stringing our suppliers out 50 days. We have to talk to them every month to assure them we are doing okay, but it has worked so far. Because our sales grew to $350k last month and we have stayed with the same suppliers, they haven't minded our slow pay."
- *[Prepaid Expenses]* "Our prepaids are so small we ignore them. Our accountant said that they weren't material, and that we could just expense this stuff as we spent it."
- *[Taxes payable]* "We are current on taxes. Dad knew a guy that lost his business because of unpaid taxes, so he has insisted on a monthly payment to keep us current."
- "Our payroll is two weeks behind, but it isn't a big deal because our staff is only 22. Otherwise, we are current on all our expenses."

Receivables • "Our customers are large companies, and they are sure slow to pay. Our receivables are running 55 days."
• "We are still getting by on the original equipment we bought."

Do you need the income statement to prepare the balance sheet in this case? Would you be able to make an intelligent decision about whether to buy the business without looking at the income statement? Explain why in one sentence.

What percentage of the total assets is tied up in inventory and receivables?

4.3 Take the following information on a company, and say what assets the company has and where the money came from to own those assets (its liabilities and equity) at the end of two years of operation (assume the principal repayment on debt has been made for year 2):

• The company has gross sales of $48 million per year, and the pattern of sales is even, i.e., there is no cyclical pattern to sales.
• Customers are large firms with a typical large-firm payment pattern.
• COGS for the business is 60% and is material only; all labor costs are in SG&A.
• Monthly payroll is $200,000.
• There is enough raw material on hand to support one month of manufacturing, and two months of actual production of finished goods is in the warehouse (remember that finished goods in inventory are carried on the books as COGS, not expected sale price).
• The company pays its suppliers 30 days after goods are received.
• The owners started the business with an initial capital injection of $5.6 million 25 months ago.
• The company borrowed $3 million of long-term debt, with the principal repayable in 10 equal annual payments.
• The company bought $8 million in assets at start-up and picked a depreciation period of 10 years. No additional assets have been purchased.
• In the first two years of the business, the company had a cumulative net income of $1,800,000 and paid dividends of $300,000 ($150,000 per year) to the owners.
• The business has a short-term credit line that runs positive or negative based on the fluctuations of the business (just like a personal checking account).

Prepare a balance sheet and use it to answer the following questions:
1. What assets does the business have? Which is larger: current assets or fixed?
2. How much short-term debt does the business have?
3. How much working capital does the business have?
4. If the cumulative dividend over two years had been $1,800,000 instead of $300,000 (if all the profits had been taken out of the business as dividends), what would the short-term debt be? Would working capital still be positive?
5. If you cut the inventory in half by a vigorous program of "just in time" manufacturing and shipping, by how much would your bank borrowings drop? Would working capital change?

4.4 For Balenceco's current fiscal year, you have the following information:

- Inventory, receivables, and payables are each up 35%, reflecting an improvement in sales.
- Net income for this year is $142,000.
- Balanceco starts the year with three owners, one of whom wants to retire. The owners agree that the retiring owner will have his shares bought back by Balanceco for $100,000. The two remaining shareholders each receive a dividend of $50,000 late this year. Other than leaving some retained earnings in the business this year, they do not inject any capital.
- A new piece of equipment is purchased for $120,000, very early this year. Its depreciation period is 10 years (all depreciation is straight-line).
- Other than the extra depreciation on the new piece of equipment, depreciation on the balance of equipment is unchanged from last year at $80,000 per year.
- Accrued wages are up 25% compared to last year's year-end, i.e., there are 25% more hours worked but unpaid at year-end.
- Cash in the bank and prepaid expenses are the same at year-end this year as they were at year-end last year.
- The long-term financing is a loan of $200K with a 10-year straight-line retirement. This year is the third year of this financing (at the end of last year, two years of financing had been completed).

Shown below is the balance sheet of Balanceco for end of year last year.

Balanceco Balance Sheet Last Year ($000)

Assets		Liabilities	
Current Assets		**Current Liabilities**	
Cash	15	Short-term credit line	96
Receivables	123	Accounts payable	66
Short-term investments	—	Accrued expenses	16
Inventory	98	Taxes payable	—
Prepaid expenses	26	Current portion of long-term debt	20
	262		198
Fixed Assets		**Long-Term Debt**	
Land, building, and equipment at cost	800	Repayable grants	—
Less accumulated depreciation	160	Long-term debt	140
	640		
		Shareholders' Equity	
Long-term investments	—	Capital shares	500
Goodwill	—	Retained earnings	64
Total assets	902	Total liability and equity	902

Complete Balanceco's balance sheet for this year. What fraction of Balanceco's assets are tied up in inventory and receivables this year?

Is Balanceco in good shape? If not, are the problems due to operational management or financial management? What could Balanceco have done differently?

4.5 Three people set out to build essentially identical apartment buildings in similar real estate markets for the same cost of $3.2 million. The three developers have the following characteristics:

- John is 45 and married with three children between the ages of 8 and 14. Ten years ago, he went bankrupt and lost the title to his home and all assets. He has reestablished himself again but promised himself that he would never again lose it all. He limits his mortgage financing (by the bank) to a maximum of 50% of project value.

- Helen is 24 and a recent graduate in civil engineering. Her uncle has decided to stake her in real estate development (give her equity). Helen thinks of herself as being a moderate risk taker and has little bad experience with failure. After discussions with her uncle, she is prepared to bank finance 70% of the project.

- Donald is 38 and determined to become very rich. He has been involved in a number of small business ventures and now wants to get into property development to get rich in a hurry. He has a strong ego and believes he can tolerate failure and bounce back again. He uses his slick and persuasive style to obtain 90% financing from the bank.

The pro forma highly abbreviated first-year income statement for the apartment complex, used in discussions with the bank that is considering the mortgage, is shown in the following table:

Pro Forma Income Statement ($)

(First year)	John	Helen	Donald
Number of units	56		
Project cost	3,200,000		
Capital cost per unit	57,143		
Annual rent per unit	11,200		
Income at full occupancy	627,200		
Less vacancy factor (5%)	31,360		
Adjusted gross income	595,840		
Cash expenses	162,366		
Depreciation	128,000		
Income before debt service	305,474		
Cash flow before debt service	433,474		
Earning power of the project (%)	9.5		

Leverage (%)	50
Equity	1,600,000
Debt	1,600,000
Interest cost	128,000
Pre-tax net income	177,474
Tax	70,989
After-tax net income	106,484
Cash flow before principal repayment	234,484
Principal repayment	34,964
Cash flow after principal repayment	199,521
Cash return on equity (%)	12.5

For each of the three developers, complete the projections by calculating first-year pro forma after-tax net income and cash flow and a pro forma first-year return on equity based on cash flow after principal repayment.

a. Does each developer have enough cash to make the principal repayment in year 1?

b. For the pro forma case, approximately how many years would it take for each developer to recover his or her equity?

Develop a downside case, where due to downturn in the local economy, the vacancy rate goes from 5% to 20%, and rental income per unit drops by 20%. For each of the three developers, calculate the same figures as for the pro forma case. Check if any developer has negative cash flow, and answer questions A and B.

What would the mortgage lender do if the developer did not have enough cash to make the mortgage payment?

A developer would frequently focus on the first one to five years of a project rather than do a long-term set of pro forma statements. He or she is mainly concerned with positive cash flow in the early years, i.e., can the development service its debt? The calculation of cash position would assume some short cuts, as is shown in the table. Thus, you can ignore current assets and liabilities (including short-term debt) and just look at the debt on the apartment building. This is pretty accurate for an apartment: inventory is negligible (some light bulbs and faucet washers), and receivables are usually zero since rent is paid in advance. Remember that interest is an expense that is deductible for calculating taxable income (but not principle repayments), so subtract interest cost from income before debt service before calculating tax. In this problem, depreciation for tax and book purposes is the same (which is virtually never true in practice), so you can calculate the tax from the book income. For those that are being taxed, tax cannot be negative, so unless you had other positive income (assume that you do not for this problem), a negative income from this apartment does not give you any tax benefit. Principal repayment occurs from after-tax dollars; if you cannot make the principal repayment, the lender will seize the apartment. Finally, return in this problem is cash return on equity: after you service the debt (principal plus interest), how much cash do you have left over, and what percentage is that of your equity? This is not identical to the return on equity ratio discussed in Chapter 6, but it is what a developer might focus on.

Why are the returns so different for the three developers? Think about the position of the three developers in good times (when Donald whizzes past you in a Porsche) and bad times (when you step over a homeless Donald on your way to the opera). When the earning power of the investment falls below the cost of money, the interest rate, can John sleep at night through the downturn? Will Helen go under in her first venture? In each case, assume a 20-year mortgage at 8% with an annual level payment of $101.85 per $1,000 original loan, first-year depreciation (book and tax) at 4%, and a tax rate of 40% on net income. Note that the cash expenses of running the apartment complex do not change significantly in the downside case.

For the earning power of the project, use EBIT divided by assets. Think about what happens when the earning power of the project exceeds the cost of debt and when it is lower than the cost of debt. This helps in understanding leverage.

Statement of Cash Flow

Key Concepts

- The statement of cash flow shows cash activities in a company over a period of time. Financial management decisions, such as how to raise funds, whether to buy new assets, or whether to pay a dividend, are clearly and consistently displayed in the statement of cash flow.

- Between two periods, an increase in an asset represents a use of cash, and a decrease is a source of cash. Similarly, an increase in a liability or shareholder equity is a source of cash, and a decrease is a use of cash.

- Cash activities are broken into three categories: operating, investing, and financing. The short-term cash and borrowing position of the company is not treated as a financing activity; it is the balancing item for the net cash change in the three categories.

- Operating activities include earnings, depreciation, and changes in non-cash working capital with the largest components usually being changes in receivables, payables, and inventory.

- Investing activities include the purchase or sale of assets.

- Financing activities include issuing or paying back long-term debt and issuing or buying back shares.

Chapter 5: Statement of Cash Flow

The income statement and the balance sheet tell managers a great deal about a company, but they do not tell the whole story, as shown by this example of two companies, Goodco and Badco.

Goodco and Badco have identical balance sheets at the end of last year and also have identical income statements for this year, which means that their operational management is identical and their ability to create value, measured by net income, is identical. They have an identical statement of retained earnings, which means that each company made the same decision about the amount of dividend. However, at the end of this year, Goodco and Badco have significantly different balance sheets in that one is healthy and the other has no working capital and would have its short-term credit line pulled. The income statement, statement of retained earnings, and balance sheets for Goodco and Badco for last year and this year are as follows:

Income and Retained Earnings Statements for Goodco and Badco

($000)	This Year
Revenue	650
Warranty/bad debt	6
Net revenue	644
COGS	320
Contribution margin	324
CM (%)	49.8
SG&A	
All admin except dep.	220
Depreciation	70
Operating income	34
Other income	12
Net income	46
Retained earnings, start of year	125
Net earnings for the year	46
Less dividend paid	16
Retained earnings, end of year	155

Goodco Balance Sheets

($000)	Last Year	This Year
Assets		
Current Assets		
Cash	9	22
Receivables	95	120
Inventory	75	88
Prepaids	40	28
Total current	219	258

Fixed Assets

Cost	700	780
Less depreciation	140	210
Net	560	570
Total assets	779	828

Liabilities

Current Liabilities

Short-term credit	51	44
Accounts payable	30	48
Accrued expenses	25	9
Taxes payable	8	2
Current portion of long-term debt	20	20
Total current	134	123
Long-term debt	170	175

Shareholders' Equity

Capital shares	350	375
Retained earnings	125	155
Total liabilities plus equity	779	828
Working capital	85	135
Working capital ratio	1.63	2.10

Badco Balance Sheets

($000)	Last Year	This Year
Assets		
Current Assets		
Cash	9	22
Receivables	95	120
Inventory	75	88
Prepaids	40	28
Total current	219	258
Fixed Assets		
Cost	700	820
Less depreciation	140	210
Net	560	610

Total assets	779	868

Liabilities
Current Liabilities

Short-term credit	51	234
Accounts payable	30	48
Accrued expenses	25	9
Taxes payable	8	2
Current portion of long-term debt	20	20
Total current	134	313
Long-term debt	170	225

Shareholders' Equity

Capital shares	350	175
Retained earnings	125	155
Total liabilities plus equity	779	868
Working capital	85	−55
Working capital ratio	1.63	0.82

Although the balance sheets last year are identical, Badco has a significantly negative working capital, a sign of inadequate financial management, while Goodco's working capital and working capital ratio have increased. Badco would in reality have been shut down by now, whereas Goodco is thriving.

This example illustrates the need for an additional financial statement. The management of Goodco and Badco has clearly made different decisions during the year, and these decisions have enormous impact, strengthening Goodco while destroying Badco. The statement of cash flow is the final financial statement, and it clearly shows what decisions management has taken during the period between two balance sheets. The statement of cash flow tracks where a company got cash from and what management did with that cash. The statement is a rate value, cash per year, which is the same as the income statement. Once the concepts of the statement of cash flow are developed, the reasons why Goodco and Badco diverged during the year will be evident.

5.1   The Concept of Sources and Uses of Funds

A fixed asset is something real that was purchased at a cost. A receivable represents real goods or services that were delivered to a customer for which the company expects to receive payment in the full amount of the booked receivable. Inventory is real in that it can be counted. Even an intangible asset such as a patent is a real item because it is intellectual property that had to be purchased with real funds (in practice, the words funds and cash are used interchangeably, even when payment is often by check or electronic funds transfer). Hence, if you look at two successive balance sheets and see an increase in an asset account, you know that cash or cash equivalents were used by the company to cause this change. For example, if fixed assets at cost in a company increase by $1 million from last year's balance sheet to this year's balance sheet, it is because the company spent $1 million to buy fixed assets, since the accountant records the value of the asset at cost. Similarly, if inventory is $100,000 higher on this year's balance sheet compared to last year's, then this is the cumulative actual cost of all the incremental material being held by the company at the end of this year and could only occur if the company spent a net incremental $100,000 in the time period between the two balance sheets. Inventory might have gone up and down over the course of the year, but an increase in its value measured between two specific points in time (which is what occurs on the balance sheet) meant that the net of all the transactions was that more cash was spent. Generally, when comparing two balance sheets, an increase in an asset account is a use of cash.

It is also true that a decrease in an asset account is a source of cash or cash equivalents. Think of receivables, the money owed a company by its customers. The only way receivables are reduced on a balance sheet is if customers pay their invoices and their payment is a source of funds. Generally, when comparing between two balance sheets, a decrease in an asset account is a source of cash.

Liabilities and equity have the opposite rule: an increase in a liability or equity account between two balance sheets represents a source of funds to a company, and a decrease in a liability or equity account means that funds were used. To illustrate this, think of long-term debt, a liability account. If this account increases between two balance sheets, it is because someone lent money to the company during that time period. The lender gives the company a check (funds), and the company gives the lender an agreement to repay. On the other hand, if long-term debt decreases, it is because the company has made a principal payment to the lender.

Depreciation appears on the asset side of the ledger for the balance sheet of a small company (it appears in a note to the financial statement for a large company), but recall that it is a negative number. Hence, an increase in depreciation is a source of cash, as you also saw in Chapter 3. Depreciation cannot decrease: companies do not "write up" the value of their assets, i.e., increase their book value.

The table below summarizes the cash implications of changes between two balance sheets.

Table 5.1 Cash Impact of Account Changes between Two Balance Sheets

	Increase	Decrease
Asset	Use of cash	Source of cash
Liability	Source of cash	Use of cash
Cumulative depreciation	Source of cash	Cumulative depreciation never decreases

Two successive balance sheets can be used to track sources and uses of funds for a company. Since the balance sheet should balance and changes in assets are always exactly offset by changes in liabilities and assets, you will find that the sources of funds always balance the uses of funds in a company. Be careful not to double count changes in current assets, current liabilities, or fixed assets. Work with each element of current assets and current liabilities, but do not also calculate the differences in the total. If the balance sheet shows fixed assets at cost, cumulative depreciation, and net fixed assets, then either work with the combination of fixed assets at cost and cumulative depreciation or with net fixed assets, but not both.

Look at this example:

Growthco Balance Sheet ($000)

	Last Year	This Year	Source	Use
Assets				
Current Assets				
Cash	—	—		—
Receivables	642	877		235
Short-term investments	—	—		—
Inventory	408	589		181
Prepaid expenses	61	54	7	
	1,111	1,520		
Fixed Assets				
Land, building, and equipment at cost	4,500	6,200		1,700
Less accumulated depreciation	900	1,520	620	
	3,600	4,680		
Long-term investments	0	0		
Goodwill	0	0		
Total assets	4,711	6,200		
Liabilities				
Current Liabilities				
Short-term credit line	192	609	417	
Accounts payable	292	387	95	
Accrued expenses	44	67	23	
Taxes payable	21	15		6
Current portion of long-term debt	40	60	20	
	589	1,138		
Long-Term Debt				
Repayable grants	0	0		
Long-term debt	340	480	140	
Shareholders' Equity				
Capital shares	3,300	4,000	700	

Retained earnings	482	582	100
Total liability and equity	4,711	6,200	
Sources/uses of funds		2,122	2,122

From looking at sources and uses of cash, several comments can be made about Growthco:

- Sources of cash/funds equal uses for the period between the two balance sheets. This is always the case. There is no significance, however, to the magnitude of the number; only that sources equal uses.
- Growthco has no cash on hand and is using a short-term credit line it has negotiated with a bank for day-to-day expenses and deposits. This is typical of many businesses.
- The company appears to have growing sales, since inventory, receivables, and payables are all up. The company is generating net income, since retained earnings increase by $100K over the year.
- Current assets increase by $409K, largely due to the increase in inventory and receivables. This increase requires funds. Specifically, all current asset categories except prepaid expenses increase. The decrease in prepaid expenses has freed up some cash, but not much in this case.
- Growthco has clearly made some major fixed asset investments in the past year to support its growth. Specifically, $1,700 of new fixed asset investments occurred in the last 12 months, which is quite significant considering that in the previous history of the company, only $4,500 of original investment had occurred.
- Growthco has a significant amount of depreciation this year ($620K). Depreciation is always a source of cash. Remember from Chapter 3 that depreciation is a deemed expense, not a cash expense. Hence, depreciation can be thought of as money that has been taken into a company and represents the recovery of past asset purchases. This money is available to the company so it can be used to pay for future asset purchases or for any other purpose. Chapter 3 showed that companies with negative earnings (net income) will have positive cash flow if depreciation is larger than the negative earnings. A company in this situation can pay a dividend or repay debt, for example, by using the cash represented by depreciation.
- Growthco's current liabilities increase by $549K. More money is owed to suppliers, and this is a source of funds; the company is, in essence, drawing on its credit with suppliers to help finance its growth. It is also increasing its short-term borrowings from the bank by $417K. The small reduction in taxes payable is a use of funds (in that last year, owed taxes can be thought of as a debt due to the government, and this year, that amount is less).
- Growthco has increased its long-term debt. If one adds up the current portion (due within one year) and the long-term portion, the total net increase in long-term debt is $160k. Last year's statement suggests that Growthco borrowed an additional $200K of long-term debt this year and paid off $40K of debt during the year, leading to a net increase of $160K.
- Growthco has had a major increase in equity over the past year. It raised $700K in new investment and retained earnings of $100K.

Note that funds flow ($2,122K) is not the same as an increase in asset value, which is $1,489K in the case of Growthco. The net increase in fixed assets is $1,080K ($4,680 minus $3,600), and the increase in current assets is $409K ($1,520 minus $1,111), for a total increase of $1,489K. Where does this money come from? Bank indebtedness goes up by $577K, which is the sum of the increase in short-term credit ($417K) and long-term credit ($140K plus $20K, which is the current portion). Equity goes up by $800K, the sum of $700K of new investment and $100K of retained earnings. The balance of the increase in the asset value comes from changes in current liabilities, mainly payables, which is money that is owed to suppliers.

From this information, it is easy to get a good feeling about the health of Growthco: they are financing their growth by a mixture of debt and equity, not just debt. If Growthco had borrowed all of the money it had required for its increase in asset value, the company would be living on borrowed time as well as borrowed money in that no person and no company can survive if all of their funding comes from borrowing from others. However, Growthco has healthy retained earnings, and a new shareholder believed enough in the company to invest an additional $700K.

An analyst might wonder why Growthco would have bought additional assets for $1,700K and only increased long-term financing by a net of $160K. It may be that Growthco found the covenants on a higher level of long-term debt too onerous. It may be that the long-term lender was unfamiliar or uncomfortable with the new assets, or it may be that Growthco has a further expansion in mind and will take out a more comprehensive long-term financing package in the future. A prospective future investor in Growthco could address this with management before committing to an investment. This is the true power of financial analysis: it allows owners, managers, buyers, or sellers of a business to focus their attention on critical details that affect the health of a business.

By calculating the sources and uses of cash, it is possible to see what management has done during the period between two balance sheets. However, some information about management choices is still lacking, such as the fraction of Growthco's earnings that were paid out as a dividend. Also, the information about management decisions is scattered throughout the sources and uses. To make management's sources and uses of cash even clearer, accounting has developed the statement of cash flow (SCF).

Sample Problem 5.1 Sources and Uses of Funds

You are provided with the balance sheets for the end of year 2001 and 2002 of Valveco, a valve manufacturing company. Determine the sources and uses of funds, and answer these three questions about the past year:

- Was investment in new equipment significantly different than depreciation?
- Did Valveco raise more equity (sell more shares)?
- Did the company pay down or take on new long-term debt?

Valveco Balance Sheet				
($000)	End of Last Year		End of This Year	
Assets				
Current Assets				
Cash		55		200
Receivables		225		139
Short-term investment		300		200
Inventory		280		400
Prepaid expenses		90		71
		950		1,010
Fixed Assets				
Land, building, and equipment at cost	5,500		6,000	
Less accumulated depreciation	1,650		2,250	
Net fixed assets		3,850		3,750
Long-term investment		200		400
Goodwill		0		0
Total assets		5,000		5,160
Liabilities				
Current Liabilities				
Short-term credit line		140		165
Accounts payable		250		55
Accrued expenses		52		—
Taxes payable		100		120
Current portion of long-term debt		100		100
		642		440
Long-Term Debt				
Long-term debt		1,800		1,700
Shareholders' Equity				
Capital shares		2,000		2,400
Retained earnings		558		620
Total liability and equity		5,000		5,160

Solution:

($000)	Last Year	This Year	Source	Use
Valveco Balance Sheet				
Assets				
Current Assets				
Cash	55	200		145
Receivables	225	139	86	
Short-term investment	300	200	100	
Inventory	280	400		120
Prepaid expenses	90	71	19	
	950	1,010		
Fixed Assets				
Land, building, equipment at cost	5,500	6,000		500
Less accumulated depreciation	1,650	2,250	600	
Net fixed assets	3,850	3,750		
Long-term investment	200	400		200
Goodwill	0	0		
Total assets	5,000	5,160		
Liabilities				
Current Liabilities				
Short-term credit line	140	165	25	
Accounts payable	250	55		195
Accrued expenses	52	—		52
Taxes payable	100	120	20	
Current portion of long-term debt	100	100		
	642	440		
Long-Term Debt				
Long-term debt	1,800	1,700		100
Shareholders' Equity				
Capital shares	2,000	2,400	400	
Retained earnings	558	620	62	
Total liability and equity	5,000	5,160		
Sources/uses of funds			1,312	1,312

Determining sources and uses of funds is a straightforward process of a line-by-line calculation of the difference in each line of the balance sheet. By convention, all entries are positive numbers, and sources of funds will always equal uses of funds. Calculate fixed assets at cost and depreciation, but do not include net fixed assets since that would be double counting (net fixed assets are fixed assets at cost less accumulated depreciation).

An increase in an asset account is a use of funds, while a decrease is a source of funds. An increase in a liability account is a source of funds, and a decrease is a use of funds. Since depreciation is a negative entry on the asset side of the balance sheet, an increase in depreciation is a source of funds, just like an increase in a liability. Depreciation never decreases, so it is never a use of funds.

The sources and uses indicate the following:

- The increase in fixed assets at cost was $500,000, and the depreciation for the year was $600,000. This is not a large difference, so the change in the net value of fixed assets is small.
- The company issued $400,000 in new equity during the year, a 20% increase.
- The company paid down long-term debt by $100,000.

5.2   Statement of Cash Flow

The statement of cash flow (SCF) takes information from this year's income statement and statement of retained earnings and this year's and last year's balance sheets and arranges key information into three broad categories: operating activities, investing activities, and financing activities.

- **Operating activities**: the first entry in this section is net earnings, the value created by the company in the last year. The next entries are depreciation and any other non-cash charges against earnings. Since depreciation and other non-cash charges, such as an allowance for future reclamation, are related to operations of assets a company already owns, they are treated as an operating source of funds. This section then includes the funds from an increase or decrease in working capital but excludes cash, the short-term credit line, and the current portion of long-term debt. This value is called changes in non-cash working capital, and it is included because working capital such as inventory and receivables is related to the company's current operations. Specific changes in inventory, receivables, payables, accrued expenses, and taxes payable are not given (just the aggregate value). However, a financial analyst who sees a significant change in non-cash working capital and wants to identify the source can easily extract this information from the balance sheets by using the sources and uses of funds approach shown in Section 5.1. Changes in cash and short-term debt are the balancing entry in the SCF, and changes in the current portion of the long-term debt are recorded in financing activities.
- **Investing activities**: this section records the net effect of the purchase or sale of fixed assets or goodwill and intangible assets. Asset purchases are shown at cost, since any depreciation taken on them during the year is recorded in operating activities.
- **Financing activities**: this section captures dividends paid, changes in long-term debt (it will sometimes show both payment of and additional creation of long-term debt, or it can simply net this out to a single number), and changes in share capital (common and preferred shares). Any change in the current portion of the long-term debt must be included in this section to accurately show all financing activity. However, changes in cash and short-term borrowings are not included here, since again the SCF balances the statement by calculating all the other changes in cash and checking that against changes in cash and short-term borrowing. However, some debt intended to be long-term debt but callable under special circumstances is now treated

in accounting as short-term debt (discussed in Chapter 4). This type of short-term debt is included in the financing activities portion of the SCF. The distinction on the SCF is between debt classified as short term but intended to be long term versus a true short-term credit line on which a company floats, i.e., the account into which it deposits and against which it writes checks.

In the SCF, the convention is that all cash/funds flowing into a company are positive, and all cash/funds flowing out of the company are negative. Hence, a dividend or asset purchase is always a negative number, while depreciation, the sale of assets, or funds from the sale of new shares is always a positive number. Note that retained earnings do not need to be included as a line item, since the SCF shows net earnings and dividends, and the difference (retained earnings) is therefore built into the SCF. The dividend payout ratio, the fraction of net earnings paid out as dividends, is easy to see on the SCF.

To complete a statement of cash flow for Growthco, its income statement and statement of retained earnings for this year are needed.

Growthco Income Statement

($000)	This Year
Revenue	4,223
Allowance for bad debt	27
Net revenue	4,196
Cost of goods sold	2,695
Contribution margin	1,501
Contribution margin (%)	35.5

Sales, General, and Administrative Expense

All items except depreciation	719
Depreciation	620
Operating income	162
Other income	−24
Net income	138

Growthco Statement of Retained Earnings

Retained earnings at start of year	482
Plus net income for this year	138
Less dividend paid this year	38
Retained earnings at end of year	582

The statement of cash flow for Growthco is as follows:

Growthco Statement of Cash Flow ($000)

	This Year
Operating Activities	
Net earnings for the year	138
Depreciation	620
Changes in non-cash working capital	−297
Subtotal	461
Investing Activities	
Additions to fixed assets	−1,700
Additions to goodwill and intangibles	0
Subtotal	−1,700
Financing Activities	
Dividends	−38
Net new long-term borrowings	160
Net new capital shares	700
Subtotal	822
Funds flow	−417
Cash on hand, start of year	−192
Cash on hand, end of year	−609
Change in cash position	−417

From a financial position, the power of the statement of cash flow is that it captures funds flow in a company and breaks it down by logical and consistent categories so that a person trying to understand a business can quickly see what critical management decisions have been made and how they affect the business.

If Growthco had cash and a short-term credit line, then the statement of cash flow would calculate the net cash position (cash minus the draw on the credit line). Since cash can normally be moved into the credit line at any time, these can be thought of as two components of a single account. You can also think of short-term borrowings as negative cash; net cash position is the sum of positive cash (cash) and negative cash (short-term borrowings).

Sample Problem 5.2 Preparing a Statement of Cash Flow

Cimci Inc. is a computer hardware manufacturing organization and has experienced high margins and high growth in sales over the past 17 years.

From the balance sheet, income statement, and statement of retained earnings for Cimci Inc., prepare a statement of cash flow. Comment on the values of Cimci's management and board of directors based on what you see from the statement of cash flow.

Cimci Balance Sheet

($000)	Year-End Last Year		Year-End This Year	
Assets				
Current Assets				
Cash		23		23
Receivables		323		237
Short-term investment		0		0
Inventory		357		549
Prepaid expenses		63		72
		766		881
Fixed Assets				
Land, building, and equipment at cost	6,300		7,200	
Less accumulated depreciation	1,300		1,757	
Net fixed assets		5,000		5,443
Long-term investment		100		100
Goodwill		0		0
Total assets		5,866		6,424
Liabilities				
Current Liabilities				
Short-term credit line		458		489
Accounts payable		432		137
Accrued expenses		53		87
Taxes payable		43		99
Current portion of long-term debt		67		123
		1,053		935
Long-Term Debt				
Long-term debt		1,456		1,235

Shareholders' Equity

Capital shares	3,000	3,500
Retained earnings	357	754
Total liability and equity	5,866	6,424

Cimci Income Statement

($000)	This Year
Revenue	6,107
Allowance for bad debt	12
Net revenue	6,095
Cost of goods sold	3,292
Contribution margin	2,803
Contribution margin (%)	45.9

Sales, General, and Administrative Expenses

Excluding depreciation	882
Depreciation	457
Operating income	1,464
Other income	2,725
Net income	4,189

Cimci Statement of Retained Earnings

($000)	This Year
Retained earnings at the start of the year	357
Plus net income for this year	4,189
Less dividend paid this year	3,792
Retained earnings at the end of the year	754

Solution:

The first step in preparing the statement of cash flow is to determine the sources and uses of funds.

Cimci Balance Sheet

($000)	Year-End Last Year	Year-End This Year	Source	Use
Assets				
Current Assets				
Cash	23	23		0
Receivables	323	237	86	
Short-term investment	0	0		0
Inventory	357	549		192
Prepaid expenses	63	72		9
	766	881		
Fixed Assets				
Land, building, and equipment	6,300	7,200		900
Less accumulated depreciation	1,300	1,757	457	
	5,000	5,443		
Long-term investment	100	100		0
Goodwill	0	0		0
Total assets	5,866	6,424		
Liabilities				
Current Liabilities				
Short-term credit line	458	489	31	
Accounts payable	432	137		295
Accrued expenses	53	87	34	
Taxes payable	43	99	56	
Current portion of long-term debt	67	123	56	
	1,053	935		

Long-Term Debt				
Long-term debt	1,456	1,235		221
Shareholders' Equity				
Capital shares	3,000	3,500	500	
Retained earnings	357	754	397	
Total liability and equity	5,866	6,424		
Sources/uses of funds			1,617	1,617

Information is then taken from all three statements to fill in the statement of cash flow.

Cimci Statement of Cash Flow

($000)	This Year
Operating Activities	
Net earnings for the year	4,189
Depreciation	457
Changes in non-cash working capital	(320)
Subtotal	4,326
Investing Activities	
Additions to fixed assets	(900)
Addition to goodwill and intangibles	0
Subtotal	(900)
Financing Activities	
Dividends	(3,792)
Net new long-term borrowings	(165)
Net new capital shares	500
Subtotal	(3,457)
Funds flow	(31)
Cash on hand, start of year	(435)
Cash on hand, end of year	(466)
Change in cash position	(31)

Note that the entry "Changes in non-cash working capital" includes the net change in all current assets and liabilities except cash, the short-term credit line, and the current portion of the long-term debt. Financing activities include changes in long-term debt (including the current portion), but not the short-term credit line.

The check for consistency is whether the net funds flow from operating, investing, and financing activities equals the change in net cash. Net cash is defined as cash minus the short-term credit line.

The statement of cash flow gives powerful insight into management values. In the case of Cimci, investment in new assets is higher than depreciation but not large relative to the net fixed assets of the company. The increase in fixed assets (investment – depreciation), approximately $450,000, is less than 10% of the net fixed assets of the company. Most of the net earnings of Cimci are being taken out of the company as a dividend. The dividend payout ratio, dividends divided by net earnings, is 90%, which is a very high ratio (many growth companies pay no dividend). New capital shares were issued during the year, and long-term borrowing was reduced slightly.

The overall conclusion from the statement of cash flow is that Cimci is harvesting its value creation as dividends to the owners and is not focused on a high growth in fixed assets.

5.3   Analyzing Problems with the Statement of Cash Flow

Using the example of Goodco and Badco again, the concept of sources and uses of funds can be used to develop a statement of cash flow to help illustrate why they diverge so significantly during this year. The following tables show the sources and uses calculations for the two companies.

Goodco Sources and Uses Calculation

($000)	Last Year	This Year	Sources	Uses
Assets				
Current Assets				
Cash	9	22		13
Receivables	95	120		25
Inventory	75	88		13
Prepaids	40	28	12	
Total current	219	258		
Fixed Assets				
Cost	700	780		80
Less depreciation	140	210	70	
Net	560	570		
Total assets	779	828		

Liabilities

Current Liabilities

			Sources	Uses
Short-term credit	51	44		7
Accounts payable	30	48	18	
Accrued expenses	25	9		16
Taxes payable	8	2		6
Current portion of long-term debt	20	20	0	
Total current	134	123		
Long-term debt	170	175	5	

Shareholders' Equity

Capital shares	350	375	25	
Retained earnings	125	155	30	
Total liabilities plus equity	779	828		
Working capital	85	135		
Working capital ratio	1.63	2.10		
Total sources/uses			160	160

Badco Sources and Uses Calculation

($000)	Last Year	This Year	Sources	Uses
Assets				
Current Assets				
Cash	9	22		13
Receivables	95	120		25
Inventory	75	88		13
Prepaids	40	28	12	
Total current	219	258		
Fixed Assets				
Cost	700	820		120
Less depreciation	140	210	70	
Net	560	610		
Total assets	779	868		

Liabilities

Current Liabilities

Short-term credit	51	234	183	
Accounts payable	30	48	18	
Accrued expenses	25	9		16
Taxes payable	8	2		6
Current portion of long-term debt	20	20	0	
Total current	134	313		
Long-term debt	170	225	55	

Shareholders' Equity

Capital shares	350	175		175
Retained earnings	125	155	30	
Total liabilities plus equity	779	868		
Working capital	85	−55		
Working capital ratio	1.63	0.82		
		Total sources/ uses	368	368

Remember that there is no significance to the magnitude of the sources and uses. The only critical factor is that they be equal. You could try to extract what management did from the scattered information in the sources and uses calculation, but it is far easier to analyze if the statement of cash flow is prepared.

Goodco and Badco Statement of Cash Flow

($000)	Goodco	Badco
Cash Derived from Operating Activities		
Net income for the year	46	46
Depreciation and non-cash items	70	70
Changes in non-cash working capital	−30	−30
Total	86	86
Cash Used for Investing Activities		
Purchase of fixed assets	−80	−120
Loss or gain on sale of assets	0	0

Total	−80	−120
Cash Derived from Financing Activities		
Changes in equity	25	−175
Changes in long-term debt	5	55
Less dividends paid	−16	−16
Total	14	−136
Increase (decrease) in cash	20	−170
Net cash, beginning of year	−42	−42
Net cash, end of year	−22	−212
Increase (decrease) in cash	20	−170

The comparison of Goodco and Badco indicates that the cash impact of the operation of the company was identical and the dividend was the same. There are two key differences between Goodco and Badco: Badco buys more assets than Goodco and has a major difference in its financing activities, with the reduction in shareholder equity being very substantial.

Goodco's asset purchases during this year, $80,000, are close to its depreciation of $70,000, so its net asset value is not growing substantially. Despite this, it brings in a very small amount of long-term debt ($5,000, perhaps a vehicle lease) and also brings in new share capital of $25,000. Its short-term borrowings decrease. Badco has asset purchases well in excess of depreciation ($120,000 versus $70,000). It increases its long-term debt by about this difference ($55,000), but it also reduces its shareholder equity by $175,000. In essence, the company has used cash to buy back some of the shares of its owners. There is not enough operating income to cover this, so almost all the funds required ($175,000) come from an increase in short-term borrowings. Badco has used an unsecured short-term credit line to buy back shares and, in the process, has put itself into a negative working capital position. It has done this at the same time that it increased assets well beyond depreciation. Badco has done too much with above-the-line money.

The management of Badco had many other choices, including the following:

- They could have not bought the shares back from the company or spread this over several years. There are two ways shares can be transferred: one has no impact on the company, and one takes cash out of the company. Suppose in the case of Badco that a shareholder wanted to be bought out. He or she could have been bought out by the other shareholders rather than by the company.
- They could have arranged more long-term debt instead of borrowing on an unsecured credit line.
- They could have postponed the asset purchase until there was enough money in the company to do this without compromising the working capital of the company.

In the example of Goodco and Badco, for simplicity the buyback of shares reduced share capital only. In strict accounting, a share buyback would be allocated in part to share capital and retained earnings. If shares were issued on more than one occasion over a long period of time, the calculation can become complex. The simplified treatment does not affect the underlying message about company management: the critical issue is Badco's over-reliance on short-term borrowing.

Company versus Owner Purchase of Shares

A company has three owners. Owner 1 wants to sell his share and retire, and owners 2 and 3 want to acquire that share and become the sole owners of the company. Owner 1 values his stake in the company at $10 million. There are two ways that owners 2 and 3 can buy out owner 1, and these will have a significantly different impact on the company, as illustrated by Badco.

The first way for owners 2 and 3 to buy out owner 1 is for them to purchase the shares directly. Owners 2 and 3 would each give owner 1 $5 million, and owner 1 would give them the shares he holds. This has no cash impact on the company because it occurs outside the company. This is exactly the kind of transaction that takes place every business day on stock exchanges around the world. Stock prices rise or fall daily as investor sentiments about a company change, but the company itself is shielded from any direct financial impact. In the case described, owner 1 might have originally put in $2 million of share capital into the company, but if the company has done well, the value of those shares, as agreed by the three owners, may be $10 million. The company does not get the extra $8 million; owner 1 does.

The second way for owners 2 and 3 to buy out owner 1 is for the company to purchase owner 1's shares for $10 million. The company writes a check to owner 1 for $10 million, and the shares are returned to the company. Once in the company, the shares are known as treasury shares, and they are, in effect, idle. There is no sense paying a dividend on treasury shares; the money just stays in the company.

The ownership impact is the same for both methods of buying out owner 1: owners 2 and 3 are the sole owners of the company at the end of the transaction. However, the impact on the company is vastly different. In the first method, owners 2 and 3 each have $5 million less, while in the second method, the company has $10 million less. There is nothing wrong with a privately held company buying out an owner as long as it does not impair the company. The case of Badco shows a company that is destroyed by such a transaction because the source of the cash for the buyout was an excessive draw on the short-term credit line.

Why Banks Have Covenants

The case of Badco illustrates why banks have covenants on short-term credit lines and why they require monthly reporting. The lender is not in the room when key management decisions are made, so he or she has no power to appoint a director to the board of a company. Badco's management shows terrible judgment, as illustrated by the statement of cash flow. Because the bank is focused on security, it will pull the credit line in response to Badco's actions.

Many companies are started by entrepreneurial people who do not have a good understanding of finance. As the Badco case illustrates, understanding the cash impact of management decisions is key to building a successful company.

Share Buyback in Publicly Traded Companies

Companies that are traded publicly on stock exchanges usually have broad ownership: many pension funds, mutual funds, and small individual investors are shareholders. Is it appropriate for such companies to buy back their own shares?

Stock markets have a great deal of investor psychology, and a popular saying that has a great deal of depth in it is that "There are only two emotions on Wall Street: greed and fear." (Wall Street is the location of the New York stock exchange, but the meaning of the words has been broadened over time to mean investing in general). Since stock buyers tend to overreact on both ends of the emotional spectrum, paying too much when a stock is "hot" and selling at too low a price when a stock is out of favor, one justification for company stock purchases is to smooth out the low values when a stock is out of favor.

Management could also give a larger dividend to shareholders and let them decide whether to buy more shares in that company or do something else with the money. When management decides to buy back shares, it is in essence saying "The best investment we can make with shareholders' money is to buy our own undervalued shares, and we are so sure this is a good investment that we are doing this rather than paying a dividend." This causes an ethical problem to arise. Management is usually inherently in a conflict of interest, since a portion of senior management income is usually in the form of a stock option or grant of shares. Stock options and share grants were originally designed to give management a strong incentive to increase the share value of a company. With an option, a manager is given the right to buy a number of shares at some point in the future at today's price; in essence, the company is setting aside shares today and giving the right, but not the obligation, to a senior manager to buy those shares at that price at a prescribed future time. If a company's stock price rises, the person holding the option has gained a benefit. If the stock price drops, the person simply does not exercise the option and suffers no loss.

Any person holding an option will potentially benefit from a significant repurchase of shares by a company because price is what changes to ensure that the number of buyers of shares always exactly equals the number of sellers, and increased interest in buying is offset by an increase in price. In other words, a decision to have a company increase its repurchase of its own shares will put upward pressure on the stock price. Hence, management is in a conflict of interest when recommending major stock repurchase programs.

Pepsico is an example of a company that has had a history of major stock repurchases. For the three-year period 2004 to 2006, the company spent more than twice as much on stock repurchase as it did on dividends. Some question whether the shareholders of Pepsico should have been entitled to a higher dividend so they could make their own decisions about whether to purchase more Pepsico shares.

5.4   *Aligning Management Decisions with Owners' Interests*

Companies A and B each have a total asset value of $1 billion, as reported on the last balance sheet for the start of the year. Each company has a net income of $200 million, or a 20% return on start-of-year assets, which is very good. However, management is making very different decisions in these two companies.

	Company A ($ million)	Company B ($ million)
Cash Derived from Operating Activities		
Net income for the year	200	200
Depreciation and non-cash items	75	75
Changes in non-cash working capital	−50	5
Total	225	280
Cash Used for Investing Activities		
Purchase of fixed assets	−500	−40
Loss or gain on sale of assets	0	0
Total	−500	−40
Cash Derived from Financing Activities		
Changes in share capital	0	0
Changes in long-term debt	250	−50
Less dividends paid	0	−150
Total	250	−200
Increase (decrease) in cash	−25	40
Net cash (beginning of year)	−90	−90
Net cash (end of year)	−115	−50
Increase (decrease) in cash	−25	40

Company A is investing heavily in fixed assets. In the past year, it has increased its asset investment by $500 million, or 50% of its total asset value at the start of the year, which is a very high increase. It is financing this by the cash coming from operating activities and by a major issuance of long-term debt ($250 million). It does not pay a dividend. It needs cash to cover an increase in non-cash working capital, which likely means its sales are growing. This pattern would be typical of a high-growth manufacturing company. Company B has a very small investment in assets, about half of depreciation. This low level of investment might be associated with maintenance capital, i.e., fixing minor problems and small debottlenecking projects (debottlenecking is the name given to projects in an existing operating plant that are intended to eliminate easily corrected limits to production capacity). Company B pays a substantial dividend equal to 75% of its net earnings (this ratio is called the dividend payout ratio). It is also paying back long-term debt and reduces its short-term borrowing during the year. This pattern would be typical of a mature pipeline company that has limited opportunities to invest in new pipelines.

Now, imagine two investors, a 35-year-old saving for a retirement long in the future and a retired 80-year-old. Company A is focused on growth and might be ideal for the 35-year-old who does not need dividend income. The 80-year-old is far more likely to want to live on the income from dividends and, if so, would be more drawn to company B, both for dividends and its lower risk (since growth in assets may or may not be successfully reflected in future sales and earnings). Management decisions about how to use cash have an impact on the nature of a company and also will help determine the kind of shareholder for whom the company is suitable.

Dividend versus Growth Stocks

Because of the business they are in, some companies are characterized by stable income (slow growth) and limited opportunities for new investment in fixed assets. Utility companies in areas of slow population growth, such as an electrical distribution company, are good examples. For this type of company, income growth is related in large part to population growth, since rates per customer are regulated by a public utilities commission. (When a company is a natural monopoly, for example, a power distribution company, the price it charges its customers typically requires the approval of a government-appointed regulatory body.) Utility companies will often have a high dividend payout ratio and try to appeal to investors who need steady income, such as seniors. Growth companies cannot have a high dividend payout ratio because they need to keep earnings in the company as retained earnings in order to finance growth. Companies that have spectacular growth, such as Microsoft, often have a history of paying no dividend in the early years of the company.

When the appeal of a stock is its dividend, cutting the dividend can often lead to spectacular drops in the price of the stock. For example, TransCanada, a major pipeline company, reduced its dividend in 1999, and its stock price dropped by more than 50%. This kind of drop in value for a company as stable as a pipeline is a reflection of the amount of emotion tied up in stock price. TransCanada's stock price returned to its former value within two years and now trades at about twice that level. The lesson here is that when investors count on a dividend, they react strongly (or even overreact) to a decrease in dividend.

Oil is a commodity that has had a highly variable price. Some oil companies are highly leveraged and focused on exploration. The focus on exploration creates a desire to use cash for new investment rather than dividends, and the high leverage means that a dividend could not be declared in years of low oil prices. However, major oil companies such as Exxon Mobil and Chevron have a long history of stable dividends. They achieve this by having relatively low leverage and a moderate dividend payout ratio. These companies have positioned themselves to convert a commodity business into a blue-chip company, where blue chip means stable and reliable.

A Real Illustration

Examine the following statement of cash flow for Suncor, a North American oil company with a strong focus on developing production from the Athabasca Oil Sands deposits in Alberta, and Enbridge, a pipeline company primarily focused on North America. The statements of cash flow for 2007 for the two companies have been simplified from their annual reports.

Statement of Cash Flow 2007 ($ million)

	Suncor	Enbridge
Cash Derived from Operating Activities		
Net income for the year	2,642	707
Depreciation and non-cash items	1,163	667
Changes in non-cash working capital	88	5
Total	3,893	1,379
Cash Used for Investing Activities		
Purchase of fixed assets	–5,362	–2,256
Cash Derived from Financing Activities		
Changes in share capital	62	601
Changes in long-term debt	1,664	762
Less dividends paid	–162	–459
Total	1,564	904
Increase (decrease) in cash	95	27
Dividend payout ratio (%)	6	65

Both companies are profitable, although income in a pipeline company is less volatile than income from an oil producer given the often rapid changes in world oil price. Suncor has a very low dividend payout ratio (roughly six cents per dollar of earnings) and a very high rate of investment (investing activity is much higher than depreciation). Suncor uses its cash flow from operations to grow its assets and also increases its long-term debt. It does not issue a significant level of common shares (the small number is related to its stock option compensation plan). Therefore, an investor in Suncor will not get a significant dividend but can expect growing oil production per common share and, hence, higher earnings provided the oil price holds and Suncor can successfully operate its new investment. The investor faces oil price risk and operational risk in a company focused on growth.

Enbridge is very different: it has a very high dividend payout ratio, paying two-thirds of its earnings back to its investors. It also has growth in assets that is higher than depreciation, but to achieve this, it issues both equity (common shares) and debt. If it only relied on debt, it would increase its leverage, since because of the high dividend payout ratio there is not enough retained earnings to significantly boost shareholder equity. When a company issues a significant amount of common shares, future earnings will be divided among more shareholders. However, given a long history of stable growth in earnings, an investor in Enbridge has a reasonable expectation of stable growth in dividend income.

Now, consider two investors: one 75-years-old and the other 35-years-old. The less volatile earnings and high dividend payout ratio would likely be appealing to the 75-year-old, while the prospect of future growth would likely have more appeal to the 35-year-old. Management and boards of directors carefully position companies to appeal to particular types of investors.

This illustration uses only one year's statement of cash flow, but an investor can easily get many years of statements from the Internet.

Can a Company with Negative Earnings Pay a Dividend?

Many investors are unknowledgeable about financial statements as are many managers. When telephone companies were regulated monopolies, they were highly secure investments. Earnings became much more volatile when deregulation of this industry occurred.

Consider this simplified statement of cash flow.

Statement of Cash Flow for Telecom Co. ($ million)

Cash Derived from Operating Activities

Net income for the year	−98
Depreciation and non-cash items	1,527
Changes in non-cash working capital	−351
Total	1,078

Cash Used for Investing Activities

Purchase of fixed assets	−886

Cash Derived from Financing Activities

Changes in share capital	74
Changes in long-term debt	−20
Less dividends paid	−305
Total	−251

Increase (decrease) in cash	−59

This company has a large depreciation, which gives it a very large cash flow from operations. Its reinvestment is below its depreciation. As a result, it can pay a dividend easily. This does not mean that earnings are not important. A company with negative earnings over a long period of time will eventually wear out its assets and find no sources of debt or equity to bring cash into the company. However, a company that has negative earnings will first look at the level of cash flow from operations. As noted in Chapter 3, positive cash flow from operations gives a company room to fix its earnings problems.

Unsophisticated shareholders in a telecom company in a situation similar to this case panicked when the management and board, after two years of negative earnings but substantial cash flow from operations, decided to reduce the dividend. As a result, the share price dropped by 80%. However, the company was not in short-term danger, and over the next few years, it returned to healthy profitability, with a ten-fold increase in share value from the low that occurred during the panic.

Sample Problem 5.4 Analyzing Companies from the Statement of Cash Flow

You have the following statements of cash flow for three companies in the same line of business:

Statement of Cash Flow ($ millions)

	Company A	Company B	Company C
Cash Derived from Operating Activities			
Net income for the year	180	185	190
Depreciation	150	160	170
Changes in non-cash working capital	−49	−34	−57
Total	281	311	303
Cash Used for Investing Activities			
Purchase of fixed assets	−369	−166	−161
Loss or gain on sale of fixed assets	—	—	—
Total	−369	−166	−161
Cash Derived from Financing Activities			
Changes in equity	—	—	—
Changes in long-term debt	70	30	−50
Less dividends paid	—	−148	−49
Total	70	−118	−99
Increase (decrease) in cash	−18	27	43
Net cash, beginning of the year	−12	−42	−14
Net cash, end of the year	−30	−15	29
Increase (decrease) in cash	−18	27	43

Use these statements to comment on the values of the companies as evidenced by management decisions. Which company is focused on growth, which is focused on dividends, and which will have a lower leverage ratio next year?

Solution:

Company A is focused on growth, with investments in fixed assets more than twice its depreciation. Note that companies B and C have investments in new fixed assets that are close to depreciation, so they are not growing the net value of their fixed assets.

Company B has a very high dividend payout ratio: of its $185 million in revenue, its dividend is about 80%. Company A, focused on growth, has no dividend, while Company C pays about 25% of its earnings as a dividend.

Company C pays down its long-term debt by $50 million, so it will be sure to have a lower leverage ratio. It takes a mix of actions: some dividend, some debt repayment, and an investment in new fixed assets that matches inflation. Companies A and B have a clear focus, while Company C has more of a mixed approach. There is nothing wrong with Company C's approach since many stable companies focused on the long term take just such a mixed approach.

5.5   The Role of Cash in a Business

People taking a first aid course are always taught that the first step is to check if a victim is breathing, and if not, deal with that first. This lesson is taught because there have been instances where people have tended to bleeding wounds only to find that the victim died from a blocked air passage. Anyone running a business should think of working capital as breath. Eight minutes without breath is almost always fatal to a human, and two days without adequate working capital can be fatal to a business. Another way of thinking of this is "If I write a check, will the bank cash it?" When a business loses access to funds, suppliers stop shipping, workers stop showing up at work, and creditors will take steps to put the firm in receivership, at which point the owners have legally lost the ability to operate the business. Normally, a company that goes into receivership is broken up, meaning the assets are sold, often at a steep discount, to recover funds to pay off creditors.

There are cases where management of a business was so focused on a longer-term issue, such as bringing a new product to market, working with an existing customer, or attracting new investors, that they lost sight of the short-term working capital position of the company, and the company went into bankruptcy. Most businesses rely on a bank credit line (an account with a bank that can go positive or negative) to support their activities. Cash is flowing in and out of that account all the time as customers' checks are deposited and suppliers cash the company's checks. Cash flow analysis is a critical business skill to ensure that the bank keeps the credit line open.

In Chapter 3, you saw a simple measure of cash breakeven: does a business generate cash from its normal operations? This simple measure excluded considerations of current and long-term assets. As sales grow, companies have higher receivables and inventory and often need more fixed assets. Financing is often available from many sources: payables (in essence, borrowing from suppliers), bank debt (short or long term), equity injection through issuing shares, and retention of earnings. The statement of cash flow tracks all the funds flowing in and out of a company, which can be used in pro forma statements to predict the future position of the bank credit line. A good management team will always have a sense of their current and future working capital position to ensure that a short term need for working capital does not ruin a business that would otherwise be healthy in the long term.

Problems

5.1 In Problem 4.4, you prepared this year's balance sheet for Balanceco. Prepare a sources and uses analysis on the balance sheets for the two years. Also, prepare a statement of cash flow, and comment on the health of Balanceco (one paragraph or less).

5.2 Growthco goes through another year of operation (next year). Prepare a statement of cash flow for next year, and comment on Growthco, comparing its performance next year to its performance this year drawn from Section 5.3 (one paragraph or less). Growthco's income statement and balance sheet for next year are shown as follows:

Growthco Income Statement

($000)	This Year	Next Year
Revenue	4,223	5,477
Allowance for bad debt	27	31
Net revenue	4,196	5,446

Cost of goods sold	2,695	3,488
Contribution margin	1,501	1,958
Contribution margin (%)	35.5	35.7

Sales, General, and Administrative Expense

All items except depreciation	719	815
Depreciation	620	620
Operating income	162	523
Other income	–24	–21
Net income	138	502

Growthco Statement of Retained Earnings
($000)

Retained earnings at start of year	482	582
Plus net income for this year	138	502
Less dividend paid this year	38	200
Retained earnings at end of year	582	884

Growthco Balance Sheet

($000)	This Year		Next Year	
Assets				
Current Assets				
Cash		—		—
Receivables		877		1,140
Short-term investments		—		—
Inventory		589		754
Prepaid expenses		54		66
		1,520		1,960
Fixed Assets				
Land, building, and equipment at cost	6,200		6,200	
Less accumulated depreciation	1,520		2,140	
		4,680		4,060

Long-term investments	—	—
Goodwill	—	—
Total assets	6,200	6,020

Liabilities

Current Liabilities

Short-term credit line	609	53
Accounts payable	387	477
Accrued expenses	67	93
Taxes payable	15	33
Current portion of long-term debt	60	60
	1,138	716

Long-Term Debt

Repayable grants	—	—
Long-term debt	480	420

Shareholders' Equity

Capital shares	4,000	4,000
Retained earnings	582	884
Total liability and equity	6,200	6,020

Sources/uses of funds

5.3 Consider the four years of statements of cash flow for the company below. Late in year 2, the ownership of the company changed. From the statements of cash flow, what do you note about the values of the new owners compared to the values of the previous owners?

Statement of Cash Flow

($ million)	Year 1	Year 2	Year 3	Year 4
Cash Derived from Operating Activities				
Net income for the year	760	812	740	880
Depreciation and non-cash items	410	510	610	610
Changes in non-cash working capital	−50	−44	28	−34
Total	1,120	1,278	1,378	1,456
Cash Used for Investing Activities				
Purchase of fixed assets	−2,000	−2,000	−580	−595
Loss or gain on sale of assets	0	0	0	0
Total	−2,000	−2,000	−580	−595
Cash Derived from Financing Activities				
Changes in share capital	0	0	0	0
Changes in long-term debt	900	710	−450	−450
Less dividends paid	0	0	−300	−500
Total	900	710	−750	−950
Increase (decrease) in cash	20	−12	48	−89

5.4 Look at the statements of cash flow for Companies A, B, C, and D. Identify which management is focused on growth, which is focused on reducing leverage, which is focused on paying a dividend, and which does not have a clear focus evidenced in its pattern of spending.

Statement of Cash Flow

($ million)	A	B	C	D
Cash Derived from Operating Activities				
Net income for the year	1,220	1,220	1,220	1,220
Depreciation and non-cash items	860	860	860	860
Changes in non-cash working capital	−120	−120	−120	−120
Total	1,960	1,960	1,960	1,960
Cash Used for Investing Activities				
Purchase of fixed assets	−941	−941	−3,400	−420
Loss or gain on sale of assets	0	0	0	0
Total	−941	−941	−3,400	−420
Cash Derived from Financing Activities				
Changes in share capital	0	0	0	0
Changes in long-term debt	−442	−90	1,420	−1,200
Less dividends paid	−380	−940	−60	−380
Total	−822	−1,030	1,360	−1,580
Increase (decrease) in cash	197	−11	−80	−40

Ratio Analysis of Financial Statements

Key Concepts

- Financial ratios are standardized calculated values that show year-over-year trends within a company and enable comparisons between companies in a similar industry.
- There are five classes of ratios: liquidity, asset management, debt management, profitability, and market value.
- Liquidity ratios focus on the short-term solvency of a company.
- Asset management ratios measure the relationship between assets and sales level and the ability of the company to collect receivables and use inventory efficiently.
- Debt management ratios measure the likelihood that a company will be able to service (pay) its long-term debt obligations.
- Profitability ratios measure the ability of a company to generate value from assets.
- Market value ratios assess the share price of a company in relation to the earnings per share and the book value of shareholder equity.

Chapter 6: Ratio Analysis of Financial Statements

6.1   Why Financial Ratios Are Used

The following examples show why it is sometimes necessary to do frequent financial comparisons of companies:

- A banker's success depends on lending money to successful clients who will pay it back. If the banker does not lend, she has insufficient income and fails. If she lends to the wrong creditors, she has insufficient income and fails. She will compare a loan applicant to other companies as part of assessing the likelihood of repayment.
- An investment financial analyst's success depends on recommending winning stocks. He will compare companies to see which are likely to grow in value.
- A credit analyst makes a crucial decision in any company: "Should we give normal commercial invoicing terms to customer X, shipping product and invoicing for payment 30 days later?" Again, companies are compared in making this assessment.

The purpose of financial ratios is to provide quick tests of various financial factors for companies. They are a fast screening technique. Buyers would never buy a company without a rigorous year-over-year analysis of an income statement, balance sheet, and statement of cash flow, but they do use ratio analysis for quick decisions on companies. A lender or a credit-checking agency will likely check some critical ratios every month, for instance, but will only go into more detailed analysis if there is a negative change in a ratio.

Different industries have historically had different ratio values. For example, a capital intensive industry such as steel making will have different values on the same ratio than a high turnover, low asset business such as a grocery chain. The biggest value of ratio tests is for year-over-year comparisons within a company and for company-to-company comparisons within an industry.

6.2   Types of Financial Ratios

Different authors have slightly different categories for ratios, but the tests themselves have become fairly standardized. There are five categories:

1. **Liquidity ratios** measure the likelihood that a business will stay solvent in the short term. A liquid asset can be quickly and easily converted to cash, such as an account receivable, which normally turns into cash within 30 days. An **illiquid asset** is difficult to turn into cash, such as a highly specialized piece of equipment that has major installation costs. The two key tests are as follows:
   - Current ratio
   - Quick or acid test ratio
2. **Activity or asset management ratios** measure how well management is using the assets it employs in the business. Management can use these ratios as an ongoing report card. The key asset management ratios are as follows:
   - Inventory turnover
   - Average collection period (also called days sales outstanding)
   - Fixed assets turnover
   - Total assets turnover

3. **Leverage or debt management ratios** measure how effective a company is likely to be in paying back its total debt. In particular, long-term lenders and equity investors look to these ratios; for the lenders, it is to satisfy themselves that the company they are lending to can repay the long-term debt, and for the investors, it is to make sure the company has some, but not excessive, leverage. The key debt management tests are as follows:
   - Debt ratio (total liabilities to total assets)
   - Times interest earned
   - Fixed charge coverage

4. **Profitability ratios** measure the profitability of the entire enterprise. The key profitability ratios are as follows:
   - Profit margin on sales
   - Return on total assets
   - Return on equity

Two other ratios do not derive from financial statements alone, but also from the market price of shares of a company.

5. **Market value ratios** measure the stock price against earnings and book value of shareholder equity. The key market value ratios are as follows:
   - Price/earnings (P/E) ratio
   - Market/book ratio

6.3   The Ratios and What They Measure

The financial ratios are illustrated by using Growthco's data for this year from Section 5.2. The ratios are calculated for one year only, but their primary value as a management tool is in tracking them over several years and trying to understand changes over time. Note also that some of the ratios include income in the numerator. There is no consistency between companies in whether net income or operating income is used, so where one or the other is specified in defining a ratio, recognize that some companies might use a different definition of income.

6.3.1   Current Ratio

Discussed extensively in Chapter 4, the current ratio, also called the working capital ratio, is of critical importance to a supplier. In effect, a supplier is lending material to a company for the time between delivery and the payment of the invoice. There are no hard assets pledged as security, so payment will come from current assets only. A current ratio of less than 1 says that for every dollar of readily accessible (liquid) assets, such as inventory and receivables, there is more than a dollar of near-term debt owing to a creditor. Banks also look to this ratio to secure their credit line.

$$\text{Current ratio} = \frac{\text{current assets}}{\text{current liabilities}} = \frac{\$1,520}{\$1,138} = 1.34$$

As noted in Chapter 4, some companies have financing intended to be long term, but it is treated by accountants as a demand loan (and hence short-term debt) because of clauses in the loan agreement that might trigger it to be due immediately under unusual circumstances. The current ratio test does not work for such companies. This is normally only a factor in large companies with complex financing; the working capital test remains a reliable test when applied to small and medium companies.

Most companies pay for the services of a credit rating agency, such as Dun and Bradstreet. Credit rating agencies look at financial statements, when available, to obtain information on the liquidity ratios and also keep track of any reports of non-payment of invoices. Before deciding on whether to extend credit to a new customer, most companies will check with a credit rating agency.

6.3.2 Quick Ratio or Acid Test

When a business fails, receivables can normally be collected. However, the value of inventory depends on its nature. While commodities such as lumber or steel can be readily sold at close to full value, some inventory, such as custom-manufactured items, is often sold at a steep discount. The quick ratio measures the extreme position: "If there is no value for the inventory, can the short-term creditors be paid out from receivables?" This test is more critical for companies for whom inventory is specialized. A firm making one-of-a-kind proprietary circuit boards would be an example of a specialized inventory. In this case, the lender or supplier might be more concerned about the quick ratio being greater than 1 than the current ratio.

$$\text{Quick ratio} = \frac{\text{current assets} - \text{inventories}}{\text{current liabilities}} = \frac{\$1,520 - \$589}{\$1,138} = 0.82$$

6.3.3 Inventory Turnover

Inventory turnover is an indirect measure of how many times inventory is restocked in a year, although the inventory turn is measured against sales value per year, not material used per year. The ratio varies from industry to industry, but within an industry, higher is better, since this means less working capital is tied up in inventory.

$$\text{Inventory turnover} = \frac{\text{sales}}{\text{inventories}} = \frac{\$4,223}{\$589} = 7.2$$

Either gross or net revenue can be used to calculate inventory turnover, and the difference is not material. Consistency in tracking this ratio over time is what is important. Frequently, during business downturns, inventory turnover drops because people are reluctant to slow down manufacturing. Good management will make a conscious effort to reduce inventory at such times to free up cash for other purposes in the business. The inverse of the inventory turnover ratio multiplied by 365 is the days of sales revenue represented by the inventory.

6.3.4 Days Sales Outstanding

Days sales outstanding (DSO), also called average collection period or days receivables, is a measure of the ability of a company to get its customers to pay. It can be calculated for Growthco with gross or net revenue (the difference is not material).

$$\text{Day sales outstanding} = \frac{\text{receivables}}{\text{sales} \div 365} = \frac{\$877}{\$4,223 \div 365} = 75 \text{ days}$$

Sometimes, 360 is used in the equation rather than 365, treating a year as 12 months of 30 days; again, the difference is not material. Unfortunately, many customers need to be reminded to pay promptly, and efforts to collect interest from good but slow-paying customers are almost never successful. Particularly in economic downturns, keeping a focus on receivables collection is a critical business management skill. In the case of Growthco, DSO is high: customers are taking 75 days to pay. Unless this reflects some special arrangement with customers, management should focus on why customers are so slow to pay. Note that if DSO were reduced by 30 days, receivables would drop by 40%, reducing short-term borrowing by $350,000 (40% of $877,000).

6.3.5 Fixed Assets Turnover

In theory, fixed assets turnover measures the extent to which management is using the fixed assets (e.g., land, buildings, and equipment). Within an industry, it can be used to compare two companies.

$$\text{Fixed assets turnover} = \frac{\text{sales}}{\text{net fixed assets}} = \frac{\$4,223}{\$4,680} = 0.90$$

This ratio is meaningless between industries, since a grocery chain, for example, will have huge turnover (low assets and high sales), whereas a highly capital-intensive business such as oil refining or power generation will be the opposite.

Analysts should keep in mind that this ratio can also have problems within an industry. Accounting is conservative, and assets never have their value increased to reflect inflation; in essence, an asset is depreciated from its original cost with no reflection of inflation. Hence, if one were to compare two companies, one with old assets and one with newer assets, there would be a depreciation and inflation impact that would distort this ratio. Fixed assets and total assets turnover ratios are therefore of limited value in inter-company comparisons if assets are long term and of different vintage. One can use fixed assets turnover in rapidly growing companies to see if additions to assets are being used effectively to generate sales.

6.3.6 Total Assets Turnover

The comments for fixed assets turnover apply to total assets turnover, except that the total assets of the company (including working capital and intangible assets) are included in the denominator.

$$\text{Total assets turnover} = \frac{\text{sales}}{\text{total assets}} = \frac{\$4,223}{\$6,200} = 0.68$$

6.3.7 Total Debt to Total Assets (Debt Ratio)

As discussed in Chapter 4, debt ratio is an important number for lenders and investors. Lenders have a strong focus on the security of a debt, or its likelihood of repayment. To a lender, a high debt ratio increases the risk that the ongoing company will not service the debt or that the debt cannot be recovered if the company fails. An investor would have the same concern if the debt ratio was very high. If the company cannot meet its debt payment schedule, the lenders will push the firm into bankruptcy, and usually, there will be nothing left for the equity holders. However, investors often do not like a very low debt ratio because their return is not leveraged.

$$\text{Debt ratio} = \frac{\text{total liabilities}}{\text{total assets}} = \frac{\$1,138 + 480}{\$6,200} = 26.1\%$$

At 26%, Growthco's debt ratio is low, and in particular, long-term debt of $540,000 ($480,000 below the line and a current portion of $60,000) is low compared to fixed assets with a book value of $4.68 million.

Debt ratio is sometimes mistakenly called debt to equity ratio. Technically, debt to equity is given as follows:

$$\text{Debt to equity ratio} = \frac{\text{total liabilities}}{\text{total equity}} = \frac{\text{total liabilities}}{\text{total assets} - \text{total liabilities}}$$

Note that for these ratios, all current liabilities are included in debt, not just the money owed to short and long-term lenders.

6.3.8 Times Interest Earned

The times interest earned ratio is a measure of the capacity of a borrower to service debt, i.e., to pay the interest charges and keep the loan current, from earning before interest and taxes. Interest payments are added back into earnings because they are available to pay interest. The theory for adding back income taxes is that if a company becomes unprofitable, its income tax bill goes to zero (since income taxes are calculated as a percentage of net earnings or profits), and the earnings that had been going to pay taxes can now be used to service debt. EBIT is an important concept in valuing companies, as discussed in Chapter 8.

To determine the times interest earned ratio for Growthco, more information would be needed than is presented in the abbreviated income statement in Section 5.2. This year, Growthco's interest charges are $28,000, and taxes (for this calculation, taxes means taxes on income) are $17,000.

$$\text{Times interest earned} = \frac{\text{EBIT}}{\text{interest charges}} = \frac{\$138 + \$28 + \$17}{\$28} = 6.5$$

(where EBIT is earnings before interest and taxes)

People lending to risky enterprises want a higher interest rate as a reward for the risk compared to those lending to low-risk borrowers. Specialized firms, called bond rating agencies, assess the long-term credit worthiness of companies and governments. Moody's, Standard & Poor's, Fitch, and Dominion Bond Rating Service (DBRS) are examples of such firms. Major lenders such as pension funds rely on these rating agencies to determine a risk level, and the interest rate on bonds issued by companies reflects those ratings. Companies spend a great deal of effort in working with bond rating agencies to ensure they get as positive a rating as possible. The senior level of government almost always has the highest credit rating in a country because it can tax a large and diverse economy to meet its debt obligations. Hence, in Canada and the United States, federal government debt has the highest rating and the lowest interest. The interest cost on federal debt is sometimes called the "riskless" interest rate, although it should more properly be called the very low risk interest rate.

Provincial/state debt ranks below federal debt in creditworthiness, and not all provinces or states get the same rating. Those that have a high per capita level of debt will have a lower rating than those with a lower debt level. Companies do not have the legal power to tax, so they are almost always a higher risk and, hence, have a lower rating than governments. Company debt ratings range from "very good" to "junk" status, a colorful term that simply means risky debt.

Times interest earned (TIE), debt ratio, consistency of sales and income (and whether these are falling or rising), the general economic climate, and the prospects for an entire industry are all considered in setting a credit rating. Of these, TIE is the most important ratio to a long-term lender or bond rating agency; it is more important to a lender than the debt ratio because it measures the ability of the company to service the debt and keep the loan out of "non-performing" status. Companies with very low net income are at greater risk of being unable in the future to service debt. Some firms, such as regulated utilities selling essential commodities, can carry very high levels of debt relative to equity because their sales are stable and the regulator is committed to approving pricing levels that give a fair return to investors after all reasonable expenses are covered. Growthco's TIE ratio of 6.5 is very high and reflects its low level of long-term debt; it would expect little trouble applying for more long-term debt.

6.3.9   Fixed Charge Coverage

As lease financing has become more popular, some analysts have switched from the times interest earned ratio to factoring in all fixed (non-avoidable) charges.

$$\text{Fixed charge coverage} = \frac{\text{EBIT} + \text{lease payments}}{\text{interest charges} + \text{lease payments}}$$

Sometimes, the before-tax income required to fund a sinking fund is also included in the denominator. As discussed in Chapter 4, a sinking fund is a reserve fund that holds cash in trust with which to redeem the principle on bonds if the entire principle is due at the end of the life of the bond. Some analysts treat a sinking fund contribution requirement as being comparable to interest in terms of a "must pay" obligation associated with debt.

Consolidated financial statements such as the Growthco statement often do not have enough detail to complete the fixed charge coverage because details on leasing payments are not included. Companies would supply supplemental information to a bond rating agency or stock analysts from a major brokerage firm to enable them to calculate this ratio.

6.3.10   Profit Margin on Sales

Various analysts define the profit margin on sales ratio differently. Some have the numerator as operating income before income tax and interest (to show the yield of the business before financing and tax-related charges that distort inter-company comparisons). Others look at an after-tax and interest number or define the numerator as net income or net income available to common shareholders, which excludes dividends on preferred shares. Once again, consistency is more important than uniformity. Companies that are capital intense, i.e., that have a high ratio of assets to sales, would be expected over the long run to have higher profit as a percentage of sales because profit can be thought of as a reward for the deployment of assets.

The profit margin on sales ratio is always expressed as a percentage.

$$\text{Profit margin on sales} = \frac{\text{operating income}}{\text{sales}} = \frac{\$162}{\$4,223} = 3.8\%$$

Profit margin on sales provides information year over year for a given company, but in addition is a very powerful tool for comparing similar companies. For example, it leads to this kind of question: "Why does a competitor very similar to us make so much more income per sale?" This can lead to a penetrating analysis of a company's efficiency.

6.3.11   Return on Total Assets

The return on total assets ratio is a measure of what a company earns on all of its assets, whether they are financed by debt or shareholder equity. It is sometimes calculated with net income rather than operating income.

$$\text{Return on total assets} = \frac{\text{operating income}}{\text{total assets}} = \frac{\$162}{\$6,200} = 2.6\%$$

This ratio, again always expressed as a percentage, is a powerful tool for comparing between similar companies. This test is also used within a company by comparing division-by-division operating income results (pre-tax, interest, and other income). This analysis asks a powerful question: "How effectively do our various divisions use assets?" Again, understanding the differences between divisions yields valuable insight into a business.

Growthco's return on total assets is low, and it would hopefully improve as growth is realized in the company. One can lend money long term to the federal government in a very low risk investment for more than Growthco's return of 2.6%; this low of a return is not an acceptable long-term target.

6.3.12 Return on Equity

Return on equity is crucial to the shareholder. Anticipated year-over-year return on equity is a key driver of the share price, and one of management's major goals is maximizing the shareholders' value over the long term. Return on assets is independent of financing, but return on equity is strongly influenced by financing. Highly leveraged companies (those with a high debt ratio) can expect to have wider swings (more volatility) in their return on equity as discussed in Chapter 4.

$$\text{Return on equity} = \frac{\text{net income}}{\text{shareholder's equity}} = \frac{\$138}{\$4,582} = 3.0\%$$

As with other ratios, some variation is possible. This formula gives return on all equity (for example, common and preferred shares). Some analysts extract the cost of servicing the preferred shares from the numerator (they subtract the preferred share dividends from net income) and make the denominator the common share equity. This gives a return on common shares only. Note again that Growthco's return on equity is disturbingly low. Growthco is focused on growth, and it may be that planned increases in assets and sales will give a higher net income that in turn gives a better return on assets and equity.

6.3.13 Price/Earnings (P/E) Ratio

The price earnings and market to book ratios are calculated for publicly traded companies. To determine these ratios, two additional pieces of information about Growthco are needed: the share price and the total number of shares outstanding. Treasury shares, in effect, shares held by the company itself and not sold to a shareholder, are not included in this number. The price earnings ratio is not a ratio that derives solely from the financial statements for a company: it assesses the market value of a company against its reported earnings. The P/E ratio is the cost of a stock divided by earnings per share. Note that the ratio is not per dollar of dividend; some companies pay little or no dividends, instead retaining their earnings for future growth. The annual dividend payment per share divided by the share price is called the dividend yield. The P/E ratio is not the sole indicator of the value of a publicly traded stock, but it is the most frequently cited number in stock market quotations.

To find the P/E ratio, assume that Growthco's share price is $8.00 per share and there are one million shares outstanding.

$$\text{P/E ratio} = \frac{\text{price per share}}{\text{earning per share}} = \frac{\text{market capitalization}}{\text{net income}} = \frac{\$8,000,000}{\$138,000} = 58.0$$

(where market capitalization is share price × number of shares outstanding)

If a bond pays 4% interest, it can be thought of as having a P/E ratio of 25. The P/E ratio averaged over all publicly traded companies usually has a value between 15 and 25. Why does anyone pay more than 25 times the dollar value of earnings for a stock? The answer is that stock buyers hope for growth in share price related to expected future earnings. Companies with good growth prospects but no earnings can have a high stock price, and the P/E ratio is meaningless because there are no earnings (negative P/E ratios are not calculated). Growthco's current price earnings ratio is very high, which is a sign that stock purchasers expect growth in earnings in the future. Unless earnings increase in the future, the share price would almost certainly go down.

While the P/E ratio is the most widely quoted market ratio for publicly traded stocks, the price earnings growth (PEG) ratio is sometimes cited. This ratio divides the P/E ratio by the annual growth rate in earnings or sales averaged over three years. A lower value of PEG is better in that the P/E ratio is being reduced by a high growth rate in the denominator. Between this year and next year for Growthco, sales increase by just under 30% (Problem 5.3); while this is not a three-year average figure, it suggests a PEG ratio of just under 2 for Growthco. The PEG ratio is new enough that standard ranges of values are not well known. Valuation is discussed further in Chapter 8.

6.3.14 Market/Book Ratio

Like the P/E ratio, the market to book ratio is not derived solely from the financial statements for a company. Market to book values assess the premium that a stock price has over the conservative valuation (depreciated assets with no adjustment for inflation less liabilities) that accounting places on the shareholder equity in a company.

$$\text{Market/book ratio} = \frac{\text{market price per share}}{\text{book value of equity per share}} = \frac{\text{market capitalization}}{\text{shareholder equity}}$$

$$= \frac{8,000,000}{4,582,000} = 1.75$$

Companies such as Microsoft and Oracle that have very high value creation from a small asset base can have very high market to book ratio values. That this ratio is greater than 1 for Growthco is a sign that share purchasers have some expectation of future growth. The market to book ratio is discussed further in Chapter 8.

Sample Problem 6.3.1 Using Ratios to Analyze Management

Widget Inc. manufactures auto parts in southern Ontario. There is a similar company in Quebec called Cogs Corp. Review the following ratios, and determine which management team is performing better.

	Widget Inc	Cogs Corp.
Inventory turnover	5	4
Days sales outstanding	25	35
Fixed asset turnover	0.41	0.33
Total asset turnover	0.32	0.24
Profit margin on sales (%)	32	25
Return on total assets (%)	7	5

Solution:

Widget Inc. is being better managed as it has higher inventory turnover, so it is keeping inventory for a smaller amount of time; it has a lower number of days that sales are outstanding, so the company is collecting its sales more quickly; it has higher fixed asset turnover, which means Widget is using relatively fewer fixed assets to achieve their sales (Widget has higher sales with a similar amount of fixed assets, or it has similar sales using fewer fixed assets, or it has higher sales and fewer fixed assets); it has a higher total asset turnover, which means it uses relatively fewer total assets to achieve their sales; Widget has a higher profit margin on sales and a higher return on total assets.

Sample Problem 6.3.2 Debt Ratios and Credit Rating

Again, consider Widget Inc. and Cogs Corp., two companies in the same industry. Widget Inc. has a total debt to assets ratio of 0.44 and a times interest earned ratio of 2.7, while Cogs Corp. has a total debt to assets ratio of 0.55 and a times interest earned ratio of 1.9. Which company will have the poorer credit rating and, hence, require a higher interest rate to raise debt?

Solution:

Cogs Corp. will have a poorer credit rating and require a higher interest rate to raise debt because they have a higher ratio of debt to assets and a smaller times interest earned ratio. These ratios mean that Cogs Corp. is a greater credit risk than Widget Inc. as Cogs Corp. has more debt relative to its assets and has lower earnings relative to its interest payments.

Sample Problem 6.3.3 Price to Earnings Ratio

Again, consider Widget Inc. and Cogs Corp. Widget has a price to earnings (P/E) ratio of 23, and Cogs Corp. has a P/E ratio of 16. Which company has more appeal to shareholders according to the P/E ratio?

Solution:

A higher price to earnings ratio usually indicates that there is a higher growth expectation for the company. Therefore, the company with the higher appeal to the shareholder is the company with the higher P/E ratio as the shareholders expect higher earnings in the future to justify the current higher price. If the higher earnings are not met, the stock with the higher P/E will experience a larger decrease in price. Therefore, higher P/E stocks can carry more risk.

6.4   *Using Ratio Analysis*

Industry average figures can be obtained from sources such as trade associations, financial or management consultants, or credit reporting agencies. Dun and Bradstreet, for instance, reports average figures for some ratios by industry type (e.g., Dun and Bradstreet's *Key Business Ratios*, published annually). Ratios are used by many different parties to gain insight into a company.

• Lenders and credit rating agencies use liquidity and debt management ratios as part of their normal working practice. As discussed in Chapter 4, a bank that issues short-term credit lines to businesses will lend to numerous small firms and will request monthly statements from each. It will then complete a check on the ratios that tell it that the covenants of its lending are being satisfied. As a minimum, a short-term lender will check the current ratio and the amount of working capital in the business on a monthly basis. Long-term lenders, or the bond rating agencies they utilize, use debt management, asset management, and profitability ratios to convince themselves that a loan is likely to be repaid. A poorly run company that is highly leveraged and whose asset management and profitability ratios are poor compared to industry average is a far higher credit risk than a company with strong equity and good performance indicators. As noted above, ratio analysis is a component of rating debt, and for long-term borrowers, a lower credit rating has a significant cost.

• Financial analysts use debt management, asset management, profitability, and market ratios in screening companies as an investment or acquisition target.

• Managers should use ratio analysis to screen their own performance both year over year and against others in the industry. In particular, asset management and profitability ratios can be a powerful stimulus to a management team to do an honest and critical analysis of their management skills.

Problems

6.1 On October 19, 2000, a Government of Canada 30-year bond maturing in 2029 had a yield of 5.56%. What is the price earnings ratio for this bond?

6.2 On October 19, 2000, a Government of Alberta bond maturing on June 1, 2004 had a yield of 5.84%. A Hydro Quebec bond with the same maturity guaranteed fully by the Government of Quebec had a yield of 5.95%. Can you think of two good reasons why these yields might be different? Note that when the Province of Quebec fully guarantees a bond, the yield is identical between a Hydro Quebec bond and a Province of Quebec bond, i.e., the lender does not even give consideration to the power industry because the bond is guaranteed by the province.

If each entity were to borrow $1 billion, what is the per-year incremental cost to the Government of Quebec (who owns Hydro Quebec) for the higher yield? If the total debt in Quebec is about $75 billion (about $12,000 per man, woman, and child that lives in the province), what is the total cost to the province of the higher yield relative to Alberta? Is it significant?

Can you imagine, after doing this problem, why governments treat bond rating agencies (who deliver opinions on the quality of bonds) with respect?

6.3 On December 5, 2005, Google shares had a price earnings ratio of 94.8. Bank of Montreal shares had a price earnings ratio of 13.3. This is representative of history over the past several years where Google has consistently had a price earnings ratio higher than the Bank of Montreal. Speculate on what makes two profitable companies have such persistent differences in P/E ratio. What factor(s) other than earnings are investors taking into account in setting the market price for these two shares?

6.4 On October 19, 2000, a Government of Canada bond maturing in 2009 had a yield of 5.70%, a Bell Canada bond maturing in 2009 had a yield of 6.39%, and a Clearnet (a telecommunications company) bond maturing in 2008 had a yield of 9.00%. Clearnet has since merged with Telus to form a large Canadian-based wireless company. Why is the Government of Canada yield less than the Bell Canada yield? Why is the Bell Canada yield so much less than the Clearnet yield? What is the bond market saying about Clearnet?

6.5 Sales are climbing in a company at a rate of 27% per year. If you managed this company, would you expect inventory to increase? Would you expect the ratio inventory turnover to increase? Would you expect receivables to increase? Would you expect days sales outstanding to increase? Is the ratio more valuable than the absolute number as a management tool?

6.6 Pick any industry that has two similar companies. Visit the website of each company, and find the market price of shares, the number of shares outstanding (from a note to the financial statements, which can be found under investor information), and the earnings, assets, and shareholder equity. Determine the P/E ratio, the return on assets and equity, and year-over-year growth in sales and profits. Look at the information you have assembled on the two companies. If you had only this information and were to make a recommendation on one of these two companies to a person who had decided to add one or the other to his or her investment portfolio, do you see enough of a difference to make a tentative choice? Many websites exist in addition to company websites where you can find information on stocks, including your bank's website, Yahoo Financial, and MSN Money.

Analyzing New Investment

Key Concepts

- Money represents available (liquid) and relatively safe wealth. Money has a time value, which is the amount required to get people to use their money in an investment, giving up its liquidity and safety.

- The time value of money is always greater than the expected inflation rate. It reflects the risk and liquidity of an investment and the general supply and demand for money. The time value of money changes over time.

- The time value of money is used to calculate the net present value (NPV) of future money by the discounted cash flow (DCF) technique.

- A high time value of money depresses investment because a future stream of money has a lower present value.

- The time value of money is used to calculate the net present value of an investment and the internal rate of return (IRR), also know as the return on investment (ROI). Payback, the time after start-up for an investment to return the invested funds, is another measure used to make investment decisions. After-tax cash flow is the stream of money used in these calculations.

- A basic knowledge of the Canadian or US tax system can be used to estimate the impact of taxation on the cash flow from a project. Whether a company doing a project is currently paying taxes has an impact on the IRR of a project.
- Revenue-generating projects are primarily evaluated by IRR, with payback period as a secondary measure. Mandatory investment projects such as environmental controls are primarily evaluated by NPV.
- When more than one alternative investment is available to achieve the same goal, analysis of incremental IRR is used to make the correct investment decision.
- All projects have risk. Two ways to account for risk are to increase the contingency in a project budget and to require a higher expected return from higher-risk projects. A company can take steps to mitigate (reduce) risk in the project design, development, and operating stages.

Chapter 7: Analyzing New Investment

7.1   The Time Value of Money

As discussed in Chapter 1, money is a measure of current commercial value. If you want an accurate assessment of the relative worth of a kilogram of nickel and a kilogram of gold, you can trust that the price, as long as it is set in a fair and liquid market that is visible and accessible to all, accurately reflects the commercial value.

Money has a time value, which is measured by **interest rate, discount rate,** or **return on investment**. These terms will be used interchangeably, even though in a narrow sense, interest rate is often reserved for debt, and return on investment is often used for equity. At a general level, debt and equity are legally different, but both are forms of investment. The term discount rate refers to the rate at which future dollars are discounted. For example, a dollar that you are certain to receive 10 years in the future is not worth as much today as a dollar that you are certain to receive one year in the future. The time value of money is the key factor in how people decide to invest in things such as building new plants, starting companies, buying stocks, or lending money. Engineering is crucially affected by decisions about whether to build new projects, so engineers need to understand the time value of money and its use in investment analysis.

7.1.1 The Time Value of Money from the Perspective of the Lender/Investor

People that invest or lend money to others give up some personal flexibility and security. They defer some other use of the money, such as a purchase or an investment in some other opportunity. They also face the risk that the person they lent the money to will not be able to repay them (or the company they invested in will fail to create value) or that inflation will reduce the purchasing power of the money they get back in the future. In practice, unless people get some benefit for lending/investing their money, they will choose the freedom, flexibility, and security of keeping it to themselves. Interest is the cost of borrowed money, and money is a commodity that has its own cycle of supply and demand.

Canada's central government bank, the Bank of Canada, controls the currency by lending money to private banks. They also set different interest rates to control the lending of money. Figure 7.1 shows the annual average interest rate posted by the Bank of Canada for the last 70 years.

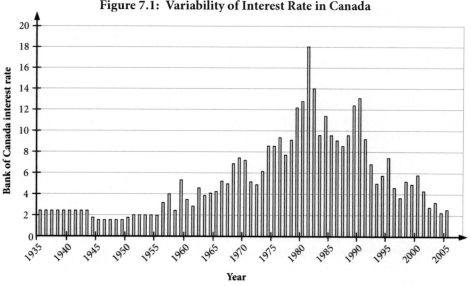

Figure 7.1: Variability of Interest Rate in Canada

(Source: Statistics Canada)

(Data for the US Federal Reserve rate can be found at http://research.stlouisfed.org/fred2/series/FEDFUNDS?cid=118)

The Bank of Canada rate is a key rate that is reflected in specific commercial rates such as commercial loans, mortgages, and consumer credit. For 15 years after the Second World War (a period of unprecedented creation of real wealth in the Canadian and US economies), the interest rate was stable and low. By the late 1960s, but especially in the 1980s, interest rates were high and unstable. It cost a lot more to use other people's money in the 1980s than it did in the 1950s. Some Canadian manufacturing practices, such as reduced inventory and "just in time" ordering, came to the fore during the period of extremely high interest rates as a means of reducing the interest cost associated with current assets. Equally as problematic as the high rate of interest is the high variability in it, since both providers and users of capital tend to adopt short-term strategies to protect against the risk of further changes in interest rates. Long-term investments are less likely in a climate of an unstable value of money.

Interest goes up and down as the competing forces between borrowers and lenders change. Similarly, the concept of **return on investment** is that an equity investment will bring a higher future value, and peoples' expectations of an appropriate rate of return vary over time. This has been dramatically illustrated over the past two decades. Until recently in Canada, many governments went from being net borrowers to net redeemers of debt at the same time that the population of pre-senior "savers" increased due to the aging of the baby boomers. The result was an increase in the supply of money available to be lent and a reduction in the demand for such money, which has resulted in a sharp drop in the cost of money.

In trying to make sense of the cost of money, or relative interest rates, consider the following factors that affect lenders (debt) and investors (equity): inflation, supply and demand, risk, and liquidity.

- **Inflation**: the purchasing power of money (its ability to be traded for real things, such as a loaf of bread or a liter of gasoline) generally reduces over time. The reasons for this are complex and not the subject of this book. However, the interest rate must be higher than the perceived rate of inflation by some amount for any thinking person to become a lender. The difference between the nominal interest rate and the inflation rate is known as the **real interest rate**. If the real interest rate is negative, then a prudent lender would be better to buy something tangible (a commodity such as oil or nickel or a home) and hold that real good as an investment. In North America, Europe, and Japan, considerable focus is placed on limiting inflation; this concern arises from the experience of some countries that had very high rates of inflation, normally because of government mismanagement (instead of raising money by taxation, governments print additional money, which is a practice that always leads to high inflation). In such periods of high inflation, lending decreases unless interest rates are also very high. There is normally a rush to convert the currency (whose value is deflating) into real goods or a more stable currency such as the US dollar. In the 1920s, Germany experienced inflation so high that workers had to be paid midday in order to be able to afford bread for dinner (since at its worst, inflation was over 100% per day). Ecuador is a recent example of this phenomenon; in essence, the country has abandoned its own currency in favor of using the US dollar.

The inflation rate is the yearly percentage change in the Canadian Consumer Price Index (CPI). Figure 7.2 shows the inflation rate since 1925.

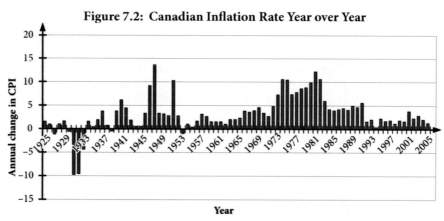

Figure 7.2: Canadian Inflation Rate Year over Year

(Source: Statistics Canada)

(Data for the US Consumer Price Index can be found at http://research.stlouisfed.org/fred2/series/CPIAUCNS?cid=9

The aftermath of World War II caused sudden inflation, partially due to the release of purchasing power when price controls and rationing were removed and savings for war bonds stopped. A period of negative inflation (called deflation) occurred during the Great Depression in the early 1930s. It is also not surprising that at the time of high instability in interest rates in the 1970s and 1980s, the inflation rate was both unstable and higher than average.

The real interest rate is the nominal interest rate minus inflation. As Figure 7.3 shows, this number is often between 2 and 5%, but in periods of high inflation or deflation, it can deviate significantly from this, as it did in the early 1970s.

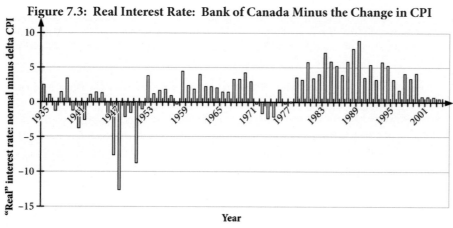

Figure 7.3: Real Interest Rate: Bank of Canada Minus the Change in CPI

(Source: Statistics Canada)

Negative real interest means that a lender loses the value of his money even in a short-term loan. Persistent periods of such instability harm investment because people naturally become reluctant to save and invest. For this reason, a major focus of current government fiscal policy is stability in inflation. Canada has had few periods of negative real interest, and they have been short in duration. Such periods are far more frequent in some developing countries that are subject to frequent political upheaval and manipulation of the currency. The absence of savings and investment in such countries is a major factor in limiting economic growth.

- **Supply and demand**: how much the interest rate exceeds the perceived inflation rate (the real interest rate) depends on the supply and demand for money. When the post–Second World War baby boom was at the age of purchasing homes, demand for money and interest rates were high. Now, that the baby boomers are at an age where saving for retirement is critical, interest rates are low. Similarly, when government spending exceeded taxation revenue and was financed by debt, demand for money and interest rates were both high. When governments are in a mode of net debt reduction, interest rates are low. Interest rates respond to many other factors, including perceptions of the relative value of currencies.

Figure 7.4 illustrates the demand side of this balance for borrowing by the Federal Government of Canada. Note the drop in new borrowing starting in the late 1990s.

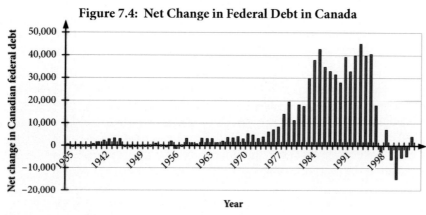

Figure 7.4: Net Change in Federal Debt in Canada

(Source: Statistics Canada)

(Data for the US Federal debt can be found at http://www.treasurydirect.gov/govt/reports/pd/histdebt/histdebt.htm)

Since Canada's **gross domestic product (GDP)**, the annual value of all goods and services, was increasing from 1998 to 2008, federal debt was declining as a fraction of the national GDP. In 2009, the Government of Canada will return to a deficit as it increases spending to stimulate the economy.

- **Risk**: the largest factor in setting relative rates between investments is the perceived risk that the lender sees in the investment. The key question is "How likely am I to get my money back?" Government borrowers with the power to tax are normally seen as the lowest risk within a given geographical area because the theory is that the legislative power to tax can ensure repayment. This theory is valid in settings like OECD countries and far less valid in regions of high turmoil like West Africa. Companies have different credit ratings for debt. A large company producing a widely used product and backed by hard assets, such as GM or Ford, is a lower risk than a start-up Internet company with a good idea but no sales. Bond rating agencies like DBRS (Dominion Bond Rating Service) in Canada and Moody's or Standard and Poor in the United States specialize in assessing the ability of a government or company to repay debt, and they assign a debt rating that is virtually directly tied to the relative interest rate. Note that equity, such as a GM share, always has higher risk than debt, such as a GM bond, and the purchaser of the stock expects a higher return on the share price. The volatility of share prices is a reflection of the rapidly changing perception of the risk and level of anticipated returns on equity.

- **Liquidity**: imagine two kinds of long-term bonds, one of which cannot be sold until the term is up and another that can be readily sold to someone else if the original lender has a sudden need for the money. The first bond is illiquid and worth less in the eyes of the lender than the liquid bond. That means that a lender would need a higher rate of interest on the illiquid bond. The reason that developed countries place such an emphasis on fair and open markets for securities is that it reduces the cost of money and promotes economic growth. Debt in government and corporate bonds and stocks in large and midsize companies are traded daily in regulated exchanges, making them highly liquid.

7.1.2   The Time Value of Money from the Perspective of the Borrower

Those who borrow money do so for one of two reasons. The first is that some personal expenditure is so important that the borrower would rather pay extra for it (in the form of interest) in order to have it early. The most common examples are home and vehicle purchases. If individuals saved until they could buy a home without borrowing, they would be old before they owned their own home. In North America, most individuals choose to pay more for a home that they own today by borrowing and incurring interest costs than wait to buy a home without borrowing and its attendant interest charges. The second reason people borrow money is to use it in some form that they believe will create commercial value. As long as the value that is created is higher than the interest cost, the borrower can create and keep excess value. This is the basis of business lending.

An investor is going to use money, either his or her own or borrowed funds, for some commercial purpose. The investor always has the option of lending the funds to others at the current interest rate. It is therefore incumbent on the investor (in his or her own best interest) to assess whether the contemplated investment is worth it; is it likely to return a stream of cash in the future that exceeds the cash that would be realized if the funds were invested at low risk in an interest-bearing loan? Is the excess value large enough to warrant the risk that the investment may not work out? These questions are at the heart of business growth and asset replacement decisions.

An Inherent Sense of the Time Value of Money

People can easily make good judgments about the time value of money if the values are extreme. Imagine that your professor asks you to lend her $100 with a promise in writing to pay you back $200 in one month's time. Who would not be tempted to take this deal? The professor has a good job, and the money is not much, so the likelihood that she will run off to a foreign country over such a paltry sum is minor. There is a chance the professor will die within the month, making it awkward to collect the money from the estate, but this is not likely. Inflation will not be a significant factor in a one-month time period in North America. Against this, the reward is very large: doubling money in one month. In an extreme case like this, you can easily weigh the critical factors of risk and reward.

Similarly, if the professor asked for $100 and promised to pay $110 ten years from now, you could easily reject this. Even if the payment were adjusted for inflation, the small amount of reward, $10, is not worth the loss of the use of the money and the risk that the professor will not repay.

However, real-life cases are not usually this extreme. Engineers face questions such as "Should we spend $127,000 extra to buy hard-surfaced pumps and piping in order to reduce maintenance costs by $5,000 in year one, $9,000 in year two, and $10,500 per year thereafter and to extend the time between replacements from 8 years to 10 years. In this case, the answer is not intuitive, and you must reflect on the risk in the time value of money and do a calculation to see if the investment is worth it. A method to quantify risk versus reward called discounted cash flow analysis is the primary means of making investment decisions.

7.1.3 Defining the Time Value of Money

Imagine that you have $1,000 today and you want to earn a return on this money. You decide that you need the money back in one year for some personal purpose, so you decide to lend it to the bank in a one-year GIC (Guaranteed Investment Certificate, called a Certificate of Deposit in the US) with an interest rate of 4%. After one year, the bank will return $1,040. You earn $40 of interest income and get your $1,000 of principal back.

If instead you take out a two-year GIC with an annual interest rate of 4%, then you will get back $1081.60 after two years. You get your $1,000 principal back, but in addition, you get $81.60 of interest. The interest on the principal is $80, and the other $1.60 is the interest earned in the second year on the interest you made in the first year. When both the principal and the prior periods' interest earn interest in the current period, this is called **compound interest**. There are cases where interest is not compounded. For example, if you buy a bond and takes the interest payment on a yearly basis (known as "clipping coupons," since bonds used to be issued with coupons attached that could be redeemed for interest), then interest is not compounded because it is paid out on a pay-as-you-go basis.

Now, think of an example where you agree to pay a charity a donation of $500 in three years. What is the present value of this pledge of future money? Suppose you decide to put money into a three-year GIC that will be worth $500 in three years. If you invest $444.50 in such a GIC at 4% annual interest, it will be worth $500 at the end of the three years. Given that you can earn interest at 4%, the future payment of $500 is worth $444.50 today.

These are examples of the fundamental principals of **compounding** (determining the future worth of a present amount of money) and **discounting** (determining the present value of a future amount of money). The interest rate is sometimes called the discount rate because a future sum (like the $500 in the previous example) is worth less today by an amount determined by the interest rate.

The fundamental equations of discounting or compounding are as follows:

Future value of a current dollar (compounding) is given by this equation:

$$F = P \times (1 + i)^n$$

Where: F = future value

P = present value

i = interest or discount rate per period

n = number of periods

Note that i, the interest or discount rate, means the return on money whether lent or invested, i.e., in this formula, i means the time value of money.

Present value of a future dollar (discounting) is given by this equation:

$$P = F \times (1 \div (1 + i)^n)$$

7.1.4 The Value of the Interest/Discount/Return Rate

The value of i depends on the inflation rate, the general supply and demand for money, the risk and the liquidity of the investment, and also any other investment alternatives there are. If you are giving money to a bank or a corporation in the form of debt, there is always a market value for the interest rate, accessible through the Internet. The choice is to offer your debt at that rate or decline to lend. Decisions about equity investment are based on expected future cash values, which necessarily involve an estimate. If the stock is publicly traded, you know what others think it is worth, but there is no certainty about future earnings.

What about a company making a decision to invest in a project? Practically speaking, most companies have a sense of a **hurdle rate of return**, or a return on investment below which they will not contemplate making an investment. The hurdle rate is also called the **minimum acceptable rate of return** (**MARR**). Sophisticated companies will have more than one hurdle rate, depending on the nature of the risk. For example, imagine a power company that is looking at building unregulated generation. In one case, the output of the plant is 80% sold under a 25-year contract to a large blue-chip industrial user; in a second case, there is no prior contract for sale of power (this plant would be called a merchant generation plant). A sophisticated company will have a lower hurdle rate of return on the first case where the prior sale contract reduces risk. Companies calculate the **weighted average cost of capital (WACC),** which is the effective aggregated interest rate from the mix of debt, preferred shares, and equity that a given company (or a given project within a company) has. The targeted or hurdle return on equity is adjusted to the risk of the overall company or a given project. An investment that had zero risk free would have to have a return at least as high as the WACC or else it would be a drag on the overall company performance. Because all projects have risk, the hurdle rate is the WACC plus the risk premium.

Liquidity is a measure of how easy it is to get out of an investment. Long-term bonds can always be sold in a secondary market. For example, you can buy a 30-year government bond today and sell it to someone else a year from now if your circumstances change. A minority interest in a privately held company, on the other hand, takes a very long time to sell. You have to find a buyer that is acceptable to the other owners, who may in turn have a right of first refusal to buy the interest at whatever price your new buyer has named. In effect, rights of first refusal typically reduce buyer interest and increase negotiation time. Hence, a bond is a highly liquid investment, and a minority interest in a privately held company has low liquidity.

Setting the right value of i is a matter of judgment, reflecting inflation, liquidity, market supply and demand for money, project risk, and any other investment opportunities that are available.

7.1.5 The Number of Periods

For interest calculations, the number of periods is set by the interest or **compounding period**. If a loan has interest compounded annually, then it is calculated once per year. If the loan has interest compounded monthly, then it is calculated once per month. A five-year loan with annual compounding has five periods, but with monthly compounding, it has 60 periods. For investment calculations, an annual period is almost always used.

There is one convention in financing that is somewhat deceptive in nature. Lending institutions typically quote a nominal annual rate of interest but often have a more frequent compounding period. Hence, a bank that offers a loan at 9% annual interest compounded monthly is really offering a loan with a compounding period of one month and a monthly interest rate of 0.75%.

Table 7.1 shows how interest would be compounded on a loan of $100 in the first year, assuming no payment until year-end.

Table 7.1: Illustration of the True Cost of a 9% Nominal Interest Rate Compounded Monthly Basis:

Initial loan amount:	$100
Nominal interest rate:	9%
Compounding period:	Monthly
No payments in the first 12 months	

Period	Interest ($)	Balance ($)
1	0.75	100.75
2	0.76	101.51
3	0.76	102.27
4	0.77	103.03
5	0.77	103.81
6	0.78	104.59
7	0.78	105.37
8	0.79	106.16
9	0.80	106.96
10	0.80	107.76
11	0.81	108.57
12	0.81	109.38

The real annual interest rate on such a loan is 9.38%. The amount of 9% can be thought of as a nominal interest rate, and 9.38% is the real or effective annual interest rate. Why do lenders compound more frequently than once a year? Imagine you are lending $100 billion per year; the impact of an additional 0.38% is $380 million per year! Years ago, lenders did not give a clear disclosure of the effective annual interest rate, but "truth in lending" laws in North America mandate full disclosure of the effective annual interest rate. For example, credit card debt at a nominal annual interest rate of 18% is 19.6% if compounded monthly.

Imagine moving from compounding yearly to monthly to daily. Ultimately, at the end of this progression is **continuous compounding**, in which the compounding period is infinitesimal. This is a special case in which a spreadsheet approach is not going to be applicable. The effective annual interest rate for continuous compounding is as follows:

$$i(\text{effective}) = e^{i(\text{nominal annual})} - 1$$

The future value for continuous compounding is given by this equation:

$$F(\text{at time } n) = P \times e^{i \times n}$$

(Where F, P, i, and n have the same meanings as in the equation $F = P \times (1 + i)^n$.)

Table 7.2 shows the effective interest rate for various compounding periods assuming 9% nominal interest.

Table 7.2: Effective Interest Rate for Various Compounding Periods

Basis: Nominal interest rate   9%

Compounding Period	Effective Interest Rate
Annual	9.0000
Semi-annual	9.2025
Quarterly	9.3083
Monthly	9.3807
Daily	9.4162
Continual	9.4174

Therefore, increasing the compounding period past monthly achieves rapidly diminishing returns.

Sample Problem 7.1.5 The Effective Rate of Interest

Ryan needs $5,000 to buy an engagement ring. His friend agrees to lend him $5,000 to be repaid with interest in one year at a nominal annual interest rate of 7% but with interest compounded quarterly. What is the effective rate of interest?

Solution:

Initial loan:	$5,000
Nominal interest rate:	7%
Compounding:	Quarterly
Periods:	4

The quarterly interest rate is 1.75% (7% ÷ 4). Using this interest rate, the following table can be developed:

Period	Interest ($)	Balance ($)
1	87.50	5,087.50
2	89.03	5,176.53
3	90.59	5,267.12
4	92.17	5,359.30

Therefore, the effective interest rate $= (5,359.30 - 5,000) \times 100 \div 5,000$
$$= 7.186\%$$

The effect of 0.186% extra effective interest is not a significant deterrent to the individual borrower in this case: it adds only $9.22 to Ryan's interest bill, which is likely not enough to deter the loan. However, banks lend billions of dollars, and an extra 0.186% would bring in $1.86 million for every billion dollars of loan amount.

7.1.6 Present/Future Worth Calculations: Other Considerations

The point in time at which n is set to zero is arbitrary and varies from company to company. The most common variants are as follows:

- n equals zero in the year of the analysis (present time).
- n equals zero in the first year of capital spending (when the first project dollars are to be spent).
- n equals zero in the first year of operation of the project, such as when the plant or project starts up (in which case n has a negative value for the years in which the capital is being spent, i.e., capital is spent in year -1, -2, etc.).

The point in time at which n equals zero defines the meaning of "present" in present value, and is arbitrary. By making n equal to zero in some future year such as the year of plant start-up, then the present value of future money means present value measured in terms of the value of a dollar in that year in which n equals zero. Changing the year in which n equals zero has an impact on present value: as n equals zero is pushed out into the future, the "present" value of a given stream of cash increases. However, when doing calculations of internal rate of return (IRR), the results are independent of the choice of n equals zero, so the rate of return is an absolute measure of the earning power of a project. Following a consistent practice within a company means that investments are compared consistently.

There is an implicit assumption in calculations that money is realized at the end of the period. For loans and bonds, this is in fact true. For analyzing investments, income is typically received over the course of the period rather than at the end of a period. For instance, imagine that you are looking at an incremental investment to add capacity to a refinery, and you model the cash flow received over 30 years. Implicit in the choice of an annual period and the application of equation $F = P \times (1 + i)^n$ is that the cash flows to the company at the end of the year, when in fact it flows in over the course of the year. In practice, the impact of this is ignored since the error introduced is typically small compared to the accuracy of the assumptions that generate the cash flow forecasts.

Prior to the age of personal computers, it was common to develop elaborate tables of the present value of future dollars or the future value of present dollars for various interest rates and compounding periods. Today, solver or goal seek features in spreadsheets allow anyone with access to such a program to do these calculations effortlessly. The further merit of developing a spreadsheet is that it is not uncommon for discussions of financial valuations to lead to "what if" questions. If a spreadsheet is set up cleverly, then a few keystrokes can lead to a change of interest rate, principal amount, etc. In this text, spreadsheets will be referred to when solving compounding and discounting problems. It is important to know how to do this for a variety of problems.

7.2 Working with Time-Adjusted Values of Money

There are a number of fairly standard problems that arise in financial analysis that can be readily solved with concepts of compounding and discounting.

7.2.1 Present Worth of a Future Stream of Dollars

To find the present value of a future stream of income, or the amount of money you would accept today in place of a future stream of income, assume an interest rate. Consider first the example of a person who wins the lottery and has the choice of an upfront payment less than $1 million or 10 equal annual payments of $100,000. What is the better choice? Assume that the person can invest either the lump sum payment or the annual payments safely in a government 10-year bond at an interest rate of 6%. Apply the equation $P = F \times (1 \div (1 + i)^n)$ to calculate the present value of each future value. The sum of the present values determines the lump sum payment that is equal in value to the future stream of payments.

Table 7.3 shows the stream of future payments, $100,000 per year, and the present values discounted at 6% for payments at the start of each year and at the end of each year. In this example the future payments are identical in value, but the present value technique is as valid for an uneven stream of numbers as it is for a constant stream.

Table 7.3: Present Worth of a Stream of 10 Equal Annual Payments

Interest rate (%)	6		
Year	Payment	Start of Year Present Value	End of Year Present Value
1	100,000	100,000	94,340
2	100,000	94,340	89,000
3	100,000	89,000	83,962
4	100,000	83,962	79,209
5	100,000	79,209	74,726
6	100,000	74,726	70,496
7	100,000	70,496	66,506
8	100,000	66,506	62,741
9	100,000	62,741	59,190
10	100,000	59,190	55,839
Net present value		780,169	736,009

The sum of the present value of each payment equals the total present value of the stream of payments. This means that if you are given $780,169, it would have the same value as if you were given 10 payments of $100,000 at the start of each year. Delaying the payment by one year (from the start of the year to the end of the year) reduces the present value of the stream of payments by about $54,000. Note that the present value of an immediate payment of $100,000 (year one in the start of year case) is $100,000 because you have immediate use of the payment, i.e., the payment is "present."

It is important to think carefully about what is the right "discount" or interest rate to use in each case of compounding or discounting. In this case, a person has a secure prospect of a future stream of money, and the appropriate interest rate to choose when considering the alternative of an initial payment is the rate of interest for a secure alternate form of investment (hence, the choice of 6%). The impact of the discount or interest rate on the present value for this example is shown in Figure 7.5. This curve is exponentially asymptotic to zero at an infinite interest rate.

Figure 7.5: Present Value of 10 Equal Payments of $100,000 at the End of the Year

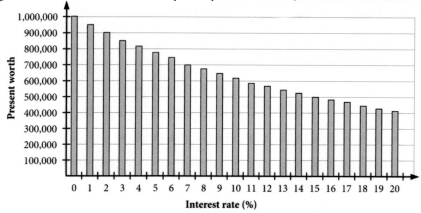

Bonds and Mortgages

When a person buys a bond, he or she receives a promise to pay money in the future. If a $1,000 face value bond has a coupon (interest) rate of 6% and a term of 20 years, the holder of the bond will receive $60 once a year for 19 years and $1,060 (the principal and the final interest payment) in the 20th year. A bond therefore represents future money. In valuing bonds, the concept of the present value of future dollars is applied by discounting future dollars to their present worth.

A 6% bond will be worth $1,000 on the day it is issued if the time value of money for the term of the bond is 6% on the day it is issued. The time value of money changes daily as investors buy or sell bonds, so a bond usually sells for close to but not exactly its face value on the day it is issued. However, over a long period of time, the time value of money can change very significantly. In the 1980s, federal government bonds were issued with coupon rates over 11%, a rate that by today's standards is very high, since long-term federal bonds today are discounted at less than 5%.

When a person takes out a mortgage, he or she gets a sum of money today but must make a future stream of payments in exchange for that. When a mortgage payment is calculated, the concept of the future value of present dollars is applied.

Bonds and mortgages are illustrations of the everyday application of the concept of applying the time value of money by discounted cash flow.

7.2.2 A Future Stream of Dollars that Amortizes an Initial Investment

How much do I have to pay in the future to pay off, or **amortize,** an initial amount? This is a standard question for mortgage lenders, for annuities (annual payments in exchange for an initial capital deposit), for those who lease equipment, and for those who want to determine a **capital recovery charge**. The capital recovery charge can be thought of as the levelized amount of money required in each period to ensure that a capital investment is recovered with a return equal to the value chosen for i. This kind of example was used to calculate a mortgage payment in Appendix 3.3. A goal seek or solver feature is used in a spreadsheet to ensure either that the present value of the payments equals the principal or the remaining balance or that principal owing is zero at the end of the loan period. In either case, an initial payment is guessed and a goal seek subroutine calculates the correct payment. Table 7.4a shows the payment present value method for an initial sum of $1,000 with 25 annual periods at 10%.

Table 7.4a: Annuity/Capital Recovery/Lease Payment/Mortgage Table

Basis:

Principal:	$1,000
Interest:	10%
Years:	25
Compounding:	Annual
Payment:	$110.17

Period	Payment ($)	Present Value ($)
1	110.17	100.15
2	110.17	91.05
3	110.17	82.77
4	110.17	75.25
5	110.17	68.41
6	110.17	62.19
7	110.17	56.53
8	110.17	51.40
9	110.17	46.72
10	110.17	42.48
11	110.17	38.61
12	110.17	35.10
13	110.17	31.91
14	110.17	29.01
15	110.17	26.37
16	110.17	23.98
17	110.17	21.80
18	110.17	19.82
19	110.17	18.01
20	110.17	16.38
21	110.17	14.89

Period	Payment ($)	Present Value ($)
22	110.17	13.53
23	110.17	12.30
24	110.17	11.19
25	110.17	10.17
Total	2,754.20	1,000

Table 7.4a takes the same approach as Table 7.3 (end-of-year calculation), namely, discounting the future mortgage payment to get its present worth. However, in practice, it is common to do this calculation in a manner that separates the interest payment from the recovery of principal, as shown in Table 7.4b. Note that the calculated mortgage payment is identical, but the cost of money (interest) is separated from the principal recovery.

Table 7.4b: Annuity/Capital Recovery/Lease Payment/Mortgage Table with Separation of Interest and Principal Portion

Period	Payment ($)	Interest Portion ($)	Principal Portion ($)	End of Year Principal Balance ($)
1	110.17	100.00	10.17	989.83
2	110.17	98.98	11.18	978.65
3	110.17	97.86	12.30	966.34
4	110.17	96.63	13.53	952.81
5	110.17	95.28	14.89	937.92
6	110.17	93.79	16.38	921.55
7	110.17	92.15	18.01	903.53
8	110.17	90.35	19.81	883.72
9	110.17	88.37	21.80	861.92
10	110.17	86.19	23.98	837.95
11	110.17	83.79	26.37	811.57
12	110.17	81.16	29.01	782.56
13	110.17	78.26	31.91	750.65
14	110.17	75.07	35.10	715.55
15	110.17	71.55	38.61	676.94
16	110.17	67.69	42.47	634.46
17	110.17	63.45	46.72	587.74
18	110.17	58.77	51.39	536.34
19	110.17	53.63	56.53	479.81
20	110.17	47.98	62.19	417.62
21	110.17	41.76	68.41	349.22
22	110.17	34.92	75.25	273.97

Period	Payment ($)	Interest Portion ($)	Principal Portion ($)	End of Year Principal Balance ($)
23	110.17	27.40	82.77	191.20
24	110.17	19.12	91.05	100.15
25	110.17	10.02	100.15	−0.00
Total	2,754.20	1,754.20	1,000.00	

Since interest payments on investments are a deductible expense (reported on the income statement) and principal repayments are not a deductible expense (reported on the balance sheet), tracking these two items separately becomes important in preparing financial statements and in completing tax returns.

This is a crucial calculation that arises in many areas of business and engineering, and it is important that every engineer be able to set up and solve such a problem. The use of a spreadsheet with the principal amounts and interest rate set up as single cell entries means that hypothetical cases can be run quite easily: what if the interest rate is a quarter point higher, or what if the principal amount changes? By dragging down the rows, one can extend the period of the loan or go from annual compounding (25 periods at an interest rate of 10%) to monthly compounding (300 periods at an interest rate of 1/12 of 10%).

Reflect on the values in table 7.4b. First, consider it from the perspective of a person paying a mortgage. For every $1,000 borrowed at 10% for 25 years, the homeowner will pay $2,754, of which $1,754 is the interest on the loan. A shorter period or a one-time balloon payment has an enormous reduction in interest paid, which is why prepayment provisions in mortgages are so important to borrowers.

Second, consider this from the perspective of a person who is weighing a capital versus an operating cost. Examples of this kind of calculation arise constantly and are at the heart of many engineering evaluations. For example, should you specify a thicker conductor wire for a transmission line (at a higher capital cost) and reduce power losses due to resistance? Should you specify a larger pipe size on a pipeline to reduce pumping horsepower? The way to approach such problems is to develop an annual charge for a capital investment, in effect, turning a capital cost into an annual operating cost. In the previous mortgage example, the annual value of an investment of $1,000 with a life of 25 years and a discount rate of 10% is $110.17. If 10% was an acceptable return on capital in a company, then the investment would be justified if the annual savings in operating costs were $110.17 or higher. If the annual operating costs savings were less than that amount, then the capital expenditure should be rejected. The specification of the target discount/interest/return rate is the critical issue in deciding the relative value of capital versus operating costs. High target rates of return on capital investment discourage capital spending. Low rates of return encourage capital investment. For this reason, one strategy governments have sometimes employed in trying to encourage some investment seen as being socially desirable, such as housing for the poor or pollution control equipment, is to provide subsidized low interest loans. Note that a rapid write-down of the investment for tax purposes through high tax depreciation rates has the same effect.

Governmental fiscal policy has an impact on a nation's economic health. Governmental decisions about borrowing and spending affect interest rates. In the early 1990s, Canada was running large federal and provincial deficits at a time when the US had made serious efforts to curb spending in order to reduce annual deficits and reduce the overall level of debt. The net impact of this was a 4% higher interest rate in Canada than in the US. This had the effect of discouraging investment in Canada because a given investment had to be more profitable to meet a hurdle rate of return compared to the US. When central banks want to reduce economic activity in order to control inflation, they raise interest rates for the same reason. In 2009, central banks of many countries have driven interest rates to very low levels to stimulate economic activity. Thus, the value of money has profound ripple effects on capital projects and the general level of economic activity in a nation.

Capital investments are one component of a society's economic wealth. The effective interest or hurdle rate of return on investment is the primary determinant of whether a given capital project makes sense. High or variable rates of inflation make investment decisions difficult because investors do not know what an appropriate interest rate is. This is the reason that so much attention gets focused on inflation and interest rates. Since engineers to a large extent make their living from capital projects, they are highly affected by these issues.

Recovering the Initial Principal

In accounting and in financial statements, depreciation is the manner in which the original value of an asset is recognized. A company that is profitable is recovering the cost of its assets through depreciation.

The mortgage calculation shows that discounted cash flow analysis has a built-in recovery of the initial payment and the time value of that money. Table 7.4b shows that the mortgage payment of $110.17 includes both the cost of money (interest) and the recovery of the principal. Because recovery of initial capital is built into DCF analysis, an entry for depreciation in cash flow calculations is never included.

7.2.3 Capital Recovery Factor

The emphasis in this text is on setting up spreadsheets to model present versus future value calculations. Setting up these spreadsheets gives the engineer a tremendous advantage in studying sensitivities and in understanding results. However, one formula called the capital recovery factor or the annuity factor is often used as a shortcut. This formula gives the same result as Table 7.4: what stream of money in the future equals a set amount of money today?

$$CRF = P \times [(i \times (1 + i)^n) \div ((1 + i)^n - 1)]$$

CRF is the amount of money required in each time period to recovery capital and earn a return on investment, P is the present value in year zero of an initial sum of money, i is the interest (return) rate, and n is the total number of periods.

The name "annuity" came from the practice of making an annual payment; however, the formula works for any period, i.e., annual, monthly, weekly, etc. If you set P at $1,000, i at 10%, and n at 25 years, you get an annual payment of $110.17, which is the same value shown in Table 7.4.

Sample Problem 7.2.1 The Present Value of Future Money

A wealthy aunt left her nephew a payment of $12,000 per year for 20 years, with the funds to be held in a secure trust fund. Once the 20th payment is made, any amount remaining in the trust fund will be given to charity. The trustee was empowered, however, to pay a lump sum if acceptable to the nephew. After making the 6th payment, the trustee proposes a one-time lump sum payment of $135,000 in order to wind up the estate and reduce ongoing expenses. The nephew consults with his banker, who indicates that the lump sum would earn 3.70% if it were invested in a secure account similar to the trust account. Should the nephew take the payment?

Solution:

The two options are a future stream of money and a current single payment. Evaluate the net present value (NPV) of the future stream of payment to compare it to the lump sum payment. The following table shows the future stream of payments, the discount factor using the interest (discount) rate of 3.70%, and the present value. The NPV is the sum of all the present values.

	Interest (discount) rate (%)	3.70	
Year (n)	Annual Receipts (F) ($)	Discounting Factor $1 \div (1 + i)^n$	Present Value (P) ($)
(1)	(2)	(3)	(4) = (2) × (3)
1	12,000	0.9643	11,571.60
2	12,000	0.93	11,160.00
3	12,000	0.8967	10,760.40
4	12,000	0.8647	10,376.40
5	12,000	0.8338	10,005.60
6	12,000	0.8041	9,649.20
7	12,000	0.7754	9,304.80
8	12,000	0.7478	8,973.60
9	12,000	0.7211	8,653.20
10	12,000	0.6954	8,344.80
11	12,000	0.6706	8,047.20
12	12,000	0.6466	7,759.20
13	12,000	0.6236	7,483.20
14	12,000	0.6013	7,215.60
		NPV	129,305

The nephew should accept the offer for lump sum payment since the NPV of the future payments is less than the value of the one-time payment. Note that although the discount factor is calculated in this spreadsheet, there is no need to calculate it; you can set up a spreadsheet to go from the future value of money (the payment) to the present value by a single calculation.

Sample Problem 7.2.2 The Present Value of Future Money

In 1982, two identical power plants, Steam Co. and Heat Co., in Germany and Canada, respectively, considered an investment in insulation for steam lines in a power plant that would save them $44,000 per year in fuel costs over the next 20 years. The cost of the insulation investment was $430,000. The long-term government bond rate in Germany was 2.5% due to very low inflation, no deficit, and a low rate of personal borrowing relative to savings. The long-term government bond rate in Canada was 10.2%, which is a reflection of very high government borrowing to finance a deficit and a high rate of personal borrowing relative to savings. Each power company used a discount rate that is 4% higher than the long-term government bond rate to discount future cash flow. For each company, is the present value of the future savings higher than the cost of the insulation? Consider the impact of a high discount rate on the willingness of a company to make an investment.

Solution:

One way to analyze this investment is to compare the present value of the savings to the cost of the investment, $430,000. The following table shows the future stream of estimated savings, discounted at 6.5% (Germany) and 14.2% (Canada).

Discount rate (%)	6.5		14.20	
	Steam Co., Germany		Heat Co., Canada	
Year	Cost Saving ($)	PV ($)	Cost Saving ($)	PV ($)
1	44,000	41,315	44,000	38,529
2	44,000	38,793	44,000	33,738
3	44,000	36,425	44,000	29,543
4	44,000	34,202	44,000	25,870
5	44,000	32,115	44,000	22,653
6	44,000	30,155	44,000	19,836
7	44,000	28,314	44,000	17,370
8	44,000	26,586	44,000	15,210
9	44,000	24,964	44,000	13,319
10	44,000	23,440	44,000	11,662
11	44,000	22,009	44,000	10,212
12	44,000	20,666	44,000	8,943
13	44,000	19,405	44,000	7,831
14	44,000	18,220	44,000	6,857
15	44,000	17,108	44,000	6,004
16	44,000	16,064	44,000	5,258
17	44,000	15,084	44,000	4,604
18	44,000	14,163	44,000	4,031
19	44,000	13,299	44,000	3,530
20	44,000	12,487	44,000	3,091
	NPV	484,814	NPV	288,090

The NPV of the future savings is more than the cost of the investment for the German company and less for the Canadian company; the investment would proceed in Germany. This problem illustrates the danger to a country from fiscal policies that cause a high cost of money: it deters investment and leads to a manufacturing sector that is less efficient than countries with a low cost of money.

Sample Problem 7.2.3 The Future Value of Present Money

You want to take out a mortgage with a once-per-year payment, a term of 10 years, and a value of $100,000. Given your high student loan and car payments, the bank considers you a substandard credit risk, and the interest rate will be 6.34%. What payment in the future will offset the value of the $100,000?

Solution:

This kind of problem can be solved with an equation, but often the amount, the interest rate, and the term change during the negotiation. Therefore, it is often worthwhile to set up this kind of problem as a spreadsheet with easily changed values.

One method to solving this is to simply reverse the present value of future money calculation by using a goal seek function to solve for the payment. Just guess the payment, and then use goal seek to set the net present value of the payment to equal the loan amount. This is illustrated in the following table.

Loan amount ($)		100,000
Interest rate (%)		6.34
Payment ($)		13,806.50

Year	Payment ($)	Present Value of Payment ($)
1	13,806	12,983
2	13,806	12,209
3	13,806	11,481
4	13,806	10,797
5	13,806	10,153
6	13,806	9,548
7	13,806	8,979
8	13,806	8,443
9	13,806	7,940
10	13,806	7,466

| Net present value | | 100,000 |

However, it is often necessary on a mortgage type loan to track interest and principal payment separately. For companies, interest is an expense on the income statement, while principal payment shows up on the balance sheet. For individuals, interest on any debt for an investment can be treated as an expense when calculating income tax, and in the US, interest on the mortgage of the primary residence is also tax deductible.

Another method to calculate the payment is a loan amortization method shown in the following table. Again, use a goal seek function to solve for the payment.

Loan amount ($)	100,000
Interest rate (%)	6.34
Payment ($)	13,806.50

Year	Interest ($)	Principal ($)	Remaining Balance ($)
1	6,340.00	7,466.50	92,533.50
2	5,866.62	7,939.87	84,593.63
3	5,363.24	8,443.26	76,150.36
4	4,827.93	8,978.57	67,171.80
5	4,258.69	9,547.81	57,623.99
6	3,653.36	10,153.14	47,470.85
7	3,009.65	10,796.85	36,674.01
8	2,325.13	11,481.37	25,192.64
9	1,597.21	12,209.29	12,983.35
10	823.14	12,983.35	0.00

The interest in each year is the interest rate times the remaining balance (the full value of the loan in the first year). The principal portion of the payment is the total payment minus the interest. The remaining balance reduces each year by the principal repayment. Again, just guess the payment, and use goal seek to set the remaining balance after the final payment to zero.

Most actual mortgages for homes have monthly rather than yearly payments, but the approach to the calculation is the same regardless of the number of periods.

7.3   Evaluating Investments

In theory, a new investment could be evaluated by looking out to the future and running a complete set of financial statements with and without the new investment. Then the dividend stream and the residual worth of the company could be looked at to decide if the new investment makes sense. However, the effort involved and the large number of projects that are screened in even a medium-sized company every year make this impractical. In practice, investments are evaluated on a straightforward analysis of the cash impact of the investment, i.e., the marginal (incremental) cash consequence of the investment is identified and analyzed.

Two conceptual approaches govern investment analysis: payback period and discounting. The **payback period** assesses the time required to get the original investment back from the future incoming cash flows. Discounting calculates the present value of future cash either by a fixed interest rate or a derived interest rate that reflects the implicit earning power of the investment. **Discounted cash flow (DCF)** techniques include:

- **Net present value (NPV),** the "extra" current value of an investment compared to a theoretical investment of the same amount of money at a prescribed interest rate.

- **Internal rate of return (IRR),** the effective interest rate at which the investment is exactly offset by the future incoming cash flows. The IRR is a direct measure of the effective earning power of the dollars being invested. This is also called the **return on equity (ROE)** or sometimes the **return on investment (ROI)**. Technically, the return on investment is the return provided by the total project (debt plus equity), and the return on equity is the return on the equity component only, which is leveraged by the debt. However, in practice, the terms are often used imprecisely and interchangeably, so be sure to clarify what the speaker means by each term.

IRR is the predominant method used to screen investments; NPV is often assessed in parallel and is the method of choice for required investments that have no revenue (such as a pollution abatement project). Payback moderates judgments based on IRR in that a risky project that has a projected very high IRR and high payback may be less attractive than a lower IRR with a short payback because future reality often deviates from current projections.

7.3.1 Cash Flow

The critical first step in any investment analysis is a calculation of the cash flows over the life of the project. This is always done on an incremental basis looking forward, which means looking at the future cash flow differences associated with some project, not total cash flow for a company. Cash flow is normally done on an annual basis for major long-term capital projects. Consider, for example, a major petrochemical project such as a new polypropylene plant. The planning, engineering, and construction of such a project will typically take three to four years, during which time the cash flow is negative, i.e., the company uses cash to pay for permitting, engineering design, procurement, construction, and start-up of the project. Often during the start-up year, cash flow continues to be negative because the plant takes a period of time to achieve operation at full capacity and also because the project must build inventory and receivables during the first year that will be collected in the last year of the project. Usually by the second and subsequent years of operation, cash flow is positive.

It is crucial that incremental tax effects be considered in any DCF analysis, since they have a major impact on cash flow; all DCF calculations should be done on an after-tax basis. Determining the incremental tax impact of a project is addressed in Appendix 7.1.

Cash flows need to be incremental, so only the extra costs associated with a new project should be considered. Imagine you are in a company that has one manufacturing plant and is considering building a second one. The company will not need a second president and vice president of finance in order to operate a second plant. In an accounting treatment, once the second plant is up and running, the company might decide to charge half of the cost of the president and VP Finance to the second plant, but in an investment analysis, this should not be done. The true marginal cost of the second plant is just the extra cash costs that the company will incur in building and operating it, and nothing else should be considered in the cash flow. In essence, this lets the economy of scale of the company be factored into the only decision the company now must make: should the second plant be built?

Cash flows should be future oriented, so they should ignore sunk costs. Suppose that a project has gone over budget, and instead of costing $100 million, the total cost will be $150 million. If this is realized when the project has committed $90 million, then the proper investment analysis is to look at whether it is worth $60 million to complete the investment and operate the project. The project may have a poor return based on the $150 million total cost, but the company's choice when the overrun is discovered is to spend an incremental $60 million and complete the project or walk away from the project. The $90 million is a sunk cost and should not show up in the cash flow analysis.

Cash flows should be developed in some detail. Operating costs should be broken down as finely as possible, since inevitably when the senior levels of a company come to review a project, many sensitivity cases are assessed. For example, they will look at a base case IRR and then look at the impact on the base case of a 10% overrun in capital cost or a 10% increase in feedstock or energy costs. The purpose of this sensitivity analysis is to see what risk factors most affect the return on investment. In some cases, a company can take steps to reduce some risks; for example, feedstock or fuel can be purchased on a long-term contract. In other cases, one must simply accept risks; no company, for example, has control over general inflation and its impact on wages or on governmental policies that can alter a project's economics sharply (for example, chlorinated fluorocarbons were banned when their impact on the ozone layer became fully understood).

Cash flow forecasts are a lot less accurate than the precision of subsequent analysis implies. It is not unusual to see DCF calculations that carry rates of return to two decimal places that are based on inputs that are at best educated guesses. There are many implicit assumptions in cash flow forecasts because they often go 30 or even 40 years into the future. Knowledge of prices of key inputs, such as labor, energy (power and fuel), and feedstock, is at best hazy, and people usually end up assuming that these have some relationship to inflation. For example, it is not unusual to assume that wages will increase in the long term at 2% over inflation.

The conventional wisdom for energy projects in 1980 was that the real price of oil, then at $40 US per barrel, would continue to rise over the next 35 years at a rate that was 2% greater than the assumed inflation rate. The dispute with this forecast was that it was too low; some oil companies and some segments within government argued that oil would increase at 3% real increase (3% over inflation). In reality, the price of oil collapsed through several stages to as low as $13 per barrel and then in 2008, reached $147 per barrel, only to collapse again. The inaccuracy of the guess of future oil price simply overwhelmed any refinement in economic analysis.

It is especially important that relative pricing be consistent within a cash flow forecast. For example, consider electrical power generation based on a combined cycle unit firing natural gas. Conventional wisdom today is that the price of gas and power are linked in that natural gas will be the fuel that sets the effective level of price for power. In other words, power price in North America will be set at a level that will give a reasonable return (say 12%) on investment in a new combined-cycle, natural-gas-fired unit. If you accept this logic, then it would be inconsistent to develop a 30-year forecast that saw natural gas prices escalating at a significantly different underlying rate than power prices.

Every input into a cash flow forecast should have a justification for its pattern of growth, and more than one person should review these to ensure as much internal consistency as possible in relative forecasts.

7.3.2 Net Present Value

Net present value takes a fixed interest or discount rate and calculates the net present value of the stream of cash flow. The normal means of referring to net present value is NPV(xx), where xx is the discount rate (as a percentage) used in the calculation. For example, NPV(10) means the net present value of the investment if the cash flow stream is discounted at 10%. Calculating NPV is essentially the same procedure as the calculation of present value shown in Section 7.2.1 and Table 7.3. The discount or interest rate used in the calculation, however, is typically either a benchmark value (10%, 12%, or 15%) or a minimum hurdle rate of return (MARR) for capital projects within a company.

NPV at MARR is in effect the present excess value of a project over the minimum acceptable rate of return, expressed as current dollars. Thus, if a project has an NPV of $12 million at the company's MARR, it means that if the company proceeds with the project and the future unfolds as per the forecast, the company will have received its MARR on the investment and will have created an additional amount of wealth (value) worth $12 million in present dollars. In practice, IRR is used more often in evaluating cash generating investments.

Table 7.5 shows the following hurdle rates of return for a power company building merchant generation plants:

Table 7.5 Hurdle Rates of Return for an International Power Company

Type of Project	Minimum Hurdle Return on Investment
Merchant generation, North America, no contract	14%
Merchant generation, Europe/ANZ, no contract	14.5%
Merchant generation, Latin America, no contract	21%
Merchant generation, Africa, no contract	Do not invest
More than 70% contracted (min. 15 years) to customers with a "B high" credit rating or better, North America, Europe, and ANZ	12%
More than 70% contracted to customers (min. 15 years) with a "B high" credit rating or better, Latin America	17%
More than 70% contracted (min. 15 years) to customers with a "B high" credit rating or better, Africa	22%
100% contracted to customers with a "B high" credit rating or better, any geography	Reduce hurdle rate by 0.5%

Type of Project	Minimum Hurdle Return on Investment
Customers are "A low" or better credit rating	Reduce hurdle rate by 0.5%
Contract term 10 years instead of 15 years	Increase hurdle rate by 0.75%
Full guarantee by World Bank or Canadian Government Agency of Power Project in Africa for minimum of 12 years.	Reduce hurdle rate by 7%

Now, imagine that you have a preordered combined cycle power generation unit that can go into a project in Egypt, Argentina, New Zealand, Ontario, or the state of Washington. One way to compare the alternatives is to prepare the cash flow projection for each of these projects (including all tax effects) and to discount them at the predefined hurdle rate of return. The result is the net present value at the hurdle rate; it would be in millions of dollars, and it represents the value over the minimum acceptable return that is available from the proposed investment. A negative NPV simply means that the project does not achieve the minimum hurdle rate of return.

Although IRR is more commonly considered by management in making this kind of decision, there is one type of investment that does not lend itself to calculating an IRR: investments required by law that have no incremental income. Consider, for example, a government order that requires that sulfur content in gasoline be reduced by a factor of 10 (as has occurred in North America). Companies can meet this by a combination of additional hydrotreating, alternate feedstock purchase, and product blending with purchased low sulfur stocks. Cases can be developed that have vastly different patterns and levels of capital spending and operating costs. Since these alternatives are a mix of capital and operating costs with no net revenue, it is best to pick the alternative with the least negative NPV, assuming that all alternatives are equal in quality and risk. The NPV will be negative because there are capital and operating costs with no income, but the least negative NPV is the alternative that results in the lowest aggregated cost to the company.

In practice, of course, alternatives are not equal in quality and risk, and such factors play a major role in the choices management makes. Despite lots of proposed methodologies for quantifying risk, humans still trust the intuitive right-hand side of their brain as the primary judgment mechanism for screening risk and choosing alternatives. Hence, NPV calculations contribute to the ultimate decision, but they do not make the ultimate decision.

Table 7.6 illustrates an NPV calculation for a taxable Canadian company evaluating a merchant power plant located in Canada.

Table 7.6: Cash Flow ($M) and Calculation of NPV for a Canadian Taxable Company Merchant Power Plant Project Located in Canada

Basis ($M)

Total installed cost	248		Operating life	15 years
Cost Profile			**Availability**	
Year 0	1.50%		Year 1	40%
Year 1	30%		Year 2–10	97%
Year 2	60%		Year 11–15	94%
Year 3	8.5%			
CCA declining balance	30%			
Effective tax rate	40%			

Discount rate	14.0%		**Real Growth**
Inflation	3%	Wage	2%
Capacity (MW)	200	Gas price	1%
		Power price	1%
		Maintenance	0.50%

Year (n)	0	1	2	3	4	5	6	7	8	9	10	11	12	13	14	15	16	17
Capital cost	-3.7	-74.4	-148.8	-21.1														
Power (GWh)				700.8	1699.4	1,699.4	1,699.4	1,699.4	1,699.4	1,699.4	1,699.4	1,699.4	1,699.4	1,646.9	1,646.9	1,646.9	1,646.9	1,646.9
Price ($/Mwh)				46.0	47.8	49.8	51.7	53.8	56.0	58.2	60.5	63.0	65.5	68.1	70.8	73.6	76.6	79.7
Gross revenue				32.2	81.3	84.6	87.9	91.5	95.1	98.9	102.9	107.0	111.3	112.1	116.6	121.3	126.1	131.2
Cash Operating Costs																		
Fuel				9.9	25.0	26.0	27.0	28.1	29.2	30.4	31.6	32.9	34.2	34.4	35.8	37.2	38.7	40.3
Wages				1.3	1.4	1.4	1.5	1.6	1.7	1.7	1.8	1.9	2.0	2.1	2.2	2.3	2.5	2.6
Maintenance				4.4	4.6	4.7	4.9	5.0	5.2	5.4	5.6	5.8	6.0	6.2	6.4	6.6	6.9	7.1
Cash from operations				16.6	50.4	52.4	54.5	56.7	59.0	61.4	63.9	66.4	69.1	69.4	72.2	75.1	78.1	81.2
UCC before CCA claim				248.0	210.8	147.6	103.3	72.3	50.6	35.4	24.8	17.4	12.2	8.5	6.0	4.2	2.9	2.0
CCA				37.2	63.2	44.3	31.0	21.7	15.2	10.6	7.4	5.2	3.6	2.6	1.8	1.3	0.9	0.6
Net revenue before tax				-20.6	-12.8	8.2	23.6	35.0	43.8	50.8	56.4	61.2	65.4	66.8	70.4	73.8	77.2	80.6
Tax				-8.2	-5.1	3.3	9.4	14.0	17.5	20.3	22.6	24.5	26.2	26.7	28.1	29.5	30.9	32.2
Cash from operations after tax				24.9	55.5	49.2	45.1	42.7	41.5	41.1	41.3	41.9	42.9	42.6	44.0	45.5	47.2	49.0
Cash flow	-3.7	-74.4	-148.8	3.8	55.5	49.2	45.1	42.7	41.5	41.1	41.3	41.9	42.9	42.6	44.0	45.5	47.2	49.0
Present worth	-3.7	-65.3	-114.5	2.6	32.9	25.5	20.6	17.1	14.5	12.6	11.1	9.9	8.9	7.8	7.0	6.4	5.8	5.3
NPV	4.5																	

Based on the information presented in Table 7.5, 14% was chosen as the appropriate discount rate. The minimum hurdle rate for a Canadian merchant generation plant is 14%. Note that the NPV (14) is $4.5 million, meaning that the project has a positive present value of $4.5 million even when discounted at 14%.

Price and cost data build in an inflation factor; it also builds in a real growth factor if one is warranted. In this case, wages have a real growth of 2% over inflation, and natural gas and electricity have a real growth of 1% over inflation. For a commodity such as natural gas, it can be argued that over a given period such as the next 15 years, it will have a real increase in value, but recognize that for most commodities, there is either no real growth in price or even a negative real growth in price. For example, over the last 200 years, the real costs of steel and wheat have dropped.

In this case, the cost of maintenance has a real increase over inflation of 0.5%. This is a means of estimating the impact of an aging plant requiring more maintenance. Maintenance costs in reality are lumpy, meaning they are high in one year if a major problem is fixed and low in others. It is usual to just capture this impact by a steady cost forecast.

Table 7.6 illustrates that the early years of any project have far more weight in a DCF analysis than later years. The operation in year 2 (n = 4) has a present worth of $32 million, while year 15 (n = 17) has a present worth of $5 million. This is because of the compound discounting of future years' income, so a dollar earned 15 years from today has a low value compared to a dollar in your hand today, especially at a high discount rate of 14%. Advancing the start-up of the unit by three months will have a greater impact on NPV than extending the life of the plant by one year.

The tax treatment in Table 7.6 is simplified in several ways. All capital is treated as a single CCA class with a 30% declining balance (available for some high-efficiency power projects). In reality, life is not normally so simple, and you might have more than one CCA class (for example, buildings versus equipment) with different schedules for claiming. Normally, managers develop a spreadsheet to track this. Tax calculations involve a pooling of CCA and are normally done by a specialist in the firm (or a consulting accounting firm) and provided to the DCF analysis.

Negative tax in years 1 and 2 means that there is a negative entry for tax that can offset taxes payable from another part of the company. If this project were purely stand alone, then taxes could not be negative, since federal and provincial governments do not return money to companies that show losses. The effect of this is that companies with fully taxable income have more favorable economics on projects, especially those with a slow ramp-up of income in the early years of the project, because the CCA claimed reduces taxes otherwise payable from other operations of the company. For a start-up company for whom this project is the only business venture, the CCA available is not all claimable against income in the early years because there is no other income.

Note that the capital spending before start-up does not lead to a CCA claim before start-up because until an asset is available for use, the CCA cannot be claimed. Also, note the half-year rule (half CCA in first year).

7.3.3   Internal Rate of Return (IRR)

The internal rate of return is the discount rate that causes the present value of the cash flow from a project to equal zero, i.e., it is the discount or interest rate that exactly matches the present value of expenditures (cash outflows) to returns (cash inflows). In effect, the IRR can be thought of as the earning power of the project. IRR can be calculated on a total investment basis (what is the total earning power of the investment in a project, independent of whether the financing is debt or equity?) or it can be calculated on an equity basis (what is the total earning power of the equity portion of the investment in a project after the cost of debt has been serviced?). Return on investment (ROI) is the name sometimes given to the former, and return on equity is the name sometimes given to the latter, although in practice, use of these terms is imprecise.

Table 7.7 uses the same case as Table 7.6, but now instead of calculating the NPV at a given discount rate, the procedure is revised to calculate the interest divided by the discount rate at which the NPV is zero. This is done by getting the goal seek or solver routine to set the NPV to zero based on varying the discount rate. (This is the reason that it is important to have the interest rate be a single cell in the calculation of present value and NPV.) For this case, the IRR is 14.4%; investing in this project gives the same financial benefit as investing on the same schedule in a financial instrument, such as a bond, with an interest rate of 14.4%. Any project that starts with a negative cash flow and has a single sign change to a positive cash flow (which is true for most engineering projects) will have only one unique value of i that gives a zero NPV. It is possible to have multiple values of interest rate for which the NPV of cash flow is zero if there is more than one sign change in the cash flow forecast, but this is a rare occurrence and can be ignored for most projects.

Table 7.7: Cash Flow ($M) and Calculation of IRR for a Canadian Taxable Company Merchant Power Plant Project Located in Canada

Basis ($M)

Total installed cost	248		Operating life	15 years
Cost Profile			**Availability**	
Year 0	1.50%		Year 1	40%
Year 1	30%		Year 2–10	97%
Year 2	60%		Year 11–15	94%
Year 3	8.50%			

Discount rate	14.4%	
Inflation	3%	
Capacity (MW)	200	
CCA declining balance	30%	
Effective tax rate	40%	

Real Growth	
Wage	2%
Gas price	1%
Power price	1%
Maintenance	0.50%

Year (n)	0	1	2	3	4	5	6	7	8	9	10	11	12	13	14	15	16	17
Capital cost	-3.7	-74.4	-148.8	-21.1														
Power (GWh)				700.8	1,699.4	1,699.4	1,699.4	1,699.4	1,699.4	1,699.4	1,699.4	1,699.4	1,699.4	1,646.9	1,646.9	1,646.9	1,646.9	1,646.9
Price ($/Mwh)				46.0	47.8	49.8	51.7	53.8	56.0	58.2	60.5	63.0	65.5	68.1	70.8	73.6	76.6	79.7
Revenue				32.2	81.3	84.6	87.9	91.5	95.1	98.9	102.9	107.0	111.3	112.1	116.6	121.3	126.1	131.2
Cash Operating Costs																		
Fuel				9.9	25.0	26.0	27.0	28.1	29.2	30.4	31.6	32.9	34.2	34.4	35.8	37.2	38.7	40.3
Wages				1.3	1.4	1.4	1.5	1.6	1.7	1.7	1.8	1.9	2.0	2.1	2.2	2.3	2.5	2.6
Maintenance				4.4	4.6	4.7	4.9	5.0	5.2	5.4	5.6	5.8	6.0	6.2	6.4	6.6	6.9	7.1
Cash from operations				16.6	50.4	52.4	54.5	56.7	59.0	61.4	63.9	66.4	69.1	69.4	72.2	75.1	78.1	81.2
UCC before CCA claim				248.0	210.8	147.6	103.3	72.3	50.6	35.4	24.8	17.4	12.2	8.5	6.0	4.2	2.9	2.0
CCA				37.2	63.2	44.3	31.0	21.7	15.2	10.6	7.4	5.2	3.6	2.6	1.8	1.3	0.9	0.6
Net revenue before tax				-20.6	-12.8	8.2	23.6	35.0	43.8	50.8	56.4	61.2	65.4	66.8	70.4	73.8	77.2	80.6
Tax				-8.2	-5.1	3.3	9.4	14.0	17.5	20.3	22.6	24.5	26.2	26.7	28.1	29.5	30.9	32.2
Cash from operations after tax				24.9	55.5	49.2	45.1	42.7	41.5	41.1	41.3	41.9	42.9	42.6	44.0	45.5	47.2	49.0
Cash flow	-3.7	-74.4	-148.8	3.8	55.5	49.2	45.1	42.7	41.5	41.1	41.3	41.9	42.9	42.6	44.0	45.5	47.2	49.0
Present worth	-3.7	-65.0	-113.7	2.5	32.4	25.1	20.1	16.6	14.1	12.2	10.7	9.5	8.5	7.4	6.7	6.0	5.5	5.0
NPV	0.0																	

Sample Problem 7.3.1 Calculating the IRR and NPV of an Investment

A pipeline company has an initial screening process for projects to ask if the pre-tax return on investment is greater than 15%. If it passes this screening, a team is formed to do a more detailed analysis including the impact on the tax position of the entire company. As a second initial screen, the company also evaluates the pre-tax net present value at 12%. You are asked to perform the preliminary screening analysis on a new project that would require a capital outlay of $400 million in year 1 and $300 million in year 2. The pipeline is expected to be fully operational from year 3 and to operate for 20 years based on reserves estimates. The incremental revenues are expected to be $130 million. Increased expenses for things like labor and general overhead costs are estimated at $5.5 million, and replacement capital (mainly materials for maintenance) is forecast at $2 million per year. Find the pre-tax IRR and NPV of the project at 12%.

Solution:

This is a straightforward NPV and IRR analysis, as illustrated in the following table. In this analysis, negative numbers indicate cash flowing out of the company. The project passes the initial screen, since the IRR is just higher than 15%.

| | | | | | IRR (%) | 15.15 | |
Year	Investment ($000)	Incremental Revenue ($000)	Additional Expense ($000)	Replacement Capital ($000)	Incremental Cash Flow Before Tax ($000)	PV at 12% ($000)	PV at IRR ($000)
1	−400,000	0	0	0	−400,000	−357,143	−347,383
2	−300,000	0	0	0	−300,000	−239,158	−226,266
3	0	130,000	−5,500	−2,000	122,500	87,193	80,238
4	0	130,000	−5,500	−2,000	122,500	77,851	69,684
5	0	130,000	−5,500	−2,000	122,500	69,510	60,517
6	0	130,000	−5,500	−2,000	122,500	62,062	52,557
7	0	130,000	−5,500	−2,000	122,500	55,413	45,643
8	0	130,000	−5,500	−2,000	122,500	49,476	39,639
9	0	130,000	−5,500	−2,000	122,500	44,175	34,425
10	0	130,000	−5,500	−2,000	122,500	39,442	29,897
11	0	130,000	−5,500	−2,000	122,500	35,216	25,964
12	0	130,000	−5,500	−2,000	122,500	31,443	22,549
13	0	130,000	−5,500	−2,000	122,500	28,074	19,582
14	0	130,000	−5,500	−2,000	122,500	25,066	17,007
15	0	130,000	−5,500	−2,000	122,500	22,380	14,769
16	0	130,000	−5,500	−2,000	122,500	19,982	12,827
17	0	130,000	−5,500	−2,000	122,500	17,841	11,139
18	0	130,000	−5,500	−2,000	122,500	15,930	9,674
19	0	130,000	−5,500	−2,000	122,500	14,223	8,402
20	0	130,000	−5,500	−2,000	122,500	12,699	7,296
21	0	130,000	−5,500	−2,000	122,500	11,339	6,337
22	0	130,000	−5,500	−2,000	122,500	10,124	5,503
					NPV	133,137	0

Sample Problem 7.3.2 Can a Company's Tax Position Affect IRR?

Two Canadian companies, Oldco and Newco, are evaluating an identical project with a cost of $20 million. The project reaches an annual pre-tax cash flow net of all expenses of $3.4 million in year 3, and has 50% of that cash flow in year 1 and 75% in year 2. Project life is 20 years. All the assets are depreciable for tax purposes at a 30% declining balance. Oldco is a large company, has substantial income from other operations, and has an annual tax bill of more than $6 million per year. Newco is a start-up, and the project is its only business venture. The effective tax rate for both companies is 32%. Calculate IRR on the project for both companies.

Solution:

The after-tax cash flow of the two companies must be calculated. Oldco has a substantial tax payment from its other income. If incremental depreciation for tax purposes (CCA) is greater than taxable cash flow, the calculated negative taxes payable will reduce taxes paid elsewhere in Oldco. Newco is not taxable, and if incremental depreciation for tax purposes (CCA) is greater than taxable cash flow, the negative taxes payable will be accumulated as a tax loss that is carried forward to offset future taxable income.

Note that the half-year rule is applied in year 1 so that only half of the CCA calculated at 30% of UCC is claimed. The terminal UCC in year 20 is small and can be ignored for purposes of calculating IRR in this case, since its impact on the two companies' cash flow forecasts is identical. The following tables show Oldco's and Newco's after-tax cash flow calculations:

Oldco:

Year	Pre-tax Cash Flow	CCA	Remaining UCC	Taxable Income	Tax Payable	After-Tax Cash Flow
0	−20,000		20,000			−20,000
1	1,700	3,000	17,000	−1,300	−416	2,116
2	2,550	5,100	11,900	−2,550	−816	3,366
3	3,400	3,570	8,330	−170	−54	3,454
4	3,400	2,499	5,831	901	288	3,112
5	3,400	1,749	4,082	1,651	528	2,872
6	3,400	1,225	2,857	2,175	696	2,704
7	3,400	857	2,000	2,543	814	2,586
8	3,400	600	1,400	2,800	896	2,504
9	3,400	420	980	2,980	954	2,446
10	3,400	294	686	3,106	994	2,406
11	3,400	206	480	3,194	1,022	2,378
12	3,400	144	336	3,256	1,042	2,358
13	3,400	101	235	3,299	1,056	2,344
14	3,400	71	165	3,329	1,065	2,335
15	3,400	49	115	3,351	1,072	2,328
16	3,400	35	81	3,365	1,077	2,323
17	3,400	24	56	3,376	1,080	2,320
18	3,400	17	40	3,383	1,083	2,317
19	3,400	12	28	3,388	1,084	2,316
20	3,400	8	19	3,392	1,085	2,315
					IRR	12.1%

Newco:

Year	Pre-Tax Cash Flow	CCA	Remaining UCC	Taxable Income	Cumulative Tax Carry-forward	Tax Payable	After-Tax Cash Flow
0	−20,000		20,000				−20,000
1	1,700	3,000	17,000	−1,300	−1,300	0	1,700
2	2,550	5,100	11,900	−2,550	−3,850	0	2,550
3	3,400	3,570	8,330	−170	−4,020	0	3,400
4	3,400	2,499	5,831	901	−3,119	0	3,400
5	3,400	1,749	4,082	1,651	−1,468	0	3,400
6	3,400	1,225	2,857	2,175	707	226	3,174
7	3,400	857	2,000	2,543		814	2,586
8	3,400	600	1,400	2,800		896	2,504
9	3,400	420	980	2,980		954	2,446
10	3,400	294	686	3,106		994	2,406
11	3,400	206	480	3,194		1,022	2,378
12	3,400	144	336	3,256		1,042	2,358
13	3,400	101	235	3,299		1,056	2,344
14	3,400	71	165	3,329		1,065	2,335
15	3,400	49	115	3,351		1,072	2,328
16	3,400	35	81	3,365		1,077	2,323
17	3,400	24	56	3,376		1,080	2,320
18	3,400	17	40	3,383		1,083	2,317
19	3,400	12	28	3,388		1,084	2,316
20	3,400	8	19	3,392		1,085	2,315

IRR   11.8%

Note that Newco does not pay tax until year 6, when the amount of cumulative tax it is carrying forward goes from negative to positive. In year 6, it pays tax on $707,000 of taxable income, which is the net positive amount from the cumulative position. For years 7 and beyond, Newco pays tax on its taxable income.

Oldco is able to shift taxes that it would otherwise pay sooner from its existing operations by using the negative taxes payable from the project, while Newco must wait to claim these. Both companies pay the same amount of incremental tax over the life of the project ($14.55 million), so the only difference between the two cash flow streams is the timing of payment of the taxes. This leads to a difference in IRR of 0.3%. If both companies had a MARR of 12%, Oldco would proceed, and Newco would decline the investment. Hence, a company's tax position affects IRR and can in turn affect investment decisions.

7.3.3.1 IRR for Incremental Investment

Opportunities to spend more incremental dollars in a project occur often and can be analyzed on an incremental basis. IRR is the most common form of analyzing such opportunities, although NPV analysis can also be used. For example, consider two oil refinery designs for processing heavy crude oil. One design is based on coking, or removing carbon by thermal cracking at low pressure, and the other is based on hydrocracking, or adding hydrogen at very high pressure in the presence of a catalyst. Hydrocracking is the more expensive process.

One of the best ways to analyze whether the extra investment in hydrocracking is worth it is to develop a full forecast of after-tax cash flow for each of the two cases and then subtract the coking cash flow from the hydrocracker cash flow. This gives the incremental cash flow between the two projects. This cash flow will have a unique NPV at any given discount rate and will also have an IRR, i.e., there will be a discount rate at which the NPV is zero. In effect, this is the return on the extra investment in the hydrocracking case versus the coking case.

Table 7.8 illustrates this calculation.

Table 7.8: Incremental IRR for a Refinery Based on Hydrocracking versus Coking ($ million)

	Case 1: Coking		Case 2: Hydrocracking			
Year	Cash Flow	PV	Cash Flow	PV	Incremental Cash Flow	PV
1	−322	−286	−344	−303	−22.0	−17.5
2	−2,324	−1,837	−2,499	−1,945	−175.0	−110.3
3	−2,122	−1,492	−2,188	−1,502	−66.0	−33.0
4	−565	−353	−570	−345	−5.0	−2.0
5	201	112	250	134	49.0	15.4
6	512	253	614	289	102.0	25.5
7	822	361	939	390	117.0	23.2
8	838	328	958	351	119.3	18.8
9	855	297	977	316	121.7	15.2
10	872	269	996	285	124.2	12.3
11	890	244	1,016	256	126.6	10.0
12	908	222	1,037	230	129.2	8.1
13	926	201	1,057	207	131.8	6.6
14	944	182	1,079	187	134.4	5.3
15	963	165	1,100	168	137.1	4.3
16	982	150	1,122	151	139.8	3.5
17	1,002	136	1,145	136	142.6	2.8
18	1,022	123	1,168	122	145.5	2.3
19	1,042	112	1,191	110	148.4	1.8
20	1,063	101	1,215	99	151.4	1.5
21	1,085	92	1,239	89	154.4	1.2
22	1,106	83	1,264	80	157.5	1.0
23	1,128	76	1,289	72	160.6	0.8

7.5 yrs   6.8 yrs

24	1,151	69	1,315	65	163.8	0.6
25	1,174	62	1,341	58	167.1	0.5
26	1,197	56	1,368	53	170.4	0.4
27	1,221	51	1,395	47	173.9	0.3
28	1,246	46	1,423	43	177.3	0.3
29	1,271	42	1,452	38	180.9	0.2
30	1,296	38	1,481	34	184.5	0.2
31	1,322	35	1,510	31	188.2	0.1
32	1,349	31	1,541	28	192.0	0.1
33	1,376	29	1,571	25	195.8	0.1
	NPV	0	NPV	0	NPV	0
	At IRR (%)	12.5	At IRR (%)	13.4	At IRR (%)	26.0

The overall rate of return on the coking case is 12.5%, and the overall rate of return on the hydrocracking case is 13.4%. Since 13.4% is higher than 12.5%, the extra investment in hydrocracking improves the overall economics of the project, and in fact, the return on just the extra (incremental) investment between the two cases is 26.0%. In other words, the return on the extra capital is more than twice the return on the overall coking project.

A company looking at Table 7.8 would not automatically choose the hydrocracking case over the coking case because they would have to consider these two factors: the relative technology risk between the two cases and the availability of capital. First, coking is a well-proven technology, while hydrocracking of bitumen at high conversions is not demonstrated. Low-conversion hydrocracking is demonstrated, and a company might convince itself that the incremental risk of moving from low conversion to high conversion is acceptable, but it would have to be carefully considered. Second, if the company simply could not raise the extra capital at a price it found acceptable, it might choose to be in the oil sands business but reject the more attractive return on hydrocracking because it only had the capital for the coking project. In general, risk and capital availability have to be taken into account in all investment analysis.

As with earlier cash flows, a large sum of money a long distance in the future has a very low present value. Consider, for example, the coking case. Almost $1.4 billion of revenue in year 33 has a present value of $32 million because of compound discounting. Extending the project life has little impact on return because the impact of compound discounting is so high. For the coking case, an extra 10 years of project life changes the IRR by 0.06%, which is not significant enough to change an investment decision from "no go" to "go," or vice versa.

The cash flow from the coking and hydrocracking cases increases by 2% per year in years 8 and beyond. This is typical of a DCF analysis: how can an oil price be accurately picked so far into the future? Normally, you can make some global assumption like a steady 2% increase in the commodity price and test the impact of this assumption by sensitivity analysis.

This kind of incremental modeling is how a great number of individual project decisions are made. For instance, the amount of tankage a refinery requires would be decided based on an analysis of the incremental cash flow as tankage increases.

Imagine that one has a large pool of capital and a minimum hurdle rate, or MARR, for that capital so that any project over a given minimum will be chosen. Five different projects have been developed with different cash flows. You use the least expensive capital case that has an acceptable return (over the hurdle rate) as a base case and look at other projects in comparison to that project. Compare the second lowest cost case to the base case. If the second lowest cost case has a return on incremental investment above MARR, it becomes the new "base case." Compare the third lowest capital cost case to the base case. Proceed in this stepwise fashion until all cases are tested incrementally.

Companies that have a surplus of cash and a desire for investment opportunities would take this approach of investing in any incremental capital that gives an incremental return over the MARR. Companies that have a shortage of funds for capital projects might well pass up a large incremental investment that lowers the return of the base case. In practice, not all companies define a MARR, and a great deal of qualitative executive judgment goes into decisions on large capital investments. The incremental approach is more often used for relatively small investment decisions such as tankage or a process selection within a refinery. There are many such decisions in designing a plant, and the senior executive is not involved in every decision.

Sample Problem 7.3.3 Using Incremental Return Rate to Choose Between Mutually Exclusive Alternatives

Acme Inc. is planning to purchase new equipment to modernize its manufacturing facility. It has asked for quotes from three different equipment manufacturers. Acme has a surplus of capital, is looking for places to invest its cash, and has a minimum acceptable rate of return of 12.5%. After completing a detailed analysis of its product, Acme Inc. prepared the following after-tax cash flow profile of all three manufacturers. What option should Acme choose? Might the choice be different if Acme was short of capital but felt it had, for competitive reasons, to invest in one of the three options?

Cash Flow ($000)

Year	Option 1	Option 2	Option 3
1	−2,763	−2,800	−3,060
2	−500	−850	−900
3	493	523	616
4	518	549	647
5	544	577	679
6	571	605	713
7	599	636	749
8	629	667	786
9	661	701	825
10	694	736	867
11	728	773	910
12	765	811	956
13	803	852	1,003
14	843	895	1,054
15	885	939	1,106
16	930	986	1,162
17	976	1,036	1,220
18	1,025	1,087	1,281
19	1,076	1,142	1,345
20	1,130	1,199	1,412

Solution:

The best way to analyze this problem is to determine the rate of return for all three options and then calculate the incremental cash flow to find out the incremental IRR. The correct approach for incremental IRR is to treat the lowest capital cost case (Option 1) as the base case, and compare the second most capital intense project (Option 2) to Option 1 by calculating its incremental IRR. Acme has a surplus of capital and is looking for places to invest its cash. If the incremental rate of return is above 12.5%, then Option 2 would become the new base case even if the overall return of Option 2 is less than Option 1. If the incremental rate of return is less than 12.5%, then Option 2 is discarded as an option. Once Option 1 or 2 is chosen, the comparison is repeated for Option 3.

Here is the comparison of options 1 and 2:

	Option 1		Option 2		Incremental	
Year	Cash Flow	PV	Cash Flow	PV	Cash Flow	PV
1	−2,763	−2,379	−2,800	−2,424	−37	−34
2	−500	−371	−850	−637	−350	−299
3	493	315	523	339	30	24
4	518	285	549	309	32	23
5	544	257	577	281	33	22
6	571	233	605	255	35	22
7	599	211	636	232	36	21
8	629	190	667	211	38	20
9	661	172	701	192	40	20
10	694	156	736	174	42	19
11	728	141	773	158	44	19
12	765	127	811	144	47	18
13	803	115	852	131	49	17
14	843	104	895	119	51	17
15	885	94	939	108	54	16
16	930	85	986	98	57	16
17	976	77	1,036	89	59	15
18	1,025	70	1,087	81	62	15
19	1,076	63	1,142	74	65	15
20	1,130	57	1,199	67	69	14
NPV	0		0		0	
IRR (%)	16.12		15.50		8.24	

The incremental internal rate of return is 8.24%, which is less than the hurdle rate of 12.5%, so Option 2 is rejected relative to Option 1. Think of the extra capital that Option 2 costs compared to 1 as earning 8.24%.

Now, compare Option 3 to Option 1:

	Option 1		Option 3		Incremental	
Year	Cash Flow	PV	Cash Flow	PV	Cash Flow	PV
1	−2,763	−2,379	−3,060	−2,621	−297	−248
2	−500	−371	−900	−661	−400	−279
3	493	315	616	387	123	72
4	518	285	647	348	129	63
5	544	257	679	313	136	55
6	571	233	713	282	142	48
7	599	211	749	254	150	42
8	629	190	786	228	157	37
9	661	172	825	205	165	33
10	694	156	867	185	173	29
11	728	141	910	166	182	25
12	765	127	956	149	191	22
13	803	115	1,003	134	200	19
14	843	104	1,054	121	210	17
15	885	94	1,106	109	221	15
16	930	85	1,162	98	232	13
17	976	77	1,220	88	244	11
18	1,025	70	1,281	79	256	10
19	1,076	63	1,345	71	268	9
20	1,130	57	1,412	64	282	8
NPV	0		0		0	
IRR (%)	16.12		16.73		19.75	

The incremental return on the extra capital cost of Option 3 over Option 1 has a return of 19.75%, well over the hurdle rate of 12.5%. When the return is higher, as it is for Option 3, the return on the incremental capital will be higher than 16.12%, so comparing Option 3 to Option 1 in this case is not required to select that option if Acme has a surplus of capital that it wants to invest. However, if Acme Inc. was tight on capital, it would be a useful exercise to help make a thoughtful decision. For example, if Acme was very limited in its ability to raise capital, it might choose to do Option 1, even though Option 3 had a more attractive return, because the cost to Acme of the extra capital it required was not justified by a 19.75% return.

Investment decisions involve many judgments, and incremental analysis helps managers to make those judgments.

7.3.3.2 When IRR Is Not Used in Investment Decisions

IRR is the most common criteria by which investment decisions are made, but it is not universally applied. There are at least five circumstances in which IRR is not the prime factor in screening investments:

- When there is no income from the investment (e.g., a mandated environmental project), NPV is used to pick the least expensive alternative.
- When an investment is for base business preservation (e.g., replacing a valve during a start-up or replacing a vehicle that is essential to continuing a large business, NPV is used to pick the least expensive alternative.
- When two projects have a nearly identical return, use payback to identify the project that more quickly returns the investment.
- When a project has an extremely uncertain future and typically a very short life (e.g., a nightclub or software), use payback, since cash flow forecasts long into the future are too uncertain to be relied upon. Short paybacks mean low risk of loss of capital.
- When projects are of a strategic nature or have a vastly different scale, strategic factors are used to screen alternatives in addition to return.

Sample Problem 7.3.4 Mandated Investment

A mining company is ordered to enhance the quality of a tailings pond in order to reduce the potential for migration of heavy metal cations into groundwater. Engineers have developed two alternative solutions, both acceptable to the government regulating agency.

Solution 1 involves drilling a well every 30 meters around the perimeter of the tailings pond and pumping groundwater from the wells through a metals precipitation process. Capital cost is $32 million dollars, and annual operating costs for power and chemicals are $5.7 million per year.

Solution 2 involves emptying the tailings pond into temporary storage, installing an impervious liner and three observation wells for sampling purposes only, and refilling the pond. Capital cost is $64 million dollars, and annual operating cost is $170,000 per year.

Construction time for the two projects is one year, the expected remaining life of the mine is 17 years thereafter, and reclamation costs are identical for the two projects. The company judges that the risk for the two projects is identical, and its practice is to apply a discount factor equal to its weighted average cost of capital of 9.64%.

Which alternative do you recommend?

Solution

Since there is no incremental revenue, an IRR calculation is meaningless, so the right choice is the project with the least negative NPV. The following table shows that the higher capital alternative is the better choice.

($ millions)		WACC (%)	9.60		
Capital	32		Capital		64
Operational cost	5.7		Operational cost		0.17

Year	Cash Flow	Present Value	Year	Cash Flow	Present Value
0	(32)	(32.00)	0	(64)	(64.00)
1	(5.7)	(5.20)	1	(0.17)	(0.16)
2	(5.7)	(4.75)	2	(0.17)	(0.14)
3	(5.7)	(4.33)	3	(0.17)	(0.13)
4	(5.7)	(3.95)	4	(0.17)	(0.12)
5	(5.7)	(3.60)	5	(0.17)	(0.11)
6	(5.7)	(3.29)	6	(0.17)	(0.10)
7	(5.7)	(3.00)	7	(0.17)	(0.09)
8	(5.7)	(2.74)	8	(0.17)	(0.08)
9	(5.7)	(2.50)	9	(0.17)	(0.07)
10	(5.7)	(2.28)	10	(0.17)	(0.07)
11	(5.7)	(2.08)	11	(0.17)	(0.06)
12	(5.7)	(1.90)	12	(0.17)	(0.06)
13	(5.7)	(1.73)	13	(0.17)	(0.05)
14	(5.7)	(1.58)	14	(0.17)	(0.05)
15	(5.7)	(1.44)	15	(0.17)	(0.04)
16	(5.7)	(1.31)	16	(0.17)	(0.04)
17	(5.7)	(1.20)	17	(0.17)	(0.04)
	NPV	(78.9)		NPV	(65.4)

A case can be made for using either WACC or MARR as the discounting basis. WACC would be appropriate when the risk between the two projects is equal and considered to be low. Low risk in this case comes from the certification of the governmental agency that either alternative is acceptable to mitigate the risk. However, regulations can change and projects can fail. If the risk were considered to be high, then MARR would be a reasonable discount rate, since capital cannot be recovered once it is spent on a project like this it. Clearly, a great deal of judgment goes in to picking an appropriate discount rate.

7.3.4 Payback Period

Payback period is the length of time that it takes to get back one's investment. It is normally measured from the start-up of the project (first production), not when construction starts. Prior to 1930, this was often the only way of judging investments: the shorter the payback, the better the investment. DCF analysis replaced payback as a far more sophisticated analysis of the earning power of an investment.

Payback calculations can be done in two forms: payback based on cash flow dollars and discounted payback based on discounted dollars. Projects will have a longer discounted payback period than a payback period; the idea of discounted payback period is that it includes the impact of a prescribed time value of money, or if a discount rate based on interest on borrowed money is used, then it includes the impact of the interest cost of the money used in the project. Discounted payback mixes two concepts, recovery of actual investment and discounting of future dollars, and in practice, discounted payback is very rarely used.

In the coking case shown in Table 7.8, payback occurs at about 7.5 years after start-up of the project (start-up is assumed to occur late in year 4). This is a relatively long payback period and reflects the capital intensity of oil refining. Payback for the hydrocracking case is about 6.8 years after start-up.

The confidence to accept a long payback period depends on the item. Consider two investments, one in a machine that makes Hula-Hoops and one in an auto parts manufacturing plant. The market demand for auto parts seven years in the future is far more certain than the demand for Hula-Hoops. Any novelty item, and more broadly any item that can go out of fashion, would warrant a shorter payback period. Nightclubs, for instance, tend to be popular for a period of time, but this can shift unexpectedly. A prudent investor would want a much shorter payback period for renovations to a nightclub than for an auto parts manufacturing plant project.

Payback period is used in different ways. When looking at two different projects that have comparable return but a different profile, payback will highlight the impact of the profile. For instance, consider Table 7.9. It shows two projects with a two-year construction period and a 20-year life that have an identical IRR. Although the return is identical, the cash flow profile is not.

Table 7.9: The Effect of Cash Flow Profile on Payback for Two Projects with Identical IRR

Year	Case 1: Early cash flow		Case 2: Late cash flow	
	Cash Flow	PV	Cash Flow	PV
1	−212	−187.2	−212	−187.2
2	−461	−359.4	−461	−359.4
3	90	62.0	12	8.3
4	92	55.8	15	9.1
5	94	50.3	20	10.7
6	96	45.3	30	14.2
7	97	40.8	50	20.9
8	99	36.7	70	25.9
9	101	33.1	100	32.6
10	103	29.8	120	34.6
11	105	26.8	150	38.2
12	108	24.2	228	51.2
13	110	21.8	232	46.1
14	112	19.6	237	41.5
15	114	17.6	242	37.4
16	116	15.9	247	33.7
17	119	14.3	252	30.3

	Case 1: Early cash flow		Case 2: Late cash flow	
Year	Cash Flow	PV	Cash Flow	PV
18	121	12.9	257	27.3
19	124	11.6	262	24.6
20	126	10.5	267	22.2
21	129	9.4	272	20.0
22	131	8.5	278	18.0
	NPV	0.0	NPV	0.0
	At IRR (%)	13.3	At IRR (%)	13.3
	Payback	7	Payback	9.5

The late cash flow project has a longer payback period of 9.5 years (and a higher ultimate cash flow) than the early cash flow project. The payback period illustrates this clearly. If the early and late projects were equally strategic and acceptable, then the early project would be the preferred choice because the investment comes back sooner. If the market shifts or an environmental regulation eliminates the product, at least the initial money has been recovered. Notice the convention here that unless otherwise specified, payback is calculated from start-up of the project, not from first construction.

For some projects, doing a cash flow forecast far out into the future involves so much uncertainty that the numbers cannot be trusted. The manager must rely exclusively on payback to become comfortable with the investment. The nightclub investment is an example of this: who would trust any forecast of revenue from a nightclub 10 years into the future? Similarly, investments in software are frequently based solely on payback period.

Sample Problem 7.3.5 When Payback Influences an Investment Decision

Ensign Corp. is considering two investment opportunities in merchant power plants, each with an estimated life of 20 years. Both projects require the same capital outlay in the first two years, but the predicted cash inflows are different because future power price forecasts for the two markets differ. Which project would you recommend, assuming Ensign will only invest in one?

Cash Flow ($000)

Year	Project 1	Project 2
−1	−1,660	−1,660
0	−586	−586
1	320	190
2	324	200
3	331	210
4	338	230
5	345	250
6	352	270
7	359	310
8	366	350
9	370	370
10	374	520
11	378	560
12	382	604
13	386	545
14	390	605
15	394	665
16	398	725
17	402	785
18	406	845
19	410	905
20	414	965

Solution:

Answering this question requires that not only the IRR be calculated but that the payback period be checked as well. The easiest way to calculate payback is to calculate the cumulative cash flow of the project and see in what year it becomes positive.

The internal rate of return for these two projects is almost the same: the difference of 13.1% to 13.2% is within the accuracy of such long-term forecasts. However, there is a significant difference in the profile of cash flow for the two projects, with project 2 having a higher cash flow further in the future. As a result, the payback period is significantly longer for project 2. Since the risk of error in any forecast increases with the time into the future, project 1 has less risk of being a bad investment than project 2, and since the two values for IRR are so close, it would be the preferred investment.

Note that payback can be cited as years after the start of project construction or years after start-up. In this case, it is cited as years after start-up.

	Project 1			Project 2		
Year	Cash Flow ($000)	PV	Cumulative Cash Flow	Cash Flow ($000)	PV	Cumulative Cash Flow
−1	−1,660	−1,877.6	−1,660	−1,660	−1,878.3	−1,660
0	−586	−586.0	−2,246	−586	−586.0	−2,246
1	320	282.9	−1,926	190	167.9	−2,056
2	324	253.3	−1,602	200	156.2	−1,856
3	331	228.8	−1,271	210	145.0	−1,646
4	338	206.5	−933	230	140.3	−1,416
5	345	186.4	−588	250	134.8	−1,166
6	352	168.1	−236	270	128.7	−896
7	359	151.6	123	310	130.5	−586
8	366	136.6	489	350	130.3	−236
9	370	122.1	859	370	121.7	134
10	374	109.1	1,233	520	151.2	654
11	378	97.5	1,611	560	143.9	1,214
12	382	87.1	1,993	604	137.1	1,818
13	386	77.8	2,379	545	109.4	2,363
14	390	69.5	2,769	605	107.3	2,968
15	394	62.1	3,163	665	104.2	3,633
16	398	55.5	3,561	725	100.4	4,358
17	402	49.5	3,963	785	96.1	5,143
18	406	44.2	4,369	845	91.4	5,988
19	410	39.5	4,779	905	86.5	6,893
20	414	35.3	5,193	965	81.5	7,858
	NPV	0.0		NPV	0.0	
	IRR (%)	13.1		IRR (%)	13.2	
	Payback	7 years		Payback	9 years	

7.4   Practical Issues in Investment Analysis

In industry, an enormous amount of time is spent analyzing and discussing investment opportunities. Investment analysis is at the heart of engineering, since engineers design, build, and operate capital facilities that create wealth. Companies that lose the heart to invest start to wither, as well as those that invest in bad projects. Only companies that renew themselves through prudent investment in good projects survive in the long run.

7.4.1   A Strategic Vision

Ultimately, companies have some strategic vision that shapes their investment decisions. In theory, one could invest in anything that has a projected high rate of return. In practice, companies are very careful and very strategic in diversifying.

In the 1970s, the conglomerate company that was in a wide variety of businesses was briefly popular, but the appeal of this kind of company soon faded. First, the synergy from vastly different businesses was near zero (what help was it to a polypropylene business that your parent company also owned a car rental and leasing business?) Second, it was difficult to find management that could understand widely different businesses. In practice, familiarity with an industry is an enormous asset to a manager, and the manager of a conglomerate could not be familiar with all of the disparate pieces of the company. Finally, the stock market never knew what to make of a conglomerate, and the stock price often was less than the value of the individual parts of the business. For example, two companies in North America tried having a pipeline business (regulated, stable, and dividend oriented) and a chemical business (highly cyclical and capital gains oriented). The stock market valued each of the companies as either a pipeline business, thereby ignoring and not placing value on the chemical business, or vice versa. Each of these companies eventually was broken in two to help shareholders realize the full market value of their investment, i.e., higher aggregate value from holding shares in each of two companies versus shares in one conglomerate.

Practically speaking, a company that makes steel-fabricated components will almost certainly evaluate an investment in equipment directly related to its current line of business and may evaluate an investment in an extension of its business (for example, a plastics fabrication business or equipment). However, they are not likely to look at a completely unrelated business such as a retail garden center or a clothing manufacturing process, no matter how good the IRR appears. Managers in this situation do not trust their knowledge of the industry, both to know future cash flows accurately and to manage the business once acquired. Most investment decisions have an implicit strategic component that does not get reflected in the numbers in a DCF or payback analysis.

In an ideal world, the strategic thinking of senior management is visible, and employees can reflect on and grow from it. Often, however, strategic thinking is less visible (sometimes even to the strategist), and an employee who is developing business opportunities through investment analysis can only learn it implicitly from the reaction of senior management to seemingly suitable investments.

7.4.2 Techniques for Investing

In larger corporations, most investment analysis will have six components:

- IRR
- Sensitivities to IRR, such as the impact on IRR of capital and operating cost changes, price increases, or schedule delays
- NPV at one or more discount rates
- Payback
- Risk factors and how they might be mitigated (for example, forward selling of product, such as electrical power, by long-term contract)
- Fit with the company's strategic plan

For small projects that are well within the capital spending limits of the company (for example, a $2 million project in a company whose annual capital spending is $200 million), a simple IRR is the critical test. If the project has a high rate of return, it is likely to be done, and this is the key criteria for evaluating the project.

For very large projects, some other factors tend to get added to the mix. Some lower IRR projects may be approved if it is anticipated that they are part of the strategic future of the company *and that future synergies will arise from the initial project.* Thus, an oil company in Canada may conclude that if it is to remain in the oil business, it must have an exposure to mineable oil sands. Also, even if such a project shows a low return and a long payback, additional investment opportunities (expansion or use of byproducts) will arise over the years that will enhance the earning power of the base project.

Some projects are investments in revenue preservation. For example, if a plant is ordered to install pollution equipment or be shut down, then the investment is mandated and must be completed to preserve the revenue from the plant, which in most cases will be large. It is not meaningful to calculate an IRR in such a case, since all choices will appear to have a high IRR because they are capturing the value of all past investment in the plant. Instead, in this case, look at NPV and pick the project with the least negative NPV (the least cost when discounted to present value).

Plant start-ups present many cases where IRR calculations are misleading. Just before start-up of a major facility such as a manufacturing plant, refinery, or power plant, engineers and operators will go through punch listing in which a number of deficiencies are noted. For each of these individual deficiencies, the value of the entire production is often cited as the benefit, since the plant will not run unless the deficiency is corrected. Conventional investment analysis is meaningless in such circumstances, since no minor revamp will appear unattractive if the entire plant revenue is tied to it. However, this ultimately is an invalid test, and various other restraints (including an outright ban on revamps just prior to start-up) are placed on last-minute revamps to keep projects in control.

In rare cases, a company may face a mutually exclusive choice between two different investments of radically different scale. For instance, an industrial site may have only enough space left for one of two projects: one is $100 million with an IRR of 22%, and the other is $900 million with an IRR of 18%. If capital is not a constraint and the projects are truly mutually exclusive, then a company might pick the project with the lower return. Imagine that the weighted average cost of capital to the company is 13%. Then, the large project with the lower return will create more NPV than the small project, and the company will be worth more if the larger project with the lower return is completed.

7.4.3   Accuracy of Cash Flow Forecasts and the Need for Judgment

The critical task in investment analysis is not the computation of NPV, IRR, or payback but the assembly of a reasonable and consistent cash flow forecast. For large projects, it is normal to take cash flow forecasts out some 30 years past plant start-up or up to 35 years in total. It is a real mark of optimism to be willing to forecast for such a long time in the future. Consider someone evaluating an energy-related project 35 years ago: electricity was a regulated cost-of-service commodity, oil prices had a long stable history, and natural gas prices in North America were driven by regulation. In the intervening 35 years, the oil price has soared and plunged, natural gas prices have been deregulated and have had both up and down cycles, and electrical power is rapidly becoming deregulated. No thoughtful forecast 35 years ago could have captured these events.

By its very nature, discounting places a lower weight on future events than on near-term events, so to the extent that forecasts of cash flow lose accuracy with increasing time, you can take comfort in the fact that errors more than 15 years after start-up are of much less concern than errors in the first five years after start-up. Even in the near term, cash flow forecasts include a great deal of judgmental information, and they need to be thought of as best estimates. DCF analysis is not a substitute for critical thinking, but rather an aid or stimulus to it. Senior management needs to understand what creates the value in a project and, in particular, the factors that would place that value at risk. Understanding long-term drivers of value is crucial in assessing investment decisions.

For example, consider the generation of electrical power from a mine-mouth surface mining coal plant. For coal, fuel price is virtually fixed at the time of the initial project, since the plant is located next to a coal mine that is developed specifically for the project, using capital equipment (trucks and shovels) that will last the lifetime of the project. The only significant cost variable in the coal price is the cost of labor, and this is minor in the overall cost of coal. A company building such a plant is not going to face a precipitous rise in the cost of fuel. Might the project experience a precipitous drop in the sale price of power? This would only occur if the price of some other fuel dropped. For example, if the price of natural gas drops sharply, then power plants using natural gas as a fuel might cut the price of power to a point where a coal-fired plant was a poor investment. A second risk in today's environmental/political scene is that a carbon tax would be levied on the coal-fired facility because of greenhouse gas emissions issues. These two concerns, the relative price of natural gas to coal and the potential for a politically imposed carbon tax, are at the real heart of the economics of a coal-fired generating unit. This is the kind of issue that the engineer who is proposing the development and the senior management who is reviewing the investment should focus on.

Cash flow forecasts are estimates of the future. Discounted cash flow analysis is capable of very precise manipulation of numbers, and the calculation of returns to any number of decimal places. It is important to remember that the limiting factor on accuracy is not the sophistication of analysis but rather the quality of assumptions that go into the cash flow forecast and, in particular, the interrelationship that is assumed between long-term costs and prices. Intuition and judgment, ultimately exercised by senior management (and a board of directors for major projects), are important elements of investment analysis.

7.5   Risk and the Concept of Mitigation

All ventures have risk, which is why they need a higher return on investment than interest on government bonds. There is always a small chance that any project will be a complete failure. Examples are a refinery in Come By Chance, Newfoundland, which failed due to a design flaw, a dry oil or gas well, and products that are not accepted by the market. Risk in investments leads to three strategic approaches:

- Include a contingency allowance reflecting uncertainty.
- Require a return on investment to offset the risk taken.
- Reduce risk by mitigation, or take steps to reduce the likelihood or impact of potential risk factors.

7.5.1 Contingency

Contingency is simply a design allowance for unexpected costs. It normally shows up in a capital cost forecast, although it may also be used in a forecast of operating costs. Normally, the level of contingency reflects the stage of the estimate. When a project has a rough estimate based on some gross factors, contingency is high, say 30%, but when every piece of major equipment in a capital project has been specified, then contingency might drop to 20%. When a final estimate is completed based on a full work breakdown, then contingency might drop to 10% or less. Contingency can be thought of as a blind allowance for risk in that you simply use experience to estimate an allowance for what you do not know.

Shocks in estimates, or large unexpected increases in cost, are very difficult for an organization to deal with. If a project is expected to cost $125 million, then this expectation gets accepted throughout an organization, from a projects group that will build the project to an operations group that is responsible for its profitable operation to the finance group that must ensure that funds are available (from debt, retained earnings, and new equity) to pay for the project. A sudden rise in a capital cost estimate is a disappointment that shakes confidence in a project and creates the fear of additional shocks in the future. Contingency can be thought of as a psychological "shock absorber" that retains support for a project as unknown costs emerge and are deducted from contingency.

Sometimes, projects are analyzed through a technique called Monte Carlo simulation to try to build a quantified basis for contingency. The theory is that a large team will spend time identifying risk factors at a highly detailed level and building a quantified bottoms-up estimate of the dollars at risk and the probability of deviation for each element of a project. For instance, in an oil sands project, each major piece of equipment, once estimated, will have some potential for a cost overrun or underrun, and the team can place a "guesstimate" on the probability of this. By going through every element of the project, such as equipment, installation labor, required infrastructure (such as civil work to drain the site), a large number of individual probability distributions and associated impact magnitudes can be assembled. The simulation then runs numerous cases in which random numbers are used to develop possible aggregate outcomes. By running a large number of cases, one can get a sense of the probability of the overall project having a cost overrun and tie the contingency level at time of project authorization to this. In practice, however, Monte Carlo simulations consume enormous staff time and hide the underlying subjective judgments (of individual probabilities and magnitudes of deviation) below a sophisticated analysis. It is not unusual for the results of such a simulation to be modified by management judgment because the initial results deviate so highly from past experience. In effect, old rules of thumb on contingency at an overall project level are often imposed onto the Monte Carlo analysis.

Quantification of an appropriate contingency level is an area of ongoing research; company-specific models based on judgments of project complexity have been tested. Any engineer going into major capital project work can expect to see ongoing evolution in analysis of contingency.

7.5.2 Risk and Expected Return

The greater the risk of failure, the greater the return on investment (IRR) expected from a project, as discussed in Section 7.1.4. Consider a company that sells a variety of materials for concrete-related products that is thinking about investing $10 million to make a fine silica dust that has an application in a particular kind of cement that is exposed to high temperatures. The existing sales force can add the product to their portfolio, and the customers for the new product already buy other products from the company. Clearly, the risk of this project is less than another project that involves a completely new untested product in a new line of business. Whether the guidelines are explicit or not, almost all companies will have a higher hurdle rate of return for a risky project and a lower return for an extension to a base business. A higher return rate can be thought of as a method of mitigating the impact of higher risk: if I invest in ten risky projects and three fail, the higher return I receive on the remaining seven projects compensates for the failure. This kind of logic guides venture capital firms that specialize in financing start-ups and early growth in companies.

7.5.3 Identifying and Mitigating Specific Risk Elements

Qualitative assessment of specific risk elements and analysis of specific steps to mitigate risk help a project sponsor to think through elements of risk and help a company identify means of reducing risk. One key concept is that risk is the product of probability and consequence. Risk is intuitively (and sometimes quantitatively) identified by both its likelihood and the magnitude of its consequence. While in theory, the numerical product of consequence and probability could be used to quantify risk, this is not the normal means of evaluation, partly because estimates of probability are almost always based on a rough judgment and vary from person to person. Risk is most often assessed by intuitive processes.

One major supplier of technology and engineering services to international customers uses a checklist as part of its project evaluation process. For each of the following categories, the person proposing the project assesses whether the risk category applies, whether it is high, medium, or low, and what mitigative measures have been taken or are proposed to reduce the risk. This risk checklist is also applicable to an engineering contractor bidding on a job.

Table 7.10: Risk Factors for an International EPC Contractor

Risk	Description	Examples of Mitigative Measures
1. Political	Break in political relationships or disruption of economic relationships due to political events in client's, major partner's, or subcontractor's country; includes war, civil war, general civil disruptions.	Get a development agency such as CIDA or the World Bank to guarantee. Progress payments ahead of work.
2. Bankruptcy	Client goes into bankruptcy or experiences severe deterioration in ability to pay. Client fails to complete their portion of scope (e.g., civil infrastructure). Bank or funding agency fails to pay. Major supplier or subcontractor goes bankrupt during construction.	Guarantee by third party (e.g., government) that is more creditworthy than the client. Completion bonds for all major suppliers and subcontractors.

Risk	Description	Examples of Mitigative Measures
3. Project cancellation	Project is stopped partway through construction.	Guarantee by third party.
4. Delayed start	Due to non-approval, legal, or regulatory challenges.	Limit EPC effort to a prescribed level prior to receipt of all approvals. Make the national government of the client's country a guarantor in the event of a change in regulation.
5. Foreign exchange	Non-convertibility of local currency or a wide fluctuation in exchange rate. Severe inflation in country of the currency of the contract.	Hedge foreign currency by buying forward in the futures market at time of contract execution.
6. Foreign taxes	Change in foreign tax regime, e.g., imposition of a tax on payments.	Make the national government of the client's country a guarantor in the event of a change in taxation.
7. Enforceability of contract	Possible unenforceability of contract in foreign jurisdiction. Unfair/biased dispute resolution, e.g., biased arbitration.	Make a known code of law the applicable law of the contract (e.g., Canada, US, or EEC). Designate an internationally-known arbitrator. Make the national government of the client's country a guarantor in the event of a legal judgment by a court in the country of the contractor.
8. Natural disaster	Flood, earthquake, storm, etc.	Insurance against specified perils.
9. Loss during transport	Severe damage to equipment during shipping or loss of ship.	Insurance against specified perils.
10. Strikes/ lockouts/labor disruptions	Unexpected disruption in labor supply.	"No strike/no lockout" contract with unions for the duration of the project. Binding arbitration procedure.
11. Major technical flaw	Major design error or construction procedure that cannot be executed.	Formalized internal or third party review of technical scope. Periodic constructability reviews.

This list is specific to an engineering and construction company. Risk for an operating company (for example, a chemical company that is building a new petrochemical plant) is more extensive because the company must operate the facility for many years in order to realize the return on investment. Table 7.11 shows some additional operational risks.

Table 7.11: Additional Risk Factors for Operating Companies

Risk	Description	Examples of Mitigative Measures
1. Rise in price of feedstock/raw materials/utilities	Sudden unanticipated price drop that affects plant economics, e.g., power, fuel, feedstock, materials.	Long-term supply contracts. Hedging by purchase of futures at time of project approval. Reopener or escalation clauses in all sales agreements that enable price adjustment in the event of an unanticipated cost change.
2. Fall in price of product	Sudden unanticipated price drop, e.g., due to subsidized, offshore supplier or oversupply.	Long-term product sale contracts.
3. Change in regulations during operating life of plant	Standards are tightened (e.g. environmental)	Assess likelihood that any regulatory change will apply to all suppliers (and hence be built into everyone's cost base), or whether some suppliers (e.g., offshore) will be exempt. Develop effective individual or industry-based presence that can lobby. Assess full life-cycle impact of all by-products/waste, and identify site reclamation plan at time of initial project approval.
4. Change in taxation regime during operating life of plant	Taxes are increased in the jurisdiction of the operating plant or decreased in the jurisdiction of competitors.	Assess likelihood that any taxation change will apply to all suppliers (and hence be built into everyone's cost base), or whether some suppliers (e.g., offshore) will be exempt. Develop effective individual or industry-based presence that can lobby.

Mitigating risk is normally not free, and some judgment is involved in how much expense is warranted. Normally, senior management makes such decisions and often reviews them with a board of directors or a subcommittee of the board. Engineers who propose and champion projects should do a full risk assessment and recommend mitigative measures, but they should also expect considerable discussion and modification of their proposals as a project goes through various stages of approval.

A Caution on Mitigating Risk of Commodity Pricing

Reducing risk by locking in pricing of feedstocks and products through long-term pricing sounds like a great idea, but many investors do not consider these aspects. Suppose your company produces oil, and you want to reduce risk by selling your oil forward with very long-term contracts. If you did this in 1979 or 1988 just before significant drops in the price of oil, you would be seen as a hero. If you did this in early 2007, just before oil climbed to well over $100 a barrel, you would be seen as a "zero." In a well-functioning economic system, the person or institution taking the risk will, on average, get a reward for doing so.

Appendix 7.1: Tax Consequences of Capital Investment: Canada

Canadian tax is highly complex (the basic guidelines for completing the Business T2 form run about 100 pages), and the calculation of tax for all but the most simple companies usually involves professional advisors. In addition, Canadian business tax is likely to undergo significant changes over the next five to ten years to better conform to practices around the world. Failure to consider other countries' tax policy in designing Canada's corporate taxation system runs the risk of driving companies from Canada, and a consensus is emerging that a redesign of the corporate tax system in Canada is required.

Because the corporate tax system is complex and subject to change, treatment here will be brief and is intended to illustrate the general principals of how tax considerations factor into investment analysis. Tax treatment of the end of a project is particularly complex, and a simplified treatment will be discussed. Anyone doing investment analysis in a company should normally seek assistance in understanding the current tax position of the company and the incremental tax impact of a new investment. Key questions would include the following:

- Does the company have net taxable income prior to the new investment?
- Does the company have unclaimed capital cost (UCC) from its prior investments that might shield income from a new investment from taxes?

The Canada Customs and Revenue Agency (CCRA) has put most tax forms and publications on the web. Helpful references include the following:

- General menu: http://www.ccra-adrc.gc.ca/menu-e.html
- Business menu: http://www.ccra-adrc.gc.ca/tax/business/menu=e.html
- Corporate income tax: http://www.cra-arc.gc.ca/E/pub/tg/t4012/t4012-e.html
- Corporate T2 tax return form: http://www.cra-arc.gc.ca/E/pbg/tf/t2/README.html
- 2004 guide to completing the T2 form: http://www.cra-arc.gc.ca/E/pub/tg/t4012/t4012-02-e.html

A7.1.1   Taxable Income

The fundamental concept of taxation for companies is similar to taxation for individuals: take revenue minus allowed cash expenses (cash income) minus non-cash charges (mainly depreciation) to calculate net income on which a percentage is levied for taxes. There are two key differences between the treatment of income on financial statements and the treatment of income on tax statements.

Some expenses in business, mainly a portion of meal and entertainment expenses, are recognized by accounting but not for taxation purposes. In effect, these expenses have to be added back into net income to get net income for tax purposes. For purposes of investment analysis, this effect is so small as to be non-material and can be ignored.

As noted in Section 3.7.1, depreciation for tax purposes follows a different set of rules than depreciation for accounting purposes. Depreciation for tax purposes is called capital cost allowance (CCA). The CCA from the new investment must be calculated.

A7.1.2   CCA

Capital cost allowance (depreciation for tax purposes in Canada) is calculated by class, usually on a declining balance basis. The following CRA table is a partial list and description of the most common capital cost allowance (CCA) classes. A complete list is in Schedule II of the *Income Tax Regulations*.

CCA Classes and Rates

Class #	Description	CCA Rate
1	Most buildings made of brick, stone, or cement acquired after 1987, including their component parts such as electric wiring, lighting fixtures, plumbing, heating and cooling equipment, elevators, and escalators	4%
3	Most buildings made of brick, stone, or cement acquired before 1988, including their component parts as listed in Class 1 above	5%
6	Buildings made of frame, log, stucco on frame, galvanized iron, or corrugated metal that are used in the business of farming or fishing or that have no footings below ground; fences and most greenhouses	10%
7	Canoes, boats, and most other vessels, including their furniture, fittings, or equipment	15%
8	Property that is not included in any other class such as furniture, calculators, and cash registers (that do not record multiple sales taxes), photocopy and fax machines, printers, display fixtures, refrigeration equipment, machinery, tools costing $200 or more, outdoor advertising billboards, and greenhouses with rigid frames and plastic covers	20%
9	Aircraft, including furniture, fittings, or equipment attached, and their spare parts	25%
10	Automobiles (except taxis and others used for lease or rent), vans, wagons, trucks, buses, tractors, trailers, drive-in theatres, general purpose electronic data processing equipment (e.g., personal computers) and systems software, and timber cutting and removing equipment	30%
10.1	Passenger vehicles costing more than $30,000 if acquired after 2000	30%
12	Chinaware, cutlery, linen, uniforms, dies, jigs, moulds or lasts, computer software (except systems software), cutting or shaping parts of a machine, certain property used for earning rental income such as apparel or costumes, and videotape cassettes; certain property costing less than $200 such as kitchen utensils, tools, and medical or dental equipment	100%
13	Property that is leasehold interest (the maximum CCA rate depends on the type of the leasehold and the terms of the lease)	N/A
14	Patents, franchises, concessions, and licenses for a limited period; the CCA is limited to whichever is less: the capital cost of the property spread out over the life of the property or the undepreciated capital cost of the property at the end of the taxation year. Class 14 also includes patents, and licenses to use patents for a limited period that you elect not to include in Class 44	N/A
16	Automobiles for lease or rent, taxicabs, and coin-operated video games or pinball machines; certain tractors and large trucks acquired after December 6, 1991, that are used to haul freight and that weigh more than 11,788 kilograms	40%
17	Roads, sidewalks, parking lot or storage areas, telephone, telegraph, or non-electronic data communication switching equipment	8%

38	Most power-operated, movable equipment acquired after 1987 used for moving, excavating, placing, or compacting earth, rock, concrete, or asphalt	30%
39	Machinery and equipment acquired after 1987 that is used in Canada primarily to manufacture and process goods for sale or lease	25%
43	Manufacturing and processing machinery and equipment acquired after February 25, 1992, described in Class 39 above	30%
44	Patents and licenses to use patents for a limited or unlimited period that the corporation acquired after April 26, 1993. However, you can elect not to include such property in class 44 by attaching a letter to the return for the year the corporation acquired the property. In the letter, indicate the property you do not want to include in Class 44	25%
45	Computer equipment that is general purpose electronic data processing equipment and system software included in paragraph f of class 10 acquired after March 22, 2004	45%
46	Data network infrastructure equipment that supports advanced telecommunication applications, acquired after March 22, 2004. It includes assets such as switches, multiplexers, routers, hubs, modems, and domain name servers that are used to control, transfer, modulate, and direct data, but does not include office equipment such as telephones, cellphones, or fax machines, or property such as wires, cables, or structures	30%

(Source: http://www.cra-arc.gc.ca/E/pub/tg/t4012/t4012-05-e.html#P1389_124653)

These two rules affect claiming CCA:

- The available-for-use rule says that CCA may not be claimed until an asset is available for use, which is defined as when the asset is used to generate income or make a product or service.
- The half-year rule says that in the first year of usage of an asset, only half the calculated CCA may be claimed. This rule reflects the fact that on average, investments are available for use for half of the taxation year in which they are commissioned.

For example, consider a company that is going to spend $600,000 on new processing equipment to go in an existing building. It will invest $60,000 on new office furniture and $70,000 on new vehicles to support the staff it will add because of the new project. What is the *incremental* CCA because of the investment?

To calculate the incremental CCA, first determine the class of each of the assets:

- The $600,000 in new manufacturing assets is Class 43, with a declining balance CCA of 30%.
- The $60,000 in furniture is Class 8, with a declining balance CCA of 20%.
- The $70,000 in new vehicles is Class 10, with a declining balance CCA of 30%.

Table 7A-1 shows the incremental CCA that is available from just this one investment for the first six years.

Table 7A-1: Calculation of CCA

Year	CCA Class	Percent (%)	Unclaimed Capital Cost Start of the Year ($)	Annual CCA Claimable ($)	Half-Year Rule	Maximum CCA Claimable ($)	Remaining Unclaimed Capital Cost ($)
1	8	20	60,000	12,000	Yes	6,000	54,000
	10	30	70,000	21,000	Yes	10,500	59,500
	43	30	600,000	180,000	Yes	90,000	510,000
			730,000			106,500	623,500
2	8	20	54,000	10,800	No	10,800	43,200
	10	30	59,500	17,850	No	17,850	41,650
	43	30	510,000	153,000	No	153,000	357,000
						181,650	441,850
3	8	20	43,200	8,640	No	8,640	34,560
	10	30	41,650	12,495	No	12,495	29,155
	43	30	357,000	107,100	No	107,100	249,900
						128,235	313,615
4	8	20	34,560	6,912	No	6,912	27,648
	10	30	29,155	8,747	No	8,747	20,409
	43	30	249,900	74,970	No	74,970	174,930
						90,629	222,987
5	8	20	27,648	5,530	No	5,530	22,118
	10	30	20,409	6,123	No	6,123	14,286
	43	30	174,930	52,479	No	52,479	122,451
						64,131	158,855
6	8	20	22,118	4,424	No	4,424	17,695
	10	30	14,286	4,286	No	4,286	10,000
	43	30	122,451	36,735	No	36,735	85,716
						45,445	113,411

Note that because of the declining balance concept, incremental CCA is highest in the early years and drops thereafter. At the end of year 6, the remaining UCC (unclaimed capital cost), i.e., the amount of the initial $730,000 of investment that has not been depreciated (written off) for tax purposes, is $113,400, or about 15%.

The exception to the available-for-use rule is when a project is declared a long-term project for tax purposes. The owner can apply to have Revenue Canada treat the project as a long-term project, which allows some CCA to be claimed as early as the third year of the project against other taxable income of the company. This is extremely rare. Tax treatment in such cases is very complex, but such large projects always have sophisticated tax help available in preparing an investment analysis.

Sample Problem A7.1.1 Calculating Capital Cost Allowance (CCA)

Serviceco, an oil field service company, bought new assets. Calculate the incremental amount of capital cost allowance (CCA) per asset class for the first two years.

Asset	Book Value on Acquisition	CCA Class
Brick building	2,000,000	Class 1, 4% declining balance
Automobiles and trucks	200,000	Class 10, 30% declining balance
Manufacturing assets	350,000	Class 43, 30% declining balance
Computing equipment	150,000	Class 45, 45% declining balance

Solution:

CCA is essentially depreciation for tax purposes, and most assets are depreciated for tax on a declining balance basis.

Year 1 (the half-year rule applies):

Asset	UCC	Calculation	CCA
Brick building	2,000,000	(2,000,000 × 4% × 50%)	40,000
Automobiles and trucks	200,000	(200,000 × 30% × 50%)	30,000
Manufacturing assets	350,000	(350,000 × 30% × 50%)	52,500
Computing equipment	150,000	(150,000 × 45% × 50%)	33,750

Year 2:

Asset	Remaining UCC	Calculation	CCA
Brick building	(2,000,000 – 40,000) = 1,960,000	(1,960,000 × 4%)	78,400
Automobiles and trucks	(200,000 – 30,000) = 170,000	(170,000 × 30%)	51,000
Manufacturing assets	(350,000 – 52,500) = 297,500	(297,500 × 30%)	89,250
Computing equipment	(150,000 – 33,750) = 116,250	(116,250 × 45%)	52,313

A7.1.3   Tax Rates

Since tax rates are subject to change, it is important to check for the most recent rates when analyzing an investment. In 2007, a reduction in Canada's corporate taxation rates was announced to be implemented over a five-year period.

The rates shown in Table 7A-2 are representative of 2007 taxation rates but should not be considered accurate for future taxes. In practice, engineers doing a detailed analysis of a project investment will be assisted by either the company's accounting staff or an external tax and accounting consultant to give the best forecast of the incremental tax impact of the project.

In the absence of any other information, a default rate of 35% in 2008 that drops by 2% per year until it reaches 25% in 2013 is a reasonable proxy for corporate income tax rates.

Rates for taxation of business income depend on which of four categories that a business fits into:

- A Canadian manufacturer and processor eligible for the small business deduction (SBD) on the first $200,000 of taxable income.
- A Canadian manufacturer and processor either not eligible for the small business deduction or eligible but with income over $200,000.
- Other company eligible for the small business deduction on the first $200,000 of taxable income.
- Other company not eligible for the small business deduction or eligible but with income over $200,000.

Table 7A-2 shows the corporate income tax rates for each of the provinces for the four categories of companies.

Table 7A-2: Corporate Income Tax Rates in Canada, July 2000 (Source Ernst & Young)

Income Allocated To	Manufacturing and Processing Income		Other Income	
	Eligible for SBD (%)	Excess (%)	Eligible for SBD (%)	Excess (%)
Newfoundland	18.12	27.12	18.12	43.12
Prince Edward Island	20.62	29.62	20.62	45.12
Nova Scotia	18.12	38.12	18.12	45.12
New Brunswick	17.62	39.12	17.62	46.12
Quebec	22.13	31.13	22.13	38.13
Ontario	20.45	34.95	20.45	43.95
Manitoba	20.12	39.12	20.12	46.12
Saskatchewan	21.12	39.12	21.12	46.12
Alberta	19.12	36.62	19.12	44.62
British Columbia	18.24	38.62	18.24	45.62
North West Territories	18.12	36.12	18.12	43.12
Nunavut	18.12	36.12	18.12	43.12
Yukon	15.62	24.6	19.12	44.12
Non-resident	N/a	N/a	N/a	39.12

Note that when a company is eligible for the SBD, it applies only to the first $200,000 of taxable income. The test for the small business deduction is that it must be a Canadian-controlled private corporation with capital less than $15 million. The SBD is reduced if capital is between $10 million and $15 million. The test for the manufacturing and processing income rate is that the company must derive at least 10% of its gross income from manufacturing or processing goods in Canada. There are many exceptions and provisions that further complicate corporate tax, especially for new companies, but the values in Table 7A-2 can be used for investment analysis.

A7.1.4   Tax Payable and After-Tax Cash Flow

For investment analysis, the focus is on incremental effects: what is the incremental after-tax cash income that I would have if I made an investment? The incremental after-tax income is the incremental pre-tax income less the incremental tax. The amount of tax payable depends on the tax position of the company prior to the investment and how much income the investment generates. A rigorous calculation of taxes payable by the overall company with and without the investment is the proper course of action if the taxes payable are uncertain. However, in most cases, this process can be shortened.

There are two questions to ask:

1.   Does the income generated by the incremental investment prior to the deduction of CCA exceed the incremental CCA in all years?
2.   Prior to the investment, is the company fully taxable at its highest marginal rate?

When new equipment is purchased by a large company, the answer is usually yes to both of these questions. In this case, the incremental tax payable is simply the marginal rate of taxation of the company times the net taxable income after deduction of CCA. Thus, incremental, pre-tax cash flow from the investment is calculated, and incremental CCA on a year-by-year basis is deducted. Then, the tax payable is calculated and subtracted at the marginal rate on a year-by-year basis, and a DCF analysis is done on the resulting after-tax cash flow.

For the case of the investment of $600,000 in Class 43 assets, with an additional $130,000 investment in furniture (Class 8) and vehicles (Class 10) as described in Table 7A-1, assume that the company making this investment is Alberta-based and publicly traded (hence, no SBD). It is fully taxable at the manufacturing and processing rate (36.62%) prior to the investment, and the investment yields an incremental pre-tax cash income of $190,000 per year. Table 7A-3 shows the calculation of after-tax cash flow for this case, using the CCA calculations from Table 7A-1.

Table 7A-3: Calculation of After-Tax Cash Flow

Year	Pre-Tax Cash Income	CCA Available	Taxable Income	Tax Payable	After-Tax Cash Flow
1	190,000	106,500	83,500	30,578	159,422
2	190,000	181,650	8,350	3,058	186,942
3	190,000	128,235	61,765	22,618	167,382
4	190,000	90,629	99,372	36,390	153,610
5	190,000	64,131	125,869	46,093	143,907
6	190,000	45,445	144,555	52,936	137,064

If the project does not generate enough cash to take advantage of the incremental CCA, but the company has other income and is in a net taxable position, then the available CCA from the incremental investment can be used to reduce taxes from any other existing income of the company. In effect, the benefit of the negative tax payable (which occurs because CCA from the incremental investment is larger than incremental pre-tax cash income) can be realized as a cash benefit to the company because it reduces taxes that it would otherwise pay on income from other sources.

If the company's available CCA deduction is greater than its taxable income both before and after the investment (it has no reportable tax income because its existing available CCA is greater than its existing cash income), then there is no negative tax because the government does not send money to companies with losses. In this case, the incremental income from the new investment will not incur tax until the excess CCA available is used up. In effect, the tax payable, which is initially negative because CCA available is larger than cash income, is cumulated, and tax is not paid until the cumulative total is positive. In other words, tax losses (negative tax payable) offset future positive taxes payable until the negative tax losses are used up. This is illustrated in Sample Problem 7.3.2.

In assessing the tax effects of incremental investment, engineers working in a large company will usually get help from a finance group, and engineers working in smaller companies will normally get help from an accounting firm that does the company's books and tax returns. For a preliminary assessment of investment, it is reasonable to assume that one can apply otherwise unused incremental CCA toward reducing taxes payable from other existing company income.

Sample Problem A7.1.1 Applying CCA to Calculate Taxable Income

Two small Alberta-based companies A and B have recently revamped operations and added some new equipment to their assets. Based on the CCA rates, the total CCA available for both the companies for year 1 and 2 is as follows:

CCA	Company A ($)	Company B ($)
Year 1	128,000	246,000
Year 2	220,000	350,000

Assume both the companies are privately held and eligible for the SBD tax rate of 19.12%. The pre-tax cash income (essentially the reported net income for the company with depreciation added back in) for both companies for year 1 and 2 is expected to be as follows:

Pre-Tax Cash Income	Company A ($)	Company ($)
Year 1	260,000	235,000
Year 2	295,000	280,000

Calculate tax payable, and show the after-tax cash flow for both companies using the given information.

Solution:

For Company A, the expected pre-tax cash income is higher than the CCA available from new investment. The company has to pay taxes on the pre-tax cash income minus CCA amount available. Company B is expecting lower pre-tax cash income than the CCA available to it from making new investment. It would not have to pay any taxes, and its after-tax cash flow would be equal to pre-tax cash income. Note that the negative taxable income rolls forward on a cumulative basis and would reduce future taxable income. If next year's pre-tax cash income is greater than the CCA, it would be reduced first by the cumulative amount of negative taxable income (called a tax loss carryforward) of –$81,000.

| | **Company A** | | | | |
Year	Pre-Tax Cash Income	CCA Available	Taxable Income	Tax Payable (at 19.12%)	After-Tax Cash Flow
1	260,000	128,000	132,000	25,238	234,760
2	295,000	220,000	75,000	14,340	60,660

| | **Company B** | | | | |
Year	Pre-Tax Cash Income	CCA Available	Taxable Income	Tax Payable (at 19.12%)	After-Tax Cash Flow
1	235,000	246,000	−11,000	0	235,000
2	280,000	350,000	−70,000	0	280,000

A7.1.5 Other Tax Factors

A7.1.5.1 Investment Tax Credit

Certain investments will trigger an investment tax credit, which is essentially a reduction of a company's taxes payable in the year in which an investment is made. Governments use investment tax credits as a means of stimulating investment. For example, in Canada, an investment tax credit can be earned for investment in certain science and research type activities and for investment in economically depressed regions of the country.

A dollar of tax revenue not collected by a government is far less difficult for a politician to justify than a dollar of revenue collected and then rebated by a grant program. Tax credits can be thought of as a negative tax, but they are only of use to offset taxes that would otherwise be paid, i.e., the government does not mail out money to companies that have a tax credit and no other taxable income.

Investment tax credits are subtracted from the capital cost of an item for purposes of calculating CCA. If you buy something for $500,000 and get an investment tax credit from the federal government of $150,000, then as far as the government is concerned, the value of the asset (the initial UCC) is $350,000, and the $150,000 is treated as an expense, reducing taxable income.

A7.1.5.2 Tax Effects on Sale/Disposition of an Asset: Practical Treatment

Chapters 3 and 4 discussed how an asset is carried on a company's books at a book value, which is the original cost less depreciation. (In rare cases, the book value will be reduced by a write-down if the asset can no longer generate revenue.) In Canada, assets are not tracked individually once they are in operation for more than one year, but rather they are in a pool of other assets of the same CCA class. When an asset is sold, unless it is the last asset in its CCA class, it does not have a specific asset value for tax purposes. Even if an asset were tracked individually for tax purposes or were the only asset in its CCA class, its value would never reach zero under the declining balance method of tax depreciation, so there is always some value at the time an asset is taken out of service and scrapped or sold.

For practical purposes in almost all investment analyses, the effect of asset disposal can be ignored because the tax treatment of disposition at the end of a project has little impact on the IRR or NPV. This is true for three reasons. First, after a typical project life of 20 or more years, there is little UCC left for most classes of assets, especially Class 43 manufacturing assets. Second, the time value of money at typical discount rates means that the impact on NPV and IRR of anything occurring 20 years in the future is negligible. Table 7A-4 shows the remaining UCC for $1,000 of assets and the discount factor at 12% time value of money for 10, 20, and 30 years. It is safe to simply ignore remaining unclaimed UCC in almost all investment analysis.

Table 7A-4: Remaining Class 43 UCC per $1,000 of Investment and Discount Factor at 12%

Year	UCC ($)	Discount Factor
10	34.30	0.322
20	0.97	0.104
30	0.03	0.033

Something that sometimes shows up in a practical treatment of asset disposal (although rarely) is that for tax purposes, the adjusted cost base (ACB) of an asset is tracked, which in almost all cases is its purchase cost. If an asset is sold above its ACB, the difference between sale proceeds and ACB is treated as a capital gain. Capital gains in Canada are currently taxed at half the rate at which income is taxed. If an asset is the only one in a CCA pool and is sold for a higher price than its remaining UCC but below its ACB, the CCA pool is effectively closed. The difference between the sale proceeds and UCC is treated as recaptured income and taxed as such. The logic behind the concept of recaptured income is that CCA depreciation shielded income from tax, and if the sale value of the asset is higher than the final UCC value at the time the pool closes, then this represents value that would have otherwise been seen as income if the asset had not been depreciated for tax purposes. For the final asset in a CCA pool, any sale proceeds over ACB are still treated as capital gains. The sale of manufacturing assets at a higher value than ACB is very rare, but sometimes this occurs for real estate.

A7.1.5.2 Tax Effects on Sale/Disposition of an Asset: Technical Treatment

When an asset is sold, tax treatment depends on whether the asset is in a CCA class with other assets or not. For the sale of assets for which there are ongoing assets in the CCA pool, Table 7A-5 applies.

Table 7A-5: Tax Treatment of Sale of Assets Assuming a Large Fully Taxable Company with Ongoing Assets in the CCA Pool from Which the Asset is Being Sold

Case	Designation	Tax Treatment
Non-depreciable asset is sold below its adjusted cost base (ACB), which is the original purchase value.	The difference between sale value and ACB (original purchase value) is a capital loss.	Capital loss can be used to reduce capital gains from the sale of other assets. In effect, taxes are reduced by the marginal tax rate times half of the capital loss, but only if there are capital gains. Capital losses can be carried forward indefinitely and can be carried back for three years.
Non-depreciable asset is sold at its ACB.	Neither a gain or loss is created for tax calculations.	None.

Non-depreciable asset is sold above its ACB.	The difference between sale value and ACB is a capital gain.	
Depreciable asset is sold below its ACB (usually the original purchase cost).	There is no capital gain or loss on the sale.	The balance in the CCA pool is reduced by the sale proceeds.
Depreciable asset is sold at its ACB (usually the original purchase cost).	There is no capital gain or loss on the sale.	The balance in the CCA pool is reduced by the sale proceeds.
Depreciable asset is sold above its ACB (usually the original purchase cost).	There is a capital gain on the sale of the difference between the sale value and the ACB.	Capital gain is taxed at half of the marginal tax rate. The balance in the CCA pool is reduced by the ACB.

The following concepts are the most important:

- When a non-depreciable asset is sold below its adjusted cost base (the original purchase value), a capital loss occurs. When a non-depreciable asset is sold above its adjusted cost base, a capital gain occurs. A non-depreciable asset sold at exactly its purchase cost creates neither a gain nor loss for tax purposes.
- Capital losses can only be incurred from a non-depreciable asset, such as land, that is sold at a loss. Sale of a depreciable asset (such as a building or machine) at a loss does not trigger a capital loss.
- Capital losses can only be applied to offset capital gains; they cannot be used to offset taxable income.
- Two treatments are distinguished for the sale of depreciable assets. One treatment occurs if there are other assets in the same CCA pool (this is the most common situation for ongoing companies). The other treatment occurs if the asset being sold is the final item in the CCA class, i.e., there are no remaining assets in the CCA class after the asset is sold.
- If there are other assets in the CCA pool, then the sale value of the asset up to the adjusted cost base (usually the purchase cost of the asset) is used to reduce the CCA pool. A sale value above the adjusted cost base is treated as a capital gain.
- If there are no remaining assets in the CCA pool, then Table 7A-5 does not apply. These are the following treatments:
  - Sale value below the remaining value in the CCA pool creates a terminal loss, which can be deducted from taxable income for that year.
  - Sale value above the remaining value in the CCA pool up to the adjusted cost base of the asset is treated as income, i.e., the remaining value in the CCA pool is subtracted from the sale proceeds, and the balance up to the adjusted cost base of the asset is treated as taxable income.
  - If the asset is sold above its adjusted cost base, the portion of the sale value above the adjusted cost base is treated as a capital gain.

Capital gain for tax purposes is any portion of the sale value in excess of the original purchase price. Capital gains are treated separately from income for businesses, much as they are for individuals. Capital gains are taxed at half the rate of income. Capital gains were once taxed as income, then the tax rate was first reduced to two-thirds that of income, and now it is half. Occasionally, there are proposals to eliminate all tax on capital gains.

Appendix 7.2: Tax Consequences of Capital Investment: United States

Taxes for corporations are governed by Section 11 of the Internal Revenue Code (IRC) and administered by the Internal Revenue Service (IRS) of the United States, regardless of whether the corporation is domestic or foreign or whether the source of income is domestic or foreign.

Because the corporate tax system is complex and subject to change, treatment here is brief and is intended to illustrate the general principals of how tax considerations factor into investment analysis. Anyone doing investment analysis in a company should normally seek assistance in understanding the current tax position of the company and the incremental tax impact of a new investment. Key questions include the following:

- Does the company have net taxable income prior to the new investment?
- Does the company have capital loss carryover?
- How long will the investment be held?

The IRS has put most tax forms and publications on the web. Helpful references include the following:

- IRS home page: http://www.irs.gov
- Topical Index to IRS Forms and Publications: http://www.irs.gov/formspubs/article/0,,id=99267,00.html
- Overview of Corporate Taxation, Publication 542: http://www.irs.gov/publications/p542/index.html
- How to Depreciate Property, Publication 946: http://www.irs.gov/pub/irs-pdf/p946.pdf

A7.2.1 Taxable Income

The IRS imposes a tax on the profits of U.S. resident corporations at incremental rates ranging from 15 to 35%. Many U.S. businesses, such as partnerships and sole proprietorships, are taxed as flow-through enterprises and are not subject to the corporate income tax: the businesses' profits are allocated to the shareholders or partners, who include their allocated income in their individual taxable income. Taxable corporate profits are equal to a corporation's gross current revenues less its current allowed expenses. Current expenses include all allowed costs associated with earning the current revenues and depreciation of capital investments, where depreciation is calculated according to IRS guidelines and is different than depreciation reported in a company's financial statements. Corporations are provided the opportunity of accelerated depreciation deductions. Furthermore, Section 179 of the IRC allows immediate expensing of some capital costs.

Dividends are paid from after-tax income in a company. Shareholders then pay individual income tax on the dividends, so dividends are in effect double taxed. This is the subject of much debate. However, it should be noted that the corporate tax structure in effect provides an incentive for debt financing over equity financing because the interest payments for debt financing are deductible as an expense. This encourages companies to finance using debt.

A7.2.2 DEPRECIATION

7.2.2.1 Overview of Depreciation for Tax Purposes

For most engineering design analyses, the application is relatively simple. Much equipment designed by engineers has a defined life for purposes of calculating tax of seven years, while land is not depreciated for tax purposes. The most commonly used tax calculation method is MACRS GDS. It involves using a table to calculate the percentage of depreciation of the cost of the asset per year. The percentage is based on a mix of declining balance and straight-line depreciation. Declining balance tax depreciation in early years gives higher depreciation in those years. For example, an asset with a defined life of seven years for tax purposes is almost 60% depreciated in the first three taxation years. The asset is assumed to be in service only for part of the first year, so depreciation is highest in year 2. The switch to straight-line tax depreciation in later years ensures the asset is fully depreciated for tax purposes. A final small residual amount is depreciated in the year after the designated asset life. There are a number of exceptions, but a simple approach will work for the vast majority of projects that engineers are involved in.

The sources for the information on IRS depreciation schedules and tax rates are IRS Publications 542 and 946.

7.2.2.2 Determining the Depreciable Cost and Asset Recovery Period

Depreciation is an income tax deduction that allows a taxpayer to recover the cost of certain tangible and non-tangible property. It is an annual allowance for the wear and tear, deterioration, or out-datedness of the property. The depreciation period begins when a taxpayer places property in service for use in a trade or business or for the production of income and ends when the taxpayer has fully recovered the property's cost or other basis or when the taxpayer retires it from service, whichever occurs first. However, no depreciation expense is allowed when property is placed in service and disposed of in the same year.

Tangible property, such as buildings, machinery, vehicles, furniture, and equipment are depreciable; land, however does not depreciate. Also, equipment used to build capital improvements cannot be depreciated. Intangible property, such as patents, copyrights, and computer software is depreciable.

Depreciation deductibility is contingent upon the following criteria:

- The taxpayer must own the property; capital improvements for leased property may also be depreciated and deducted by the lessee.
- The property must be used in business or in an income-producing activity. If the property is also used for personal purposes, depreciation expense can only be deducted on the business use portion of that property.

Before a deduction for property depreciation can be taken, the taxpayer must determine the following six items:

1. The depreciation method for the property—the IRS has determined that the Modified Accelerated Cost Recovery System (MACRS) is the proper depreciation method for most property. The taxpayer's use of either the General Depreciation System (GDS) or the Alternative Depreciation System (ADS) to depreciate property under MACRS determines the appropriate depreciation method and recovery period to use. Generally, the GDS is used unless specifically required by law to use ADS.

2. The class life of the asset—the following tables illustrate the class life categories and recovery periods of properties under the General and Alternative Depreciation Systems. Under GDS, property that is not qualified Indian reservation property is depreciated over one of the following recovery periods.

Table A7.2.1 Recovery Periods under GDS

Examples of Property	Recovery Period (years)
Tractor units for over-the-road use Any racehorse over 2-years-old when placed in service Any other horse (other than a racehorse) over 12-years-old when placed in service Qualified rent-to-own property	3
Automobiles, taxis, buses, and trucks Computers and peripheral equipment Office machinery (such as typewriters, calculators, and copiers) Any property used in research and experimentation Breeding cattle and dairy cattle Appliances, carpets, furniture, etc., used in a residential rental real estate activity Certain geothermal, solar, and wind energy property	5
Office furniture and fixtures (such as desks, files, and safes) Agricultural machinery and equipment. Any property that does not have a class life and has not been designated by law as being in any other class Certain motorsports and entertainment complex property placed in service before January 1, 2008 Any natural gas gathering line placed in service after April 11, 2005	7
Vessels, barges, tugs, and similar water transportation equipment Any single-purpose agricultural or horticultural structure Any tree- or vine-bearing fruits or nuts	10
Certain improvements made directly to land or added to it (such as shrubbery, fences, roads, sidewalks, and bridges) Any retail motor fuels outlet, such as a convenience store Any municipal wastewater treatment plant Any qualified leasehold improvement property placed in service before January 1, 2008 Any qualified restaurant property placed in service before January 1, 2008 Initial clearing and grading land improvements for gas utility property Electric transmission property (that is section 1245 property) used in the transmission at 69 or more kilovolts of electricity placed in service after April 11, 2005 Any natural gas distribution line placed in service after April 11, 2005	15
Farm buildings (other than single-purpose agricultural or horticultural structures) Municipal sewers not classified as 25-year property Initial clearing and grading land improvements for electric utility transmission and distribution plants	20
Water utility property, which is either property that is an integral part of the gathering, treatment, or commercial distribution of water, and that, without regard to this provision, would be 20-year property; or municipal sewers other than property placed in service under a binding contract in effect at all times since June 9, 1996.	25

Residential rental property, which is any building or structure, such as a rental home (including a mobile home) that has 80% or more of its gross rental income for the tax year from dwelling units (a house or apartment used to provide living accommodations in a building or structure). Excludes units in a hotel, motel, or other establishment where more than half the units are used on a transient basis. If you occupy any part of the building or structure for personal use, its gross rental income includes the fair rental value of the part you occupy.	27.5
Non-residential real property, which is section 1250 property (such as an office building, store, or warehouse) that is neither residential rental property nor property with a class life of less than 27.5 years.	39

The recovery periods for most property generally are longer under ADS than they are under GDS. The following table shows some of the ADS recovery periods.

Table A7.2.2 Recovery Periods under ADS

Property	Recovery Period (years)
Rent-to-own property	4
Automobiles and light duty trucks	5
Computers and peripheral equipment	5
High-tech telephone station equipment installed on customer premises	5
High-tech medical equipment	5
Personal property with no class life	12
Natural gas gathering lines	14
Single-purpose agricultural and horticultural structures	15
Any tree- or vine-bearing fruit or nuts	20
Initial clearing and grading land improvements for gas utility property	20
Initial clearing and grading land improvements for electric utility transmission and distribution plants	25
Electric transmission property used in the transmission at 69 or more kilovolts of electricity	30
Natural gas distribution lines	35
Any qualified leasehold improvement property	39
Any qualified restaurant property	39
Non-residential real property	40
Residential rental property	40
Section 1245 real property not listed in Appendix B	40
Railroad grading and tunnel bore	50

3. Whether the property is listed property—includes cars and other property used for transportation, property used for entertainment, and certain computers and cellphones.

4. Whether the taxpayer elects to expense any portion of the asset—the US government is allowing certain property affected by natural disasters and the September 11, 2001 terror attacks to be

expensed with accelerated depreciation. Cellulosic biomass ethanol plant property acquired by purchase after December 20, 2006 can also be expensed with accelerated depreciation.

5. Whether the taxpayer qualifies for any "bonus" first-year depreciation—instead of recovering the cost by taking depreciation deductions, a section 179 deduction allows taxpayers to elect to recover all or part of the cost of certain tangible personal property up to a limit by deducting it in the year the property was placed in service. Property eligible for the section 179 deduction must have been acquired for business use by purchase. Section 179 of the IRC describes what property is not eligible for the Section 179 deduction. Some of these are land and land improvements, certain property leased to others, air conditioning and heating units; property used by tax-exempt government or foreign entities and property used mostly outside of the US.

6. The depreciable basis of the property—the basis of the property is the cost of the property plus any costs, such as sales tax, freight, installation charges, and any debts associated with acquiring the property and readying it for business use. Basis excludes service contracts. If property is converted from personal use to business use, then the depreciation basis is the lower of cost basis or fair market value on the date of the conversion. Prior depreciation reduces the basis of the property. For example, in 2008, Corporation ABC purchased machinery in California for $500,000 by paying $100,000 cash down payment and financing the rest. The tax rate in California was 7.75%. The manufacturer charged $10,000 to ship the equipment. Additionally, it cost $20,000 to calibrate the equipment to ABC's specifications. ABC purchased a service agreement for the equipment for five years at $5,000 per year. ABC's depreciable basis is as follows:

Equipment	$500,000
Taxes	$ 38,750
Freight	$ 10,000
Calibration	$ 20,000
Depreciable basis	$568,750

7.2.2.3 Determining the Depreciation Amount per Year

Once the cost and asset life are defined, then depreciation is calculated year by year until the asset is fully depreciated for tax purposes. The MACRS applicable percentage for the General Depreciation System (GDS) using a half-year convention that assumes the asset is placed in service in the middle of the company's tax year is shown in the following table. For calculating actual tax, modifications are applicable when assets are placed in service at different times in the tax year. However, the half-year convention is adequate for investment analysis purposes, since precise start-up times are typically not known.

Table A7.2.3 IRS Depreciation Rates for 3-, 5-, 7-, 10-, 15-, and 20-Year Property under the Half-Year Convention

Depreciation Rate for Recovery Period (%)

Year	3-Year	5-Year	7-Year	10-Year	15-Year	20-Year
1	33.33	20.00	14.29	10.00	5.00	3.750
2	44.45	32.00	24.49	18.00	9.50	7.219
3	14.81	19.20	17.49	14.40	8.55	6.667
4	7.41	11.52	12.49	11.52	7.70	6.177
5		11.52	8.93	9.22	6.93	5.713
6		5.76	8.92	7.37	6.23	5.285
7			8.93	6.55	5.90	4.888
8			4.46	6.55	5.90	4.522
9				6.56	5.91	4.462
10				6.55	5.90	4.461
11				3.28	5.91	4.462
12					5.90	4.461
13					5.91	4.462
14					5.90	4.461
15					5.91	4.462
16					2.95	4.461
17						4.462
18						4.461
19						4.462
20						4.461
21						2.231

Sample Problem A7.2.1 Determining US Tax Depreciation

Use MACRS GDS to calculate the depreciation for a project with a total cost of $27.92 million consisting of $820,000 of trucks, $1.23 million of land, and the balance of manufacturing plant assets.

Solution

Under MACRS GDS, land is not depreciated for tax purposes, trucks have a designated recovery of five years, and the manufacturing assets will have a designated recovery of seven years. Use the values in Table A7.2.3.

($000)

Asset type	Land		Trucks		Manufacturing	
Asset value	1,230		820		25,870	
Recovery period	No recovery		5 year		7 year	
Year	(%)	Depreciation	(%)	Depreciation		Total Tax Depreciation
1	20.00	164.0	14.29	3,696.8		3,860.8
2	32.00	262.4	24.49	6,335.6		6,598.0
3	19.20	157.4	17.49	4,524.7		4,682.1
4	11.52	94.5	12.49	3,231.2		3,325.6
5	11.52	94.5	8.93	2,310.2		2,404.7
6	5.76	47.2	8.92	2,307.6		2,354.8
7			8.93	2,310.2		2,310.2
8			4.46	1,153.8		1,153.8

A7.2.3 Tax Rates

Since tax rates are subject to change, you should check for the most recent rates when analyzing an investment. The following tax table shows the US corporate tax rates for 2008 but should not be considered accurate for future taxes.

Tax Rate Schedule*

If taxable income (line 30, Form 1120, or line 26, Form 1120-A) is:

Over—	But not over—	Tax is:	Of the amount over—
0	50,000	15%	0
50,000	75,000	7,500 + 25%	50,000
75,000	100,000	13,750 + 34%	75,000
100,000	335,000	22,250 + 39%	100,000
335,000	10,000,000	113,900 + 34%	335,000
10,000,000	15,000,000	3,400,000 + 35%	10,000,000
15,000,000	18,333,333	5,150,000 + 38%	15,000,000
18,333,333	—	35%	0

*Note: A qualified personal service corporation is taxed at a flat rate of 35% on taxable income

The federal and state governments offer many tax incentives to corporations based on their business sector. The economic stimulus legislation in 2008 and 2009 have added and removed various incentives. Engineers are advised to apprise themselves of the tax effect of recent legislation in their application of rates posted in table 7A2. There are many exceptions and provisions that further complicate corporate tax, especially for new companies, but the values in Table 7A-2 can be used for investment analysis.

Table 7A-2: Corporate State Income Tax Rates as of January 1, 2008

State	Tax Rate	State	Tax Rate
Alabama	6.500	Montana	6.750
Alaska	9.400	Nebraska	7.810
Arizona	6.968	Nevada	0.000
Arkansas	6.500	New Hampshire	8.500
California	8.840	New Jersey	9.000
Colorado	4.630	New Mexico	7.600
Connecticut	7.500	New York	7.500
Delaware	8.700	North Carolina	6.900
Dist. of Columbia	9.975	North Dakota	6.500
Florida	5.500	Ohio	8.500
Georgia	6.000	Oklahoma	6.000
Hawaii	6.400	Oregon	6.600
Idaho	7.600	Pennsylvania	9.990
Illinois	7.300	Rhode Island	9.000
Indiana	8.500	South Carolina	5.000
Iowa	12.000	South Dakota	0.000
Kansas	4.000	Tennessee	6.500
Kentucky	6.000	Texas	0.000
Louisiana	8.000	Utah	5.000
Maine	8.930	Vermont	8.500
Maryland	8.300	Virginia	6.000
Massachusetts	9.500	Washington	0.000
Michigan	4.950	West Virginia	8.500
Minnesota	9.800	Wisconsin	7.900
Mississippi	5.000	Wyoming	0.000
Missouri	6.250		

(Source: Individual state tax forms)

A7.2.4 Tax Payable and After-Tax Cash Flow

For investment analysis, engineers are concerned with incremental effects: what is the incremental after-tax cash income that I would have if I made an investment? The incremental after-tax income is the incremental pre-tax income less the incremental tax. The amount of tax payable depends on the tax position of the company prior to the investment and how much income the investment generates. A rigorous calculation of taxes payable by the overall company with and without the investment is the proper course of action to follow if the taxes payable are uncertain. However, in most cases, this process can be shortened.

There are two questions to ask:

1. Does the income generated by the incremental investment prior to the deduction of CCA exceed the incremental CCA in all years?
2. Prior to the investment, is the company fully taxable at its highest marginal rate?

When new equipment is purchased by a large company, the answer is usually yes to both of these questions. In this case, the incremental tax payable is simply the marginal rate of taxation of the company times the net taxable income after deduction of tax depreciation. Thus, incremental pre-tax cash flow from the investment is calculated, and incremental tax depreciation on a year-by-year basis is deducted. Then, the tax payable is calculated and subtracted at the marginal rate on a year-by-year basis, and a DCF analysis is done on the resulting after-tax cash flow. Sample problem A7.2.2 illustrates the technique.

Sample Problem A7.2.2 Calculating After-Tax Cash Flow

As described in Sample Problem A7.2.1, a manufacturing facility is worth $27.92 million with $1.23 million of land, $820,000 of trucks, and the balance in manufacturing assets. For the project, calculate the after-tax cash flow and return on investment if the pre-tax cash flow is $3.1 million in year 1, $4.6 million in year 2, and $5.2 million in years 3 to 20. The effective tax rate for the plant is 22%. Assume that the land is bought one year before start-up, and the plant and trucks are paid for at start-up. Assume that the company has substantial taxable income from other sources and that any excess of depreciation for tax purposes in excess of taxable income can be used to defer taxes elsewhere in the company that would otherwise be payable.

Solution

The depreciation for this investment was calculated in Sample Problem A7.2.1. The tax calculation, after-tax cash flow, and IRR are shown in this table:

($000)

Year	Pre-Tax Cash Flow	Tax Depreciation	Taxable Income	Tax at 22%	After-Tax Cash Flow
−1	−1,230.0				−1,230.0
0	−26,690.0				−26,690.0
1	3,100.0	3,860.8	−760.8	−167.4	3,267.4
2	4,600.0	6,598.0	−1,998.0	−439.6	5,039.6
3	5,200.0	4,682.1	517.9	113.9	5,086.1
4	5,200.0	3,325.6	1,874.4	412.4	4,787.6
5	5,200.0	2,404.7	2,795.3	615.0	4,585.0
6	5,200.0	2,354.8	2,845.2	625.9	4,574.1
7	5,200.0	2,310.2	2,889.8	635.8	4,564.2
8	5,200.0	1,153.8	4,046.2	890.2	4,309.8
9	5,200.0		5,200.0	1,144.0	4,056.0
10	5,200.0		5,200.0	1,144.0	4,056.0
11	5,200.0		5,200.0	1,144.0	4,056.0
12	5,200.0		5,200.0	1,144.0	4,056.0
13	5,200.0		5,200.0	1,144.0	4,056.0
14	5,200.0		5,200.0	1,144.0	4,056.0
15	5,200.0		5,200.0	1,144.0	4,056.0
16	5,200.0		5,200.0	1,144.0	4,056.0
17	5,200.0		5,200.0	1,144.0	4,056.0
18	5,200.0		5,200.0	1,144.0	4,056.0
19	5,200.0		5,200.0	1,144.0	4,056.0
20	5,200.0		5,200.0	1,144.0	4,056.0
				IRR (%)	14.5

In Sample Problem A7.2.2, the project does not generate enough cash to take advantage of the incremental tax depreciation created by the project, but the company has other income and is in a net taxable position. In this case, the incremental depreciation can be used to reduce taxes from any other existing income of the company. In effect, the benefit of the negative tax payable can be realized as a cash benefit to the company because it reduces taxes it would otherwise pay on income from other sources. This occurs because in some years, tax depreciation from the incremental investment is larger than incremental pre-tax cash income.

What if the company's available tax depreciation is greater than its taxable income both before and after the investment? This means it has no reportable tax income because its existing available depreciation is greater than its existing cash income. Then, there is no negative tax because the government does not send money to companies with losses. In this case, the incremental income from the new investment will not incur tax until the excess tax depreciation available is used up. In effect, the tax payable, which is initially negative because depreciation available is larger than cash income, is cumulated, and tax is not paid until the cumulative total is positive. In other words, tax losses (negative tax payable) offset future positive taxes payable until the negative tax losses are used up. This is illustrated in Sample Problem 7.3.2.

In assessing the tax effects of incremental investment, engineers working in a large company will usually get help from a finance group, and engineers working in smaller companies will normally get help from an accounting firm that does the company's books and tax returns. For preliminary assessment of investment, it is reasonable to assume that one can apply otherwise unused incremental CCA toward reducing taxes payable from other existing company income.

A7.2.5 Tax Effects on Sale of an Asset

Remember that an asset is carried on a company's books at a book value, which is the original cost less depreciation. In rare cases, the book value will be reduced by a write-down if the asset can no longer generate sufficient revenue to justify its book value. For tax purposes, there is an equivalent "tax book" value of an asset, which is the original cost less cumulative tax depreciation.

In the United States, assets become fully depreciated for tax purposes long before their expected operational life is over, so there is almost never any remaining taxable book value when assets are sold. When an asset is sold, its sale price then represents recaptured income and is treated as income for tax purposes. The logic here is that if the asset is fully depreciated, the depreciation shielded income from tax. If the sale value of the asset is higher than the book value for tax purposes (normally zero by the time the asset is sold), then this represents value that would have otherwise been seen as income if the asset had not been fully depreciated for tax purposes.

Problems

7.1 You and your significant other are contemplating the purchase of a home. Your combined family income is $80,000 per year. You know that mortgage lenders use a rule of thumb that the limit on the size of a mortgage loan is that no more than 30% of a family's income should go to the payment of principal and interest (PI, also sometimes known as IP). What is the maximum purchase value of a home that you and your partner could purchase assuming that you have a 10% down payment through savings? Assuming one annual mortgage payment instead of 12 monthly payments per year, answer this question for these four cases:

- 20-year amortization
- 30-year amortization
- mortgage interest rate of 7%
- mortgage interest rate of 11%

7.2 Your uncle, a farmer, wins the lottery and is offered a choice of a cash payout: either 10 annual payments of $13,000 with the first installment paid immediately or a lump sum payment of $100,000. You uncle is very conservative and would simply invest the money in a bank account or a conservative bond mutual fund (that would allow annual withdrawals) if he takes the lump sum payment. He wants to use the money over a 10-year period but does not know if the stream of payments is a good or bad deal. Your uncle asks for your advice.

Assume that the going rate of a bond mutual fund is 6%, which is the current interest rate on provincial and government bonds that the fund invests in, and that the current interest rate for bank deposits is 3%.

- What is the effective discount rate being offered?
- What do you recommend to your uncle if the entity offering the stream of payments is a provincially guaranteed lottery corporation?
- What do you recommend to your uncle if it is a local charitable group? If your advice is different based on the guarantor of the payment, explain why in one sentence.
- Would your advice be different if the $13,000 payment stream was paid at the end of each year? What is the effective discount rate in this case?

7.3 a) You are contemplating the purchase of a company that has a $600,000 balloon payment on debt due in four years. Interest on the original loan is calculated at 8.5%, and all due interest payments to date have been paid. As part of your plan to purchase this company, you are contemplating paying off the debt early in order to take out a larger long-term debt with longer repayment provisions, at the current long-term interest rate for company borrowing of 7.5%. What payment would be a fair offer to repay the balloon payment, assuming that you are going to refinance the new long-term debt from the same financial institution at current rates?

b) You are contemplating the purchase of a company that owes a lender 9 equal annual payments of $100,000, with the first one due in one year's time. The company cannot be sold without consent of this lender, and you are planning to meet the lender to discuss your plans to purchase and to seek consent. What is a fair offer to pay out this debt? Pick a value of i, and justify it (one or two sentences).

7.4 a) A 10-year bond was issued two years ago with a face value of $1,000 and an annual coupon (interest payment) of 6%. Two years later, higher inflation and a surge of borrowing in a strong economy has shifted the market interest rate for eight-year bonds to 9.2%. What is the market value of the bond? Assume that you are at the start of year 3, i.e., the second interest payment was just made. Does the higher interest rate today versus two years ago increase or decrease the face value of the bond?

b) Determine the market value of a 20-year $1,000 bond with a 6% annual interest rate two years after issue when the market rate of interest for 18-year bonds is 9.2%. Is the impact of changing interest on bond value greater or less for increasing term?

7.5 You own a small fabrication shop that has specialized in custom work for construction projects. You are contemplating purchasing a CNC water jet cutter machine. This machine uses an ultra high-pressure water stream with suspended fine grit to cold cut materials. It is especially useful in alloy work and to cut intricate patterns of architectural materials such as marble, since in each of these applications, the heat generated by other cutting techniques is harmful (it changes the properties of the alloy and discolors the architectural materials).

You have the following estimates for the machine:

Installed cost	$112,000
Operating cost	$31/h (includes maintenance and power)
Saleable Machine Hours	
Year 1	800
Year 2	1,200
Year 3+	1,450
Useful life of the machine	15 years

At the time you are contemplating this decision, the going interest rate for long-term debt to your company that would be secured by assets is 8.5%. You have not decided yet whether to borrow extra funds for the purchase.

How would you price the machine, i.e., what charge-out rate per hour would you propose for the machine? Specify and justify an appropriate discount rate (one to two sentences). Since hours are increasing over the first two years, would it make sense to have an initial higher price followed by a lower price?

Ignore inflation in your analysis, i.e., do the analysis in present dollars, and assume that minor inflationary costs (increase in operating costs) can be passed on to customers. Also, ignore tax (i.e., the discount rate you specify is a pre-tax return). Note that this problem does not require the calculation of any interest payment owing to others, i.e., you would use the same approach to this problem regardless of whether you financed the purchase by equity (your own money), debt (other peoples' money), or a combination of the two. The interest rate quoted above is included simply to help you set an appropriate time value of money.

7.6 a) You are working up a detailed cash flow forecast for a large and complex capital investment that involves building a new electronics manufacturing facility.

Your accounting department advises you that the project will be charged $400,000 per year as an allocation of existing head office overheads. This is your project's share of the head office executive and finance department. Do you include this amount as a negative entry in your cash flow statement? Why? NO. p. 209

The manufacturing plant is a super clean low contamination facility, and you know that once every two years, the plant will be shut down for two months for a cleaning and an overhaul of the clean room support equipment. The cost of the overhaul is $14 million. Your accounting department tells you that it will create a reserve (a non-cash charge against income) of $7 million per year to smooth the impact of this shutdown. What does your cash flow forecast show as a shutdown expense: $14 million every other year or $7 million per year? Why?

b) Your company pays an annual cash payment of $6 million to a fund as a security that the site will be cleared and restored at the end of the life of the manufacturing plant. Your accounting department says that if the new manufacturing facility proceeds, $1 million per year of the current payment to this fund will be allocated to the facility. Do you factor this into your cash flow forecast? Why? No --- this is not an extra cost to the co.

c) Over the past two years, your company has spent $12 million in development costs on this project, including R&D, architectural fees, environmental studies, and engineering. The capital cost of completing the project is $78 million. Do you factor the $12 million into the cash flow forecast you will use to determine an IRR? No. Sunk cost, p. 209

7.7 A northern mining project producing a nickel/cobalt concentrate has a capital cost of $5.242 million, consisting of the following assets by class:

Item	CCA Class		Amount ($000)
Building (cement)	1	4%	821
Aircraft	9	25%	1,209
Large trucks	16	40%	824
Parking area	17	8%	180
Process machinery	43	30%	2,208
			5,242

The project started in November of last year, and the company's financial reporting period is January 1 to December 31.

- What is the maximum incremental capital cost allowance arising from this investment that can be claimed over the next 10 years, with the financial year of last year being year 1.
- In what year does the maximum CCA claim occur, and what percentage of the initial investment is it?
- After 10 years, what percentage of each asset class is not yet depreciated for tax purposes?
- After 10 years, what percentage of the overall assets are not yet depreciated for tax purposes?

In answering, remember the half-year rule. Note that this is a repetitive problem as illustrated in Table 7A-1; it can be made much easier by copying year 2 repeatedly!

7.8 Prepare a 10-year after-tax incremental cash flow (10 years of production after start-up or a total of 12 years of cash flow) and discounted cash flow forecast for the project of Problem 7.7, given the following additional information:

- The company's minimum acceptable rate of return for northern mining projects is 14%.
- The project construction takes two years, with 50% of the capital cost spent in each of the two years.
- The design throughput of the plant is 1,200,000 tonnes of concentrate per year.
- The expected production buildup is 80% of design throughput in year 1, 85% in year 2, 90% in year 3, 95% in year 4, and 100% in year 5 and thereafter.
- The estimated sale value of the concentrate is $6 per tonne FOB Winnipeg.
- The variable operating cost is $3.24 per tonne, which includes shipping to Winnipeg.
- The fixed operating cost is $1,620,000 per year.
- The corporate tax rate is 40%.

Given this information, answer these questions:

a) What is the NPV at 14% (the company's MARR)?

b) What is the IRR?

c) Without adjusting CCA, how much does the IRR increase if capital cost is reduced by 10%? (Note, do not adjust CCA. This makes the calculation approximate, but the purpose of the sensitivity is to get an indication of the impact, and you can get an indication without a great deal of rework by ignoring the tax impact.)

d) How much does the IRR increase if the variable operating cost is reduced by 10%?

e) How much does the IRR increase if the price per tonne of concentrate increases by 10%?

f) How much does the IRR increase if the corporate tax rate drops to 25%?

g) How much does the IRR increase if the production profile changes to 90% in year 1 and 100% in year 2 and after?

Note: In setting up this problem, it is very important that you carry the main variables as single cells and then refer to these in your year-by-year calculations. This will allow you to easily do the sensitivities. Your spreadsheet should include capital cost, production (tonnes), gross revenue, variable operating cost, fixed operating cost, pre-tax net cash flow, CCA (from Problem 7.7), tax, after-tax cash flow, and discounted after-tax cash flow. Make year 1 the first year of production, which means that the capital will be spent in years –1 and 0.

When you have calculated the sensitivities, give some thought to what you would focus on if you were the person responsible for this project. Would you recommend the project? With whom would you spend the most time or effort to improve the return from this project?

7.9 a) You work for a large manufacturing company that has a high cash flow from previous investments and is actively looking for opportunities to invest. The concern of the senior management is that the company will have its assets depreciate and may fail to reinvest to sustain income in the future. The company has directed that all investments in its business line above a MARR of 14% should be pursued.

You have developed two cases for investing in a new assembly line. The first case has a lower degree of automation, so it has lower capital cost and higher operating costs (due to higher operating labor costs). The second case has a higher degree of automation, so it has a higher capital cost and lower operating cost. You have carefully worked up the following detailed cash flow forecasts for the estimated 15-year life of the equipment.

Year	Low Automation Case Cash Flow (FV) ($ million)	High Automation Case Cash Flow (FV) ($ million)
−1	(9.1)	(16.2)
0	(57.4)	(81.4)
1	14.8	20.2
2	16.2	21.6
3	17.5	22.9
4	18.5	23.9
5	18.5	23.9
6	18.5	23.9
7	18.5	23.9
8	18.5	23.9
9	18.5	23.9
10	18.5	23.9
11	18.5	23.9
12	18.5	23.9
13	18.5	23.9
14	18.5	23.9
15	18.5	23.9

Which case do you recommend? Why?

b) Would your answer be any different if your company had many opportunities to invest and very limited funds for capital investments? Why?

7.10 a) Your company is looking at acquiring a deep oil well in a region near some existing producing wells. The well being considered is projected to have a flat production profile for its remaining 12 years of life. You have the following information:

- The acquisition cost of the well is $1,000,000.
- Royalties, payable to the government, are 40% of gross production.
- Operating costs are estimated to be labor at $40,000 per year, parts and supplies at $60,000 per year, and electrical power at $200,000 per year.
- Your company assumes a general inflation rate of 2% per year. If the purchase is treated as year 0 (at the end of year zero), then the first year's expenses and revenue are as stated above, and in year 2 and beyond, they are increased by 2% per year.
- Projected gross revenue is $800,000 per year.
- The effective CCA rate is 24% declining balance, and the effective tax rate is 20%.
- Your company's MARR is 15%.

For a base case, set up a cash flow forecast, and calculate IRR, NPV at the MARR, and simple payback. Also, calculate a discounted payback using the MARR as a discount factor. Do you recommend the investment?

b) A vice president of energy supply in your company is concerned about power price. Specifically, she believes that electrical power may experience a far higher escalation rate than other factors due to the application of greenhouse gas emission controls. She asks you to run a case in which all other factors stay the same as the base case except electrical power expense, which is escalated at 6% per year. For this sensitivity case, calculate IRR, NPV at the MARR, and simple payback. Also, calculate a discounted payback using the MARR as a discount factor. Do you recommend the investment?

In your personal opinion, is the sensitivity case realistic? (One to three sentences)

Note: As with other factors in cash flow spreadsheets, it is not unusual for sensitivities to be run on different inflation assumptions. To make it easier to work with these sensitivities, enter the general inflation factor (2%) in a single cell, and then refer to that cell in your inflationary calculations. Then, you can run a different inflationary assumption by changing a single cell, not rewriting numerous formulae in the spreadsheet.

Valuation, Sale, and Cyclical Patterns in Business

Key Concepts

- There are two ways to acquire the operations of a company: purchase the assets or purchase the entire company.

- Asset purchase leaves past liabilities, including debt and any possible lawsuits, in the hands of the selling company. Depreciation for tax purposes is reset for the buyer at the purchase price, and the seller will often realize recaptured income.

- When a buyer purchases all the shares and thereby owns the company, past liabilities stay with the company, and depreciation for tax purposes remains unchanged.

- Earnings before interest and taxes (EBIT), earnings before interest, taxes, depreciation, and amortization (EBITDA), the replacement cost of assets, and whether there is a strategic fit between buyer and seller may all factor into the purchase price, depending on the status of the company being sold.

- Bonds are valued on the basis of the net present value of future interest and principal payments and adjusted for risk. Stocks are valued on expected future earnings, dividends, and growth in share price. Investors in stocks have different investment styles.

- Cyclical pricing is a predictable outcome in industries that have multiple players, a fungible product, a high capital cost, and a long construction duration.

Chapter 8: Valuation, Sale, and Cyclical Patterns in Business

8.1 Overview of Valuation

Valuation is a subject complex enough to warrant its own course, so this chapter will only superficially address some issues that affect valuation.

At a general level, one can approach valuation from two fundamentally different concepts:

- What are the assets of the business (tangible and intangible) worth from the perspective of their purchase/replacement cost?
- What is the business worth from the perspective of its earning power?

These two approaches often lead to different answers. For example, in the extreme, one could spend a great deal of money buying an ice manufacturing facility and installing it in Antarctica. The installed cost of the assets would be substantial, but the earning power of the assets is negligible.

As a general rule, it is the *long term* earning power of a business that is critical in setting value. Cyclical industries (such as most commodity industries) may have negative earnings for significant periods of time, but it is the belief that the price of the commodity will increase in the future, leading to positive earnings, that sustains value in a downturn. Publicly traded companies will at times trade below the replacement value of the assets they hold, or even below their book value (which should always be a conservative value because it does not reflect inflation), but this is unusual if the industry and company are each seen as going concerns.

Hi-tech businesses often have negligible fixed asset values compared to their market capitalization, especially in the case of information-based business. Compare Microsoft and GM, for instance. GM has tens of billions of dollars of fixed assets and struggles to create any income. Its market capitalization (the total value of shares) has dropped sharply because it struggles to generate value. Microsoft has less than $10 billion of fixed assets and generated $17 billion in net income in 2008; its market capitalization far exceeds the book value of its total assets, reflecting its high earnings. The information revolution has forced people to think of business value as unrelated to fixed assets.

8.2 Fundamental Concepts of Valuation

8.2.1 Asset versus Share Sale and Its Impact on Tax and Liability

The first fundamental watershed decision when buying or selling a business is what is for sale: the assets of the business or the business itself. In either case, one presumes that the overall business is changing hands and that the existing owners are getting out of the business. However, there is a significant tax impact depending on what alternative is chosen.

If assets are sold, then they are free of the previous company debt and can be refinanced by the new owners. (The sellers normally pay off any debt that had been secured by the assets being sold.) The assets regenerate tax depreciation based on their fair market value, i.e., in the hands of the new owner, the capital cost available for tax depreciation is the purchase cost. Thus, if assets are sold for a fair market value of $5 million and they had been depreciated for tax purposes down to a remaining value of $1 million, the purchaser will be able to start claiming depreciation for tax purposes from a value of $5 million, not $1 million. The seller will have recaptured tax depreciation of $4 million, which will be treated as income for purposes of tax calculation. Thus, sale of assets will usually give a purchaser relief on taxes and will give the seller taxable income.

If a company is sold, the purchaser assumes the tax position of the company as is. In the previous example, the purchaser has $1 million in remaining value for the asset even though its fair market value is $5 million. The purchaser has a new adjusted cost base for the shares, and the seller will have a capital gain on the shares of the company. Capital gains are normally taxed at a lower rate than income, so this is a benefit to a seller. Thus, sale of a company will normally give a seller relief on taxes and will give the purchaser more taxable income.

In companies, losses or expenses can be used to offset earnings, thereby reducing tax. The Revenue Canada rule for buying a company in entirety and merging it for tax purposes is that if a loss is being captured, the company being bought must be in a **like business** to the buyer. This stopped the practice of failed companies with tax losses being bought by any firm just to reduce the tax that would otherwise be paid. Capturing tax losses, however, is still a powerful reason for some company purchases. In such cases, the buyer often has no intention of using any of the assets of the company being purchased; the only "asset" of value is the accumulated tax loss.

If a company is bought, then the buyer assumes all the historical liabilities of the company including debt. Thus, if a product made five years ago fails and causes severe damage, then it is the company that is sued, regardless of the change in ownership. In the case of the sale of a company, the seller indemnifies the buyer against legal actions that arise prior to the time of sale by agreeing to pay any consequences of such a lawsuit, but if the seller goes bankrupt, this indemnification is of no value.

These factors play a major role in determining value, and anyone buying or selling a business should get professional help from both an accounting and a legal firm to identify all the options and sort out all the issues that arise in a sale situation.

Tax treatment is subject to a test of fair market value coupled with what is known as the "anti-avoidance rule." Any attempt to skew the value of a company or its assets at time of sale that creates a deferral or avoidance of taxation is subject to reversal. In practice, a sale between parties that are truly "at arm's length" (not related) is rarely subject to review because the presumption is that their interests are competing rather than aligned. A sale between related parties (blood relatives or partners) is more likely to be reviewed.

8.2.2 EBIT and EBITD as Drivers of Value

Valuation of a business with a steady income is relatively straightforward: how much will the business earn in the future? This can be done based on a detailed projection of future cash flow, which in turn derives from the development of pro forma income statements and balance sheets. In practice, many small businesses with a reasonably long operating history are valued based on their historical earnings before interest and taxes (EBIT). EBIT measures the ability of a business to generate earnings before any financing or tax charges are levied on the business. This is particularly relevant if assets are going to be sold, since the financing will normally be quite different for the buyer of the assets than the seller. Hence, the interest payment is not of concern to the buyer, who will have a different interest expense depending on the type of financing put in place.

The multiple of EBIT that a business is worth depends on the time value of money/interest rates at the time of sale and on the perception of the likelihood of growth in EBIT. For small businesses, values from three to seven times EBIT are quite common. Special circumstances can drive this number higher.

The low end of EBIT multiples reflects businesses with low barriers to entry. **Barrier to entry** is a measure of the difficulty for a new entrant to come into the same business; it often reflects capital intensity or the amount of fixed or total assets required per dollar of sales. At one extreme, a personal service offered in the home (such as housecleaning) has no real barrier to entry; anyone wishing to clean houses can put up a sign in a grocery store and enter the business. At the other extreme, entering the new car manufacturing business has huge barriers to entry: not just the capital intensive manufacturing facilities, but also the sales dealership network and new car financing program would have to be recreated by a new entrant.

Using EBIT as the driver of value has an implicit assumption in it; namely, that depreciation will more or less match the ongoing need for investment. EBIT is a measure of pre-tax cash flow for a business where reinvestment matches depreciation. In special circumstances, a buyer may be able to convince himself that no significant new asset purchases will be required for a long period of time. An example of this is the sale of a business during a cyclical downturn, when there is a high surplus of capital equipment. In this case, buyers will sometimes value a business on multiples of EBITDA, earnings before interest, taxes, depreciation, and amortization. (Recall that the difference between depreciation and amortization is blurry, and the terms are sometimes used interchangeably.) This is equivalent to pre-tax cash flow for a business that does not require reinvestment in new assets.

8.2.3   Replacement Value of Assets as an Alternative to Earnings Multiples

There are two circumstances where earnings tests fail. The first is a start-up company that has the prospect for growth in sales but has not yet reached breakeven. The second is a company in a cyclical industry that is in a downturn and that has depressed earnings or even a loss. Such downturns are common in the resources industries.

A buyer in such a circumstance will frequently look at the replacement value of the assets as the driver of value. It is important to recognize that replacement value is used in the broadest sense, not just to buy the equivalent equipment to the company being sold, but also to build up knowledgeable staff and intangible benefits such as know-how, customer lists, etc. Particularly for start-up technology projects that are not truly capable of being protected by a patent, cost and time to develop a competing product are costs that a buyer weighs against the purchase price of a company.

Replacement value of assets in effect measures the barrier to entry: if I wanted to enter this business and not buy your company, how much would it cost?

8.3   Other Considerations in the Valuation, Sale, or Purchase of a Business

8.3.1   Consistency and Quality of Records

Nothing helps the seller of a good business more than good financial records that allow year-by-year comparison, especially for the income statement. However, in reality, obscure and inconsistent financial records going back a short period of time (to the most recent legal reorganization of the business) are often all that a buyer has to go on. The impact of this is overwhelmingly to depress the sale price of the business.

8.3.2   Management Bonuses and Other Small Company Issues

As discussed in Appendix 3.4, owner/managers of small businesses in Canada get better tax treatment if they take money out of a company as a bonus (income) than if they allow the money to be taxed within the company and paid out as a dividend. Thus, it is normal to see a small owner-managed business with a very low ongoing EBIT and a high salary bill. What the owners who are selling such a business will often do is add back in *all* owner compensation to give an adjusted EBIT. What the buyer should do is assume that if she or he works full-time at the business, then a "normal" salary and bonus is warranted. Hence, this would be a legitimate charge against earnings so that the adjusted EBIT would remove "excess" owner/manager compensation. When money has been removed from a company as a questionable expense (for example, a condominium in a warm location that is charged in part or in total to the business because it is occasionally used for business meetings), a buyer will have to make careful judgments about the true historical earning power of a company.

To someone operating a company, there is a lesson here: if potential buyers have to do an analysis of many dubious expenses to see what is an "add backs" to EBIT, the business will be harder to sell. Clean books make clean sales, and good books make good sales. If an owner thinks she is going to sell a business within five years, then keeping consistent and fully appropriate books is a good strategy for maximizing value.

8.3.3   Strategic versus Financial Purchase

Buyers of a business whose initial intent is to continue to operate the business as it was being run, perhaps with a vision of expanding the business in the future, are called financial buyers. They are motivated by the ability of the business to make money "as is." From a seller's perspective, it is ideal to find a strategic buyer, one who can find some synergy between the prospective business and his or her other current operations.

This is perhaps best illustrated by an example. Some years ago, an Alberta oil patch product and service company was sold by a major multinational firm. Management led a leveraged buyout bid backed by a combination of debt and venture capital plus management equity. The venture capital firm was inherently a financial buyer, not motivated by synergies with other operations but rather looking for the business to be profitable and give a return as is. A second bidder was a large US firm with a product line that in some areas complemented the products and services of the business being sold. Specifically, the US bidder thought that products from the Canadian firm could go to market through its existing US distribution channels, and products from the US firm could go to the Canadian market through the business being sold. A substantial premium was paid by the strategic buyer relative to the bid made by management because of the anticipated synergies.

From the perspective of a seller of a business, efforts to identify a strategic buyer will normally boost the sale price of a business.

8.3.4   The Acquisition of Publicly Traded Companies

For the purchase of a publicly traded company, shareholders normally expect a premium to the current market value of the shares. Since the value that the market places on the company is a consensus view of the financial value of the company, most takeover bids for publicly traded companies are inherently from a strategic purchaser.

When publicly traded companies purchase a business, they need to be well informed on the likely impact of the purchase on their share price. When one publicly traded company offers to buy another publicly traded company, it is not unusual in the very short term for the share price of the target company to rise and the share price of the offering company to drop. In the mid to long term, sales, sales growth, and earning per share become critical to share price impact. Evaluating these is normally done with the help of skilled advisors.

Companies that generate cash and do not require capital investment have value even if they have negative earnings. As an example, a pipeline company with annual depreciation of $3 million, no need for reinvestment, and a loss of $1 million per year is generating $2 million in cash per year. To a private investor, this stream of cash flow has significant value. However, recall that the price earnings ratio is a key metric influencing the share price of publicly traded companies. If a publicly traded company purchased the pipeline company, it would reduce its annual reported annual earnings by $1 million even though its annual cash flow went up by $2 million. In such a case, the purchase of assets would make more sense in order to reset the value of assets for purposes of depreciation.

8.3.5 Breakup Value: A Special Case

Bankers are concerned with loan security (the certainty that the interest costs will be serviced and the principal recovered). Banks also lend to so many businesses that they are no strangers to business failure, where a business is not sustainable and a receiver is appointed to sell off the assets and return as much as possible to the creditors of the business. In such cases, experience says that the breakup value of a business rarely exceeds the book value of the assets and more typically would be some percentage of the book value (ranges of 50 to 80% are typical, but lower recoveries are possible).

Many factors influence the extent of asset recovery on business failure. Here are some examples:

- Is the business failure part of a general decline in the industry, or is it due to factors unique to just one company? If there is a general decline, often competitors will not be interested in the inventory or fixed assets because they are carrying surplus inventory and their own fixed assets are underutilized. The rapid decline in energy prices in the 1980s led to many business failures, for example, in the drilling sector. At times, rig utilization rates were so low that there was negligible interest among survivors in bidding on rigs. In the extreme case, working rigs were sold at 4 cents per pound, the approximate value of scrap steel, and immediately hauled to scrap yards.

- Does the customer base have high integrity? Sometimes, businesses take the bankruptcy of a supplier as an excuse not to pay for the last orders that they received from the supplier. In general, to the extent that the customer base is many small customers versus a few large customers, this is more likely to be a problem.

Breakup values are not a normal part of business valuation because most sellers of a business are concerned with receiving value for a going concern, but it is an approach to valuation in special cases of distressed businesses.

8.3.6 Summarizing Valuation

It is important to recognize the complexity of conceptual approaches to valuation and the added complexity that arises from the purchase of assets or of an entire business. All parties in a significant transaction should have legal, tax, and accounting advice.

The following flow chart summarizes different elements of analysis in valuing businesses:

Factors Considered in Valuation of Companies

8.4   Stock Markets and Stock and Bond Values

8.4.1   Securities (Stock) Markets

Securities markets, commonly known as **stock exchanges** or **stock markets**, are a key part of the ability of companies to raise equity for capital projects. Over time, countries have recognized that if stock markets are regulated to be fair and visible, then ordinary small investors will feel comfortable in putting their savings into the purchase of shares in companies. Small investors want many things: honesty, no unfair insider trading based on advance knowledge, clear disclosure of information, and liquidity (the ability to sell shares on short notice when they need the money for other purposes).

Stock markets have been increasingly regulated to ensure that fairness and visibility are maintained. There are strict disclosure rules for any **prospectus**, which is a document circulated to investors outlining a new investment opportunity. These rules are so strict that entrepreneurs need to be careful when raising money that they do not violate laws about disclosure. "Full, plain, and true" is the test applied to any disclosure statement. Regulations came from a long history of the unscrupulous playing on the greed of the naive (one famous saying is that there are only two emotions on Wall St: greed and fear). Once a company becomes publicly traded on a stock exchange (a privilege for which it must apply and obtain approval), then it must file periodic statements with the stock exchange that are also carefully regulated. Significant events must be reported to the exchange, which will occasionally issue a cease trading order so that all investors have time to hear the news; otherwise those who get the news first may reap an unfair benefit. Thus, if one company makes an offer to acquire another publicly traded company, then trading in both the acquiring company and the target will be halted until news of the proposed takeover is disseminated. When a stock price has a sudden unexplained movement, officials from the stock exchange will contact the management of the company to determine whether management has any idea why the change in price is occurring. If some big, planned transaction has been leaked, then the stock market officials will order a halt in trading until the news is disseminated to all. Finally, there are strict rules about insider trading, and any shares bought or sold by senior officers and directors must be reported to the stock exchange, which makes this information public. Some stock market analysts pay careful attention to insider trading as an indicator of management's expectations about future share price.

8.4.2   Initial versus Resale Values of Stocks and Bonds

People first learning to analyze financial statements sometimes get confused between the market value of a security (share or debenture) and its value on a financial statement. The first time a company issues a share or debenture, it has a nominal value, which is what the company receives for the security. Thus, a company might issue 10 million shares at $10 per share at start-up. The company would show $100 million in share capital on its financial statement. Now, imagine that this company develops a software product that has enormous market acceptance and takes off or the company finds a major new oil pool. Someone who holds shares in this company finds that the market value of the shares (what someone is willing to pay for shares) is far higher than $10 per share because of the value created by the successful software product or oil discovery. On the other hand, imagine that the company spends its original capital on products that are not accepted by the market or on exploratory oil wells that are dry holes. Then a smart purchaser will not be willing to pay as much as $10 per share. In any event, this has no impact on the book value of the original share capital; the company still got the $100 million, whether it spent it wisely or foolishly.

8.4.3 Valuation of Bonds

There is a difference between the face yield of a bond and the market yield of a bond. Imagine that the Government of Canada issues a 30-year bond for $1,000 at 6% interest. This means that Canada is committed to paying $60 in interest every year for 30 years and then returning the original $1,000 principal. Now, imagine that two years later, long-term interest rates, through a combination of government fiscal policy and the supply and demand for money, have risen to 8%. The bond is now worth less. This means a person who is going to receive a payment stream of $60 per year and $1,000 in 28 years will not be willing to pay $1,000 if the general value of government debt is 8% instead of 6%.

Table 8.1: Recalculation of the Value of a Bond

Year (n)	Original Bond Value		New Bond Value (after two years)	
	Interest (%)	6	Interest (%)	8
	Payment ($)	Present Value ($)	Payment ($)	Present Value ($)
1	60.00	56.60	60.00	55.56
2	60.00	53.40	60.00	51.44
3	60.00	50.38	60.00	47.63
4	60.00	47.53	60.00	44.10
5	60.00	44.84	60.00	40.83
6	60.00	42.30	60.00	37.81
7	60.00	39.90	60.00	35.01
8	60.00	37.64	60.00	32.42
9	60.00	35.51	60.00	30.01
10	60.00	33.50	60.00	27.79
11	60.00	31.61	60.00	25.73
12	60.00	29.82	60.00	23.83
13	60.00	28.13	60.00	22.06
14	60.00	26.54	60.00	20.43
15	60.00	25.04	60.00	18.91
16	60.00	23.62	60.00	17.51
17	60.00	22.28	60.00	16.22
18	60.00	21.02	60.00	15.01
19	60.00	19.83	60.00	13.90
20	60.00	18.71	60.00	12.87
21	60.00	17.65	60.00	11.92
22	60.00	16.65	60.00	11.04
23	60.00	15.71	60.00	10.22
24	60.00	14.82	60.00	9.46
25	60.00	13.98	60.00	8.76
26	60.00	13.19	60.00	8.11

27	60.00	12.44	60.00	7.51
28	60.00	11.74	1,060.00	122.87
29	60.00	11.07		
30	1,060.00	184.56		
	NPV	1,000.00	NPV	778.98

The concepts of present value, outlined in Chapter 7, can be applied to determine the market value of the bond, as shown in Table 8.1. A purchaser of the bond in the climate of 8% interest rates would only pay $779. Again, there is no impact on the Government of Canada: it has the original $1,000 and continues to pay $60 per year and the principal repayment of $1,000 as per the original schedule. It is the holder of the bond who is affected by the change in interest rates.

In a period of rapid change in interest rates, those holding a bond can experience a large **c**apital gain or loss. When interest rates change rapidly, the value of investments change rapidly, especially those that pay regular interest or a steady dividend; that is the reason why interest rate changes are headline news in the business section and sometimes on the front page.

Companies borrow billions of dollars of debt to finance their asset purchases. Governments also borrow billions of dollars to finance public works and sometimes social programs that are not paid for from current taxes. Every day, the market value for corporate and government debt changes, reflecting the current market value of interest. However, there is a second factor that affects interest rates between borrowers: the market perception of ability to pay. As was discussed in Chapter 7, various bond rating agencies will assess the creditworthiness of a company or government. For companies, one key test is the income of the company and its ability to cover interest costs. For government, one key test is the ratio of total debt to annual gross domestic product (the value of what is produced in a country in a year) and to annual taxation revenues, plus the political stability of the country. Intuitively, people know that lending money to Sierra Leone is a far riskier undertaking than lending money to Canada or the US. Within Canada, the ability of the "have" provinces to pay is higher than those that have weak economies or that have some political uncertainty, such as Quebec. Similarly for companies, Microsoft is less at risk of default on debt than a start-up dot-com company.

8.4.4 Valuation of Stocks

Stock (equity) values, like bond values, vary widely. This is a subject of great complexity and fascination to many people, and one can spend a lifetime trying to understand and profit from the stock market. One key factor in evaluating stocks is the **price/earnings ratio**, which is cited in almost every stock. For example, a bond that pays 6% interest has a price/earnings ratio of $1/i$, or 16.67. If you own the bond, you will get the interest payment, i.e., the earnings are fully liquid and paid out to the holder of the bond.

Now, consider a company that has a price/earnings ratio of 20 and a share price of $40, which means that for each share, the company has earnings in the last 12 months of $2.00. It is theoretically possible that the board of directors could pay all earnings out to shareholders as a dividend. However, this is virtually never the case, since the company is trying to finance some growth from retained earnings. If the company declares a dividend of $1, it has a **dividend yield** of 2.5% ($1 of dividend per $40 of share price) and a **dividend payout ratio** of 50%. This means 50% of earnings go to dividends and the balance to retained earnings.

Another key factor in stock valuation is the potential for **capital gains**, or an increase in the value of the asset, in this case, the stock. Growth rate and/or prospects for future growth (in revenue and net earnings) are the key issue. For a start-up company, earnings are always negative; investors decide to invest based on future prospects, not current performance. Companies with strong prospects for growth will have high price/earnings ratios or a strong stock price with no earnings. A metric that has emerged recently is the **PEG ratio (price/earnings/growth ratio)**. In this formula, price is in dollars, earnings are in dollars per year (normally the last 12 months), and growth rate is the average for the last three years of percent annual growth in earnings, but not expressed as a fraction. Hence, a company with a price/earnings ratio of 100 (very high) but with a three-year average growth rate in earnings of 50% per year would have a PEG ratio of 2.

Compare the potential return on investment of holding a Government of Canada 6% bond versus the same value in company shares for the company with a P/E ratio of 20 and a dividend payout ratio of 50%. The bonds yield more cash payment per year but have no potential for growth in earnings, i.e., the bond will pay the same interest period after period. If the term of the bond is long and interest rates change, its market value will change, as illustrated in Table 8.1. However, the value at maturity is unchanged. If the same amount of money is put into the company shares, then there are lower earnings per dollar invested (5% vs. 6%), and the shareholder gets less cash because half the earnings are kept in the company. However, in the company, there is the potential for future growth from retained earnings. There is also the risk of a turndown that will reduce the earnings (and hence increase the price/earnings ratio) of the shares. The bond might have more appeal to a 65-year-old with a high need for secure cash from dwindling savings, while the company shares might have more appeal to a 45-year-old who is 20 years away from retirement. Meanwhile, a 25-year-old with no children might want to take a chance and invest in a dot-com start-up that has no earnings and pays no dividend but, if successful, might experience ten-fold capital gains.

This kind of tradeoff (would I rather own a bond or company shares?) takes place every day in the securities market for tens of thousands of bonds and stocks. The relative desire to own things is what makes the market. Securities tend to be owned by companies, rich individuals, and ordinary individuals, who hold them in two forms: directly and indirectly through pension plans. The desire to own a stock or bond is what sets the price, so there is a great deal of psychology in the market, and investors often act as a herd. In March of 2000, tech stocks such as dot-com companies were very hot, the NASDAQ index tied to technology shares was over 5,000, and investors piled into each new initial public offering (IPO) of shares. Two months later, the NASDAQ index was below 3,400, and tech shares were comparatively out of favor; it eventually went below 2,000. The only substantial change in this time period was in investor sentiment. More recently, 2008 and 2009 have seen highly volatile stock markets driven in part by high levels of fear of bank failure and depression. Because stock valuation is the subjective judgment by a mass of humans (each responding to fear and greed) of objective criteria, stock valuation is an art, not a science.

Different styles in purchasing of securities emerge, reflecting both the needs of the investor and the tolerance for risk. To be clear, risk means the potential for a substantial loss on a stock. Some investors fret more over one stock that goes down than 10 that go up; this kind of investor should not purchase highly risky stocks. Other investors have the view that if three out of ten shares fail completely but two of the remaining seven have high gains, then the overall portfolio return is better than average. Seniors are sometimes **fixed income** investors, looking for a reliable dividend return or bond interest payments. A second investing style is **value investing**, where the fund manager looks for low price/earnings ratio companies (usually paying a steady dividend) that represent solid value. Often, these companies will not have glamour and hype, but they tend to perform solidly and steadily over time. Warren Buffet is cited as an example of a value investor.

A third investment style is **speculative**, with an emphasis on high capital gains and no focus on dividends. A fourth style, **growth oriented**, lies between value investing and speculative. The focus is on companies with growth prospects that are less risky than the speculative category. Dividends are normally not important to growth-oriented investors.

Capital gains on stocks are normally taxed at a lower rate than dividends to encourage economic growth through investment.

8.5   *Pricing Cycles and the Concept of the Tragedy of the Commons*

Many items, but especially commodities, show cycles in pricing from low prices where most producers have book losses to high peaks where returns on assets are quite high. Figures 8.1 and 8.2 show such price swings for nickel and ammonia, based on the price at year-end (not the average price) in both dollars of the day and constant purchasing value dollars (adjusted for inflation).

Figure 8.1: Fluctuation in Year-End Nickel Price (Actual and Inflation Adjusted)

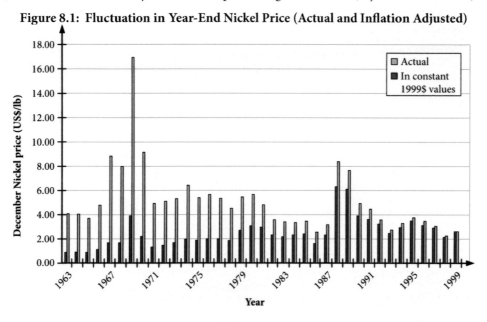

Figure 8.2 Fluctuation in North American Ammonia Price (Actual and Inflation Adjusted)

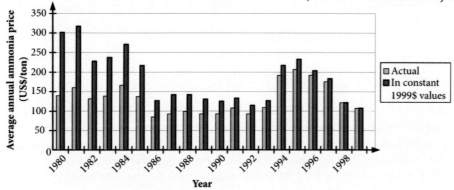

In both cases, there is very high variability in a basic fundamental commodity. Input costs are one factor. The price of natural gas and oil, for instance, went through major swings during the period shown in figures 8.1 and 8.2. But input costs alone do not account for the total fluctuation in cost, since the nickel and ammonia industries went from periods of high profitability to book losses due to supply and demand. The "Tragedy of the Commons" is an anecdote first developed by an English mathematician in the 1800s and discussed at length by Garret Hardin that is often cited to explain both environmental degradation of common resources and persistent patterns of irregular investment (The Tragedy of the Commons, Science, v 162, p 1243–48 (1962)).

Think of a common grazing area that has the capacity to support many sheep. If only one sheep grazes this common area and a second is added, meat production per year doubles. However, at some point, additional sheep will lead to overgrazing, causing the total meat production from the common to drop with each additional sheep. Figure 8.3 shows that the optimum number of sheep grazing on the common is 13. If you add a 14th sheep, then the total meat production stays the same, but each sheep is thinner. Essentially, 14 sheep will produce the same total amount of meat as 13 sheep, and total meat production drops if there are more than 14 sheep.

Figure 8.3: The Tragedy of the Commons
Meat Production Per Year
Common Grazing Area

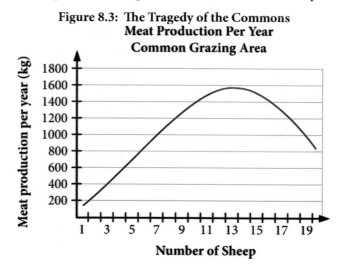

Now, consider what would happen if nine independent farmers each have one sheep in the common and decide to each add one sheep to the common. This would double each farmer's flock (and earnings from lambs). Each farmer acts in the belief that the sheep population will increase from 9 to 10 sheep and will produce an incremental gain of over 100 kg of meat per year, for his personal benefit. However, the total number of sheep in the common actually increases to 18, and the total meat production is about 100 kg lower than it was when 9 sheep grazed the common. Each farmer acted in self-interest to increase his own earnings, but the result is that each farmer loses income.

The tragedy of the commons is used to illustrate two phenomena in business: the overuse of natural sinks and cyclical pricing in some industries. For example, each industry along a river will dump their waste in the water, believing that its waste stream is small compared to the river and that the total level of contaminants will be well below acceptable levels. However, when all the industries along the river do this, the result is catastrophic for the river, making it polluted to a point where it cannot be used for recreation or food production.

The same kind of issue arises for investment in commodity production. Typically, commodities are produced in large, world-scale plants or mines. For example, no one builds a small fertilizer (ammonia/urea) plant since the economy of scale would mean that the plant would have a cost disadvantage compared to larger facilities. Similarly, mines that produce ores that must be processed to the metal (for example, nickel production) are developed on large scale. This sets up a cyclic pattern. Many producers watch the commodity price rise above the point where it provides a good return on investment. At that point, many or all producers commit to a world-scale production facility because they want to retain their market share. When all these plants start up, they flood the market with the commodity, and the price drops, often to the cash cost of production of the marginal producer (the point at which the highest cost producer still in business has a book loss but is at cash breakeven). Then, no one invests in additional capacity because the low product price means that the return on investment is below an acceptable level. Gradually, increased world economic activity or the exhaustion of some facilities, such as a depleted mine, brings the demand in line with supply, and the price rises back to the point where it justifies new investment, which starts the cycle all over again. The two key points in this cycle are the cash cost of the marginal producer (since companies do not run at a cash loss for long), which sets the low point in the cycle, and the cost at which new investment has an attractive return, which sets the decision point when companies commit to new investment. Since new facilities take time to build, it is normal for the price of a commodity to overshoot the price at which new investment is justified. During such price spikes, producers can show startling profitability, but only until new capacity is developed.

The nine farmers could legally form a stock grazers' association and limit the number of sheep on the commons in some equitable manner. The reason this would be legal is that nine farmers (and 13 sheep) are not big enough relative to the market to control the price of sheep. Commodity producers are sometimes tempted to try to smooth out price swings because these are so disruptive to industry. However, it is illegal in many jurisdictions for commodity producers to take steps to limit price swings; this constitutes price fixing. In essence, industrialized economies take the position that the inefficiency due to price swings does less damage to society than the inefficiency due to price control. OPEC, the Organization of Petroleum Exporting Countries, clearly does limit production to reduce price swings, so the view that price fixing is the greater harm is not universally held.

All industries show price swings due to changes in supply capacity (number of plants producing the good) and demand (often influenced by the general level of economic activity). These swings are particularly severe in commodities because supply increments are large.

Using Financial Statements to Manage an Operating Company

Key Concepts

- Successfully managing a company requires an understanding of financial statements and the ability to initiate a number of required actions based on concerns identified by looking at financial statements.
- The most critical short-term issue in any business is maintaining adequate working capital.

Chapter 9: Using Financial Statements to Manage an Operating Company

9.1 Overview

The purpose of assembling financial information is to guide action, and a good management team will look to financial statements and their analysis as the source of information for indications of what actions are needed. Vertical analysis, also called common size analysis, reduces all elements on an income statement to a percentage of sales or some unit of production, such as a ton of steel or a barrel of oil, and all items on a balance sheet to a percentage of total assets or annual sales. Horizontal analysis compares year-over-year performance and, in particular, tracks percentage changes in revenue, operating, asset, and liability accounts. Ratio analysis looks at standard values, as discussed extensively in Chapter 6.

The combination of vertical and horizontal analysis is quite powerful. It can raise questions such as "Even though our sales are going up, why are our fixed costs (SG&A) increasing as a percentage of sales?" or "Even though our sales are going down, why is our inventory up?" Ratio analysis leads to questions such as "Why does it take 52 days to get our customers' money in the bank from the time we book a sale when the industry average is 42 days?" These kinds of questions are based on internal data and are independent of market size. However, the other key questions that management must know are related to the market: "What share of sales in our industry do we (and our competitors) have?" This in turn depends on the features, price, and quality of the products or services the company sells and the effectiveness in selling it.

Managing an ongoing business often comes down to asking the right questions, having the information and the persistence to answer them, deducing the right actions from the process of asking and answering questions, and implementing the actions. Sometimes, the proper action becomes so obvious once the questions are asked that the organization simply changes. Often, great persistence is needed not only to answer the questions but also to determine and implement the right action. This is the art of management.

Most experienced managers develop a broad knowledge base and skill set. The following elements of management are based on financial statements only and do not address the numerous market, human, and legal issues that managers also face.

9.2 Specific Financial Statement Elements in Managing a Company

9.2.1 Sales

Sales growth is virtually a universal goal of business, but the more important issue is market share (the percentage of total sales of a given product or service that come from your company), not absolute sales level. In a competitive market, products and services are positioned based on features, price, and quality, and despite earnest attempts to say that "We can have it all" (best quality and lowest price), there is in reality almost always a trade-off. Luxury cars are better, cost more, and have a smaller share than standard models, and no amount of advertising will change this.

Given that a company's product or service has been positioned at a particular market niche based on its features, quality, and price, a change in share is a powerful signal that something is changing in the market that will affect the company's long-term position. This is usually more important than a short-term drop in sales that comes from an industry-wide downturn. To illustrate this, there have been companies who have experienced a slow growth in sales who did not realize that their share was dropping in a rapidly expanding market because competitors were taking up incremental sales. Steady erosion of market share lets competitors offer more attractive volume-based pricing, and the share loss can start to grow exponentially.

A financial statement does not convey any information on market share, and one of the key inputs to management's financial analysis from outside its statements is a knowledge of total market size so that share can be determined. This is often the reason companies join industry associations.

Analysis of market share leads to tough questions about customer preferences and buying decisions and the appropriateness of a company's positioning of features, quality, and price. This is at the heart of marketing.

9.2.2 Margin

Erosion of margin is not unusual as products mature. As competition increases and market growth slows, prices often drop, and highly profitable products become less profitable. However, efforts to maintain margin are a key part of maintaining income from operations. Margin is easily tracked as long as costs are consistently allocated to COGS versus SG&A.

In a mature product, changes in margin usually occur because of a disconnect between suppliers' and customers' prices. If suppliers increase prices and a company is unsuccessful in getting its customers to pay a comparably increased price, it will watch its margin drop. More importantly, if a downturn in a market forces a company to drop its prices to maintain its market share, the first thing it should do is try to get its suppliers to support them by rolling their prices back too. Suppliers are often surprisingly willing to do this if it is clear that the price rollback at the supply level is temporary and tied to the price rollback at the customer level. Some companies have taken the same approach with labor cost inputs, asking workers to accept lower wages in cyclical downturns, sometimes committing to "catch-up pay" during upturns.

"Pass it on" is the key management tool in maintaining margin. Management that loses sight of this will sometimes defer price increases year over year only to find that they must have a large increase in one year to get their company back on track. This is more painful for customers than a longer history of lower price increases. One of the key indicators that buyers usually look at is consistency in margin. Owners who are selling a company who say "We could have had a price increase but didn't get around to it," or even worse "If you buy this business, you can put through a price increase" are not likely to get maximum value for their company.

9.2.3 Sales, General, and Administrative

Managing a business is a constant tension between too much and too little. In good times, when earnings abound in a company, the temptation to add the extra market analyst, buy the news service that has industry-specific information, support more employee training, and hire extra front office staff is enormous: people who have been through bad times want relief and want to share in the good times. When the momentum to add staff goes on and on, inefficiencies steadily build up as costs grow, and some economists believe that it is these cost inefficiencies that lead to downturns, when cost-cutting begins anew. No extra spending in good times discourages staff, and no discipline on SG&A costs in good times builds the foundation of the next downturn. Walking that tightrope is the art of management.

In an ideal world, SG&A would stay very flat (be a pure fixed cost), and increased sales would contribute all incremental margin directly to profitability. In the real world, SG&A increases as sales grow, but not proportionately.

9.2.3.1 Depreciation

Judgments about depreciation have no impact on the cash position of a company, but they do affect how its earning power and value is represented through its financial statements. Accounting by nature is conservative, and rapid depreciation of assets is often encouraged so that the books do not overstate the value of the business. However, rapid depreciation reduces reported income and EBIT (but not EBITD) and reduces the book value of a business relative to a slower write-down. When it comes time to sell a business, the lower EBIT and book value can be a factor in a lower valuation. At the other extreme, a very low depreciation rate means that assets that are scrapped are overvalued, and accounting will require a special write-down (in essence, accelerated depreciation) when the asset is replaced. Historical financial statements full of significant special write-downs will likely make the potential buyer feel uneasy, especially if the buyer wants management to stay with the business. Setting the right value for depreciation is part of the art of management. High tech is a particularly difficult challenge when setting depreciation rates. Modern business changes so quickly, especially in anything related to telecommunications and information technology, that picking the right depreciation rate is more art than science.

9.2.4   Integrating Volume, Margin, Cost, and Income

It is easy to talk about managing share (sales volume), margin (price), and cost to maintain or grow operating income as if these things existed in isolation. In reality, they are interconnected, and any action in one area has an impact in another. Here are some examples:

- In order to hold market share in a falling market, one can cut price, but this drops margin and operating income unless the lower price stimulates a more-than-offsetting increase in sales.
- One can increase promotion/advertising to hold share, but this increases cost and drops operating income unless sales increase to generate contribution margin higher than the increased cost.
- One can hold margin (price) and lose share to competitors, which again drops operating income.

Margin (price), share (sales volume), and costs are not independent of each other. Action in any of these areas will have an uncertain impact on the other two. The art of management is trying to choose an appropriate action, with decisions often made by trial and error. Learning from experience is important: almost no business has enough empirical data to mathematically optimize this kind of judgment.

9.2.5 Net Income

For companies that put financing cost as a negative entry in other income, the primary difference between operating and net income is interest cost. Long-term interest costs are often not subject to change, but management action can have a significant impact on short-term interest cost because management of receivables, inventory, and payables can substantially reduce short-term debt. Remember that net income measures value creation, so it becomes the critical number to measure the long-term sustainability of an enterprise.

9.2.6   Receivables

The management of receivables is a major opportunity for reducing the cash requirements of a business, and it is especially important when a business is sold. The best management practice is to age receivables, or track the dollar amount of receivables as a function of billing date so that each month, management knows the fraction of the receivables that are less than 30 days old, between 30 and 60 days old, and over 60 days. Depending on the business, there will be a day value that causes alarm: receivables over a certain age are often a sign that a customer is in trouble and may never pay the bill.

In some cases, companies must continually remind their customers to pay their bills. These customers envision the receivable as a form of borrowing money from the company and will delay on paying as long as it does not object.

In cyclical industries, everyone gets scared in a downturn and wants to hold on to someone else's cash. Collecting in a downturn is important in order to distinguish bad debt from slow debt. If you know debt is bad, stop shipping more product to the customer. If you know the debt is good but slow, keep shipping, since you need the sales.

Large companies are almost always reliable but slow payers. Large, integrated oil companies, for example, usually take 55 to 60 days to pay, but the risk of non-payment is negligibly small. Financing these customers is a cost of business. Businesses like Dell that are trying to forge Internet-based alliances with suppliers have addressed this problem by quick-pay systems that solve the suppliers' needs and require less processing cost on the part of the payer. Over the next 20 years, the problem of slow but reliable payments from large customers will likely disappear.

Incentives are sometimes offered for quick payment, for example, if payment is received within 10 days, the price will be 2% less. A business thinking of offering such an incentive needs to be cautious here. Ideally, the discount will be a credit so that the customer does not shift the price point; otherwise in hard times, the company will be under pressure to take the 2% off without the quick pay. Second, such discounts can reduce margin if they are too high; as interest rates have fallen, quick-pay incentives have grown to far exceed the value that they originally conveyed in a time of high interest.

9.2.7 Inventory

Inventory is simply a cash cost that a company must finance. Inventory reflects money tied up, and any steps to reduce it (except a write-down) free up cash that the business can use for other purposes.

The very high interest rates of the late 1970s forced companies to ask why they needed so much inventory on hand. The phrase "just in time" came from this era: instead of having assembly line A produce parts and stockpile an inventory to go into assembly line B, just connect up the two assembly lines and have A feed B directly ("just in time"). The old argument for the intermediate inventory between A and B was that the reliability of line B could then be decoupled from line A. One benefit of the "just in time" movement was a higher focus on reliability. Suddenly, when line A stopped, the whole plant stopped, and management, which had perhaps ignored the frequent stoppage of line A in the past, came down on the floor, discovered why line A stopped so frequently and did something about it.

"Just in time" manufacturing supported by sophisticated computer-tracking systems has advanced to a point where auto parts companies consider trucks on the road as their warehouses. Forward-thinking companies share their order information with suppliers so that an order for a finished product from a company (for example, an order for a Dell computer) is automatically translated into an order for the components. This allows Dell not to maintain a large inventory of parts to ensure it can make every computer in its line. There is an implicit change in this approach: volume ordering discounts of the past ("If you order a large quantity, I will give you a lower price") have shifted to reliable order discounts ("If you have an alliance with me and I can count on being a significant supplier, I will give you a lower price"). Part of what has allowed this transition is lower processing costs for invoices and payments as the information age has become automated and, in some cases, eliminated the paper work from the process of invoicing and paying bills.

Other innovative techniques have been adopted to reduce inventory. When a steady relationship has been set up between a supplier and a company, sometimes they both have an inventory: the supplier has inventory to ensure that the good customer is always serviced, and the good customer has inventory because there is a volume discount on buying or because of a fear of a transportation disruption. One "win-win" strategy that has been adopted in such cases is to have the supplier own the inventory at the customer's site. A steel supplier, for example, will store steel that it still owns at its customer's site. The customer does not own the steel until it pulls it out of the yard onto the production floor. The steel supplier is free to remove the steel at any time should it need it, but in practice, overall inventory is reduced, and both parties win.

As products change, **stale inventory**, which is mainly obsolete components or product that is unsellable, inevitably builds up. The proper step to take is to scrap this material and write down the difference between the book value of the material and the scrap value recovered. Managements sometimes defer this step because it causes a drop in net income, but failing to do so distorts the true value of useful inventory and makes year-over-year comparisons increasingly meaningless. "Take the medicine in small doses" is a guideline management should remember in steadily writing down stale inventory, thereby avoiding a major write-down in the future.

Start-up companies sometimes find that their biggest financial peril is the large order they had dreamed of receiving because they do not have the funds to buy inventory and carry the receivable after the sale. As illustrated in Chapter 4, one technique for bridging short-term problems like this is to ask key suppliers to participate in the financing of the sale by extending special terms on their supplies. For instance, imagine a product that takes 30 days to assemble and ship that is being sold to a large "slow pay" customer. If the company making the product can convince its suppliers to extend 90-day terms for this order (often justified by the prospect of additional future sales), then the company can make and ship the product and collect its receivable before its payable becomes due, solving the short-term problem. Many suppliers will support this if they believe that the request for special terms is one time or infrequent and associated with growth.

9.2.8   Prepaid Expenses

Prepaid expenses mean that someone else holds your money. The only reason to do this is because you get a benefit from the prepayment. If your once-per-year insurance premium is not at a discount, then insist on paying it monthly.

9.2.9   Payables and Accrued Expenses

Payables and accrued expenses are a form of borrowing money from your suppliers. For all the reasons that you want to collect your receivables promptly, you want to pay your payables slowly. Rapid changes in payment approach may disrupt long-term supplier relationships, but management should be aware of payables as a source of short-term credit that they have some control over. On the other hand, stretching payables unreasonably may lead a supplier to nudge prices up, so managers need to exercise careful judgment in determining a payment strategy.

9.2.10   Fixed and Intangible Assets

Management decisions about assets, both tangible and intangible, are obviously key to the success of a business. Once bought, the main financial decision to make about assets is the rate at which to depreciate them. There are numerous non-financial decisions to make about utilization, optimal maintenance, etc., but these derive from manufacturing management, not financial management.

Goodwill is an asset, and it should be depreciated just like a tangible fixed asset. In addition, management must attest to the value of goodwill each year; that is, declare that in their opinion, the goodwill value reported on the balance sheet accurately reflects its true value. Most goodwill arises when a company is purchased for more than book value; almost all purchases of companies are at higher than book value because book value is typically a conservative valuation of a business.

9.2.11 *The Short-Term Credit Line*

No issue is more critical to the survival of a business than its working capital, reflected in its cash and short-term borrowing position. In good times, this is not a day-to-day problem, so management sometimes ignores this or puts it at the bottom of its daily priorities. Instead, management properly focuses on the growth issues of a business:

- What do customers want?
- How is our product performing?
- What are our competitors doing?
- How can we sell more?
- What new products should we be developing?

In bad times and in times of rapid growth, management needs to quickly move cash (and short-term borrowings, which is simply negative cash) to the top of the list to ensure that there is always adequate working capital in the business. Banks take deposits from people who accept a low interest rate in exchange for high security. Bankers do not want to have non-recovery on loans because it violates the basis on which they got the funds and because their own personal performance is judged in part on this criterion. Bankers lend to many and learn early in their career to apply tough criteria to businesses seeking loans. You may think that your business is revolutionary, visionary, and just deserves a break, but to your banker, it is one of a wide portfolio of loans for which complying with covenants is very important, being current in repayment (not being in default) is extremely important, and being secure (fully recoverable) is career shaping. Bankers are also human and very keen to maintain a long-term relationship with a good business. If a business is going to go briefly offside on a covenant, the most important thing management can do is talk to their short-term lender in advance. Although a business should never count on this, a bank might in rare circumstances relax its covenants provided the business can give a good reason for the temporary nature of not meeting its covenants.

Many small businesses cannot have such a discussion in advance with their short-term lender because they do not have the discipline and skills to forecast their cash position. For a small business, the owner/manager should master this skill and think of it as maintaining working capital, which is as critical to a business as breath is to a human. For a large business, the senior manager should insist that the chief financial officer, not just the treasurer, be fully aware of the working capital position of the company. There is ample history to show that even large publicly traded companies can overload themselves with debt and run out of working capital, leading to failure.

Most banks will look for a personal guarantee (usually unlimited) from the owners of a new small company or new owners of an established small company. The banks' logic in this is that a small business can get offside very quickly and can go into a working capital deficit position from which it cannot recover. This is the responsibility of the owners. The bank's view is that the owners get all the benefit of a business's success other than interest charges, so the personal assets of the owner/manager should provide security for the loan. Banks will kick owners out of their house and sell it and its contents to recover a defaulted loan. However, when a business gets established, it is often possible to get the personal guarantees lifted or reduced. This may require a change in covenants for a period of time; for instance, the owner/manager may have to agree to maintain a higher minimum level of working capital or accept a higher current ratio within the company in exchange for a lifting of the personal guarantee. This is a goal that many owners aim for, especially in middle age, so that a failure of their company does not consume all of their net personal wealth.

Owners of small companies should strive to master the skill of knowing the current and likely future working capital position, since no other skill is so critical to the day-to-day survival of the company: in a business, "working capital is breath."

Appendices

List of Abbreviations and Glossary of Financial Terms

(With thanks to Michael Lipsett, University of Alberta)

List of Abbreviations

CCA: capital cost allowance

COGS: cost of goods sold

ΔIRR/IIRR: incremental internal rate of return

EAIR: equivalent annual interest rate

EBIT: earnings before interest and taxes

FV: future value

GDS: general depreciation system

IRR: internal rate of return

MACRS: modified accelerated cost recovery system

MARR: minimum acceptable rate of return

NPV: net present value

ROE: return on equity

ROI: return on investment

SCF: statement of cash flow

SG&A: sales, general, and administrative expense

STCL: short-term credit line

WACC: weighted average cost of capital

WIP: work in progress

UCC: unclaimed capital cost

Glossary

Acceleration: A change in the due date of debt, typically from some time in the future to immediately due. The usual reasons for acceleration are a violation of a covenant in a debt agreement, default (failure to make a required payment) or cross default (failure to pay another debt).

Accounting: Categorizing and interpreting transactions to provide the financial context for business decision making.

Accounts payable: A current liability. See payable.

Accrual: A current liability. See accrued expense.

Accrued expense: A current liability. Booking an obligation of a payment that has yet to be made, such as wages owed but not yet paid.

Acid test: A liquidity ratio. See quick ratio.

Activity ratios: Financial ratios that measure how effectively assets are being used in the business (inventory turnover, average collection period, fixed asset turnover, total asset turnover); also called asset management ratios.

Adjusted cost base (ACB): In Canadian tax, the value above which capital gains are calculated when selling an asset. The ACB of an asset is almost always simply the cost of acquisition.

Age receivables: Categorizing receivables by the amount of time they have been outstanding. Banks often require this process so that receivables that have been outstanding for more than 90 days can be excluded from current assets for purposes of calculating working capital.

Allowances and returns: An adjustment for wrong shipments and returned goods that for some reason cannot be returned to inventory; one of the costs that is subtracted from gross revenue to calculate net revenue. Some companies treat an allowance for bad debt and warranty work in the same manner.

Amortization: The period of time over which a series of payments are made; also used as a synonym for depreciation.

Amortize: To recover the principal value of long-term debt or the capital cost of a long-term asset.

As spent: Money as it was valued at the time of expenditure as opposed to its present or future value.

Asset: An item of value that is held by the business and recorded at the lower cost or market value. The sum of assets always equals the sum of liabilities (what is owed to others) plus equity (what owners have contributed to the business).

Asset management ratios: See activity ratios.

Authority: The delegated ability to do a job function and be held accountable for its responsibilities. Signing authority for expenditures is an example of authority delegated to an employee.

Average collection period: An activity ratio. See days sales outstanding.

Bad debt: A loan or receivable that cannot be collected at all or only at a steep discount. It can be treated as an expense as incurred, but some companies create an allowance for bad debt that is subtracted from gross revenue to calculate net revenue, along with allowances and returns and warranty work.

Balance sheet: A financial statement documenting the assets that a business has at a point in time and where the money came from to acquire those assets.

Bankruptcy: A legal status that is typically declared by a company or imposed by a court when a company fails to meet its obligation to pay liabilities.

Barrier to entry: The difficulty of a newcomer to enter a line of business, typically high for capital intense businesses and low for businesses such as distributors or retail outlets.

Billable hours: The basic unit of sales for a business that provides services, such as a consultancy or a law firm.

Book breakeven: The point at which operating income becomes positive, under the assumption that interest on long-term debt is expensed before calculating operating income.

Bookkeeping: The process of tracking (monetary) transactions in a business.

Budget: A financial document that estimates the expected expenses and revenues for an upcoming interval, usually three months or a year.

Budgeting: The process of developing a budget.

Business plan: A projection of expected business operations, based primarily on sales revenue and operating expenses, often looking out five or 10 years.

Capital cost allowance: In Canada, depreciation for purposes of calculating taxable income.

Capital gains: The gain realized in selling an asset. For a non-depreciable asset, the capital gain is the difference between the proceeds of sale and the cost of acquisition. For a depreciable asset, the capital gain is the amount realized in excess of the adjusted cost base.

Capital recovery charge: An annual allocation that will recover the cost of an item over its lifetime plus provide a return on investment. Calculation of the capital recovery charge requires specification of the capital cost, the lifetime, and the time value of money.

Capitalized cost analysis: A present worth analysis in which the alternatives each have infinite analysis periods.

Cash: A liquid asset that can be spent immediately. The ability to raise cash to keep operations going is the most important short-term management function.

Cash breakeven: The point at which cash flow from operations (operating income plus depreciation and any other non-cash charge against income) becomes positive, under the assumption that interest on long-term debt is expensed before calculating operating income; more important for small businesses, which otherwise would have to dip into reserves to keep the business going.

Cash flow diagram: A graphical representation of how cash enters and leaves an organization over a period of time; very useful for understanding how to calculate interest and present worth.

Cash flow from operations (CFFO): Operating income plus depreciation and any other non-cash charge against income; cash generated from normal business (usually calculated before tax).

Chapter 11: The name given in the United States to creditor protection. The name comes from the chapter of the legislation on bankruptcy in the United States.

Common shares: The form of ownership of a company. Common shareholders have the right to elect the directors of a company, who have a duty to look after the best interests of the shareholders.

Compounding: The practice of calculating interest even though a cash payment of interest is not made and then paying interest in future periods on this calculated interest.

Compounding period: The time period for which interest is calculated, e.g., monthly, quarterly, or annually.

Compound interest: The calculation of interest in a period based on the initial capital and the calculated but unpaid interest from all previous periods.

Contribution margin: Net revenue minus cost of goods sold. A measure used for evaluating sales and marketing effectiveness and for setting a minimum price for incremental sales. Typically, contribution margin is sensitive business information that should not be revealed to competitors; also called margin.

Constraint: A limit on a resource, e.g., the rate at which a machine can produce a product or the volume of a storage tank.

Continuous compounding: A calculation that treats interest as earning instantaneously and then earning interest on interest in subsequent periods.

Corporation: A business organization that has the legal status of a person. The owners of a corporation are not legally responsible for its debts or actions.

Cost of goods sold (GOGS): The expenses directly related to purchasing or producing products or services for sale; also called direct costs or marginal costs.

Cost plus: A type of contract where allowable costs are reimbursed and an incremental percentage is paid for overhead and profit.

Cost tracking: Monitoring expense transactions.

Covenants: Terms and conditions that a business must meet to maintain a contract (such as a short-term credit line) with a lender.

Covering the nut: See cash breakeven.

Credit: 1) Generally, but not always, a positive influx of money into an account. 2) A type of loan.

Creditor protection: A legal status in which a company goes to court to get a temporary right to suspend payment of liabilities without having a receiver appointed to run the business. Laws in most developed countries provide for creditor protection to maximize the possibility of a business surviving a short-term problem. Creditor protection is known as Chapter 11 in the United States.

Cumulative deficit: The name given to retained earnings if the sum of retained earnings is negative, i.e., a cumulative net loss.

Current: On a balance sheet, an asset or liability that will convert to cash or require a cash payment within a year. For debt, the word current means that all interest and principal payments to date have been made.

Current assets: Cash, receivables, short-term investments, inventory, and prepaid expenses.

Current line: The dividing line on a balance sheet between current assets and liabilities and longer term assets and liabilities.

Current ratio: A liquidity ratio calculated as current assets divided by current liabilities.

Current portion of long-term debt: A current liability.

Days of sales: Money owed as receivables divided by monthly sales and multiplied by 30.

Days payables: The time a firm takes to pay its bills. If COGS is materials only, days payable can be calculated as payables (in dollars) divided by the product of monthly sales times (1 – contribution margin) and then multiplied by 30.

Days sales outstanding: An activity ratio calculated as receivables divided by (annual sales ÷ 365) or (monthly sales ÷ 30) that measures how well the company gets its customers to pay.

Debit: Generally, but not always, an outflow of money from an account.

Debt: Money legally owed to others. Long-term debt is typically secured against specific assets, so holding debt in a company is less risky than holding equity.

Debt management ratios: See leverage ratios.

Debt ratio: A leverage ratio calculated as total debt divided by total assets; also called total debt to total assets ratio. Sometimes, debt ratio is called debt to equity ratio, but technically, debt to equity is total debt divided by (total assets – total debt).

Debt to equity ratio: A leverage ratio calculated as total debt divided by (total assets – total debt). The term is often mistakenly used when debt ratio is actually meant.

Demand loan: A loan that can be called (i.e., payment due) at any time. Short-term credit lines are typically demand loans that can be called if the borrower is in violation of covenants regarding the loan.

Depreciation: A non-cash expense that recognizes that an asset such as equipment wears out over time, which can be thought of as a charge against revenue that recovers the cost of the original assets that are wearing out. There are different classes of depreciation, which depend on the type of asset.

Direct costs: See cost of goods sold.

Discounted cash flow (DCF): A conversion of the value of a stream of payments in the future to their equivalent value in today's dollars (present value) based on a time value of money.

Discounting: The process of converting a future value of money to a present value.

Dividend: A payment to shareholders reported as a negative entry in the statement of cash flow.

Dividend yield: The annual dividend per share calculated as the dividends paid in the previous 12 months divided by the share price and expressed as a percentage.

Dividend payout ratio: The dividends a company pays divided by the net income of the company, expressed as a ratio or a percentage; the fraction of earnings paid to shareholders as a dividend.

Double entry: Tracking a transaction simultaneously as a debit in one category and a credit in another to maintain balance between assets and the sum of liabilities plus equity. The parts of a transaction can be all in one category or in two different ones. A physical analogy is conservation of energy in which energy can be transformed into different forms, but neither created nor destroyed.

Downsized: A name given to staff reductions in companies.

Earnings before interest and taxes (EBIT): Net income before payments of interest and taxes. It represents the value created by a company independent of financing and tax charges.

Earnings before interest, taxes, and depreciation (EBITD): Net income before payments of interest and taxes plus depreciation. It represents the cash generated by a business independent of financing and tax charges.

Equity: The value that owners have in a business; the sum of share capital plus retained earnings; also called capital or shareholder's equity.

Equivalence: The property of money that allows a shift of any sum to an equivalent sum at some other point in time; the premise under which investment analyses can be compared at different points of time.

Equivalent annual interest rate: The actual interest rate charged annually that would have the equivalent yield to multiple compounding periods during the year.

Expenses: Money that leaves the business.

Externalities: Things outside an organization that it can use for free. If used excessively by one or many, externalities come under pressure and cause harm to society in which case, government regulation (which may include taxation) is necessary to preserve it. Highways and the atmospheric environment are examples of externalities.

Financial management: The oversight activities in a company that ensure that sufficient funds are available to the company to meet its needs and that the needs of lenders to the company are met so that the company remains solvent.

Fiscal year: The annual period in which business is conducted and reported. Many companies start their fiscal year at the beginning of a quarter, not necessarily January. Governments start their fiscal year on April Fool's Day.

Fixed asset: A real, physical thing that a company owns, such as a piece of equipment, a building, and land. Land does not depreciate, but most other fixed assets do. Fixed assets are sometimes pledged as security for long-term debt.

Fixed asset turnover: An activity ratio calculated as annual sales divided by net fixed assets.

Fixed charge coverage ratio: A leverage ratio calculated as (EBIT plus lease payments) divided by (interest charges plus lease payments).

Fixed costs: Costs that do not vary with the amount of production (e.g., number of units produced). In reality, a fixed cost does have a constraint related to production. See sales, general, and administrative expense.

Fixed income investors: Investors who are looking for a known and predictable return on investment, such as is realized from a bond.

Forecast: A revised budget for the remainder of the fiscal year.

Fundamental equation of accounting: Assets = liabilities + equity

Future worth: The equivalent sum at some future point in time.

Gain: Creating value in a business.

Gain or loss on sale of assets: The difference between the sale price of an asset and its remaining book value; a gain if positive and a loss if negative.

Goodwill: 1) In accounting of a balance sheet, an intangible asset arising when a company is purchased for more than its book value. 2) In business parlance, goodwill is the ability to exert influence on someone or within a group without having to resort to the use of an asset.

Governance: The manner in which the board or other forms of owner representation directs an organization to align the actions of its parts to support overall objectives. Defining authority and responsibility are key elements of governance.

Gross domestic product (GDP): The value of all the goods and services produced by a country.

Gross revenue: The total revenue in a reporting period.

Gross sales: Sales revenue before subtracting bad debt.

Growth-oriented investing: An investment style that tries to identify companies that will experience significant growth in value, typically by growth in sales and earnings.

Horizontal analysis: The comparison of data over a period of years, with the data frequently being normalized values that result from vertical analysis.

Human resources: The part of an organization that deals with developing and applying policies and procedures for fair and equitable treatment of the people in the organization.

Hurdle rate: See minimum acceptable return on investment.

Illiquid asset: An asset that cannot be readily converted into cash.

Income statement: A financial statement documenting how much income is accumulated by a business in a meaningful period of time, i.e., rate of earning.

Incremental internal rate of return (ΔIRR/IIRR): The IRR of the difference in incremental cash flow between two investment alternatives, so ΔIRR is the return on the additional spending. The general rule is to choose the most expensive (capital cost) option if ΔIRR is above the minimum acceptable rate of return.

Indirect expenses: See sales, general, and administrative expenses.

Inflation: The loss over time in the purchasing value of a given amount of money caused by an increase in prices.

Initial public offering (IPO): The initial sale of shares to the public as a company goes from being a privately held company to a publicly traded company whose shares will trade on a stock exchange.

Intangible assets: Trademarks, patents, franchise fees, valued as assets despite not being tangible objects.

Intellectual property: Legally protected information owned by a business, including (but not limited to) trademarks, patents, documented business processes, proprietary technical information, and trade secrets.

Interest: The time value of money for a debt investment as payments at an agreed schedule from a borrower to a lender; an operating expense to the borrower (payer) reported on the income statement in SG&A or a negative entry in other income; income to the lender; similar to return on investment, which is the time value of money for equity.

Interest on long-term debt: A financing expense reported either in SG&A or as a negative entry in other income.

Internal rate of return (IRR): The effective interest rate at which the net present value of an investment's cash flow (including costs) is zero; the most common criterion by which investment decisions are made; the return provided by the entire cost of the investment; often called return on investment (ROI).

Inventory: Parts, raw material, partially completed products, and finished goods not yet sold; a current asset that could be sold for cash if absolutely necessary (but probably at a steep discount); often measured in days of sales.

Inventory turnover: An activity ratio calculated as annual sales divided by inventory.

Levelized payment: A mortgage type payment in which the dollar value of the payment remains constant per period and the amount allocated to interest and principal changes over the term of the loan.

Leverage ratios: Financial ratios that measure how effectively a business is likely to repay its total debt (debt ratio, times interest earned, fixed charge coverage); also called debt management ratios.

Liabilities: Value borrowed from others to support the business.

Like business: A term used in characterizing an acquisition of one company by another. In Canada, acquisition of 100% of a company in the same (like) business as the purchaser allows tax losses in the purchased company to be utilized by the purchaser to reduce taxes payable.

Limited liability partnership (LLP): A form of partnership in which individual partners are not exposed to the liability of the partnership; therefore, LLPs mimic the limited liability realized by shareholders of corporations.

Liquid asset: Value in the business that can be converted readily into cash, which is the most liquid asset of all.

Liquidity: A measure of the ease with which an asset can be converted into cash.

Liquidity ratios: Financial ratios that measure the likelihood that a business will remain solvent in the short term (current ratio, quick, or acid test ratio).

Loan: Borrowing to finance a business.

Loan repayment: A sum of money with two components: interest to the lender and repayment of the principal. There are different methods for principal repayment.

Long-term debt: Debt for which the total principal repayment period is longer than one year.

Long-term investments: Financial investment assets such as bonds; not commonly held by manufacturing and technology businesses.

Loss: Negative earnings measuring the destruction of value in a business.

Maintenance: An operating expense associated with keeping equipment and facilities operating within performance specifications.

Management: 1) A business activity concerned with planning, financing, organizing, and operating an organization through working with people. 2) A term for the group of employees within the company that have formal supervisory roles and responsibilities related to those activities.

Margin: See contribution margin.

Marginal costs: Variable costs of an operation. See contribution margin.

Market capitalization: The value of a company on a stock market equal to the number of shares outstanding times the share price.

Market value ratios: Financial ratios that measure stock price against earnings and book value of equity (price/earnings, market/book).

Market/book ratio: A market value ratio calculated as market price per share divided by book value of equity per share. Market to book value assesses the premium that a stock price has over a conservative valuation; not derived solely from financial statements; relates to a company's market value.

Mark to market: The name given to the difference in value between a contracted price of a purchase or sale contract or the original price of an asset held for resale and the current market price.

Materiality: The allowable error in tracking transactions, which is defined by the business. Any material errors in transactions (those larger than the standard) are corrected after the reporting period by a post-period adjustment.

Minimum acceptable rate of return (MARR): The lowest return that you are willing to earn on an investment; also called hurdle rate.

Net cash flow (NCF): The measure of the short-term viability of a business. Negative net cash flow is very bad if it persists for more than a short time.

Net income: The measure of creation of value by a business.

Net present value (NPV): The total present worth of a series of sums. See also present worth.

Net revenue: Gross revenue minus bad debt, allowances and returns, and warranty work.

Net sales: Gross sales minus bad debt.

Non-performing loans: A loan for which interest payments are not being made.

Offset: An expenditure that can be sacrificed in favor of another (typically unbudgeted) expenditure.

On budget: The happy situation when the income statement matches the original projection in the business plan.

Operational management: The oversight activities in a company that ensure that goods and services within a company and between a company and its customers are provided at the targeted cost and revenue.

Operating income: Calculated before tax, the income a business is generating from normal activities. Net revenue minus COGS minus SG&A.

Other income: Unusual or one-time cost or revenue that is not related to normal operations and the expense of interest on long-term debt. By separating the cost of financing from the operating costs, the normal earning power of the business is not distorted.

Outlook: Predicted expenditures for the remainder of the fiscal year.

Over budget: The unhappy situation when the income statement does not match the original projection in the business plan because higher than expected costs have reduced net revenue.

Overhead: See sales, general, and administrative expense.

Partnership: A business organization in which the owners share the equity and liability directly as well as being responsible for any debt and any legal actions against the business.

Payable: A current liability of money owed to a supplier, expressed in days (days of COGS not days of sales).

Payback period: An estimate of how long it will take to recoup an investment. A long payback period typically holds more risk for the investor. Payback comes in two forms: simple (using as-spent dollars) and discounted. Simple payback is more commonly used.

Payroll: A business function that controls cash payments to employees in exchange for their labor.

PEG ratio (price/earnings/growth ratio): The price earnings ratio divided by the percentage average growth in revenue over the past three years; the PEG ratio adjusts the price earnings ratio by factoring in company growth.

Point of sale: The contracted point at which ownership of a good passes from buyer to seller, such as at time of shipment or at time of receipt.

Post-period adjustment: An adjustment to a financial statement made after the initial financial statements are released.

Preferred share: A form of equity investment in a company that receives a defined dividend that is paid in priority to any common share dividend but that does not increase if earnings in the company grow; preferred shares are typically cumulative (any unpaid dividend must be paid in the future before any common share dividend can be paid) and redeemable (the company can buy them back at a prescribed price, often the original price, at any time.

Prepaid expenses: A current asset representing the remaining fraction of an ongoing expense that was paid up front to distribute the booking of the expense over the year.

Present worth: The equivalent sum as of the present time. Present worth analysis compares the net present value of a set of multiple mutually exclusive options. Only future income and expenses are used; the past is considered to be irrelevant.

Price/earnings (P/E) ratio: A market value ratio calculated as price per share divided by earnings per share, which equals market capitalization divided by net income; not derived solely from financial statements; relates to a company's market value.

Principal: The original amount of a loan. Principal repayment is not treated as an expense to the borrower, and it does not create income for the lender.

Principle: An idea that guides behavior.

Procurement: 1) The business function that acquires assets. See Purchasing. 2) The stage of a project when raw material and other assets are purchased, which comes prior to construction and commissioning.

Pro forma statements: Forecast statements that are based on past history and expected future performance of a company.

Profit: Creating value in a business.

Profit margin on sales ratio: A profitability ratio calculated as operating income divided by annual sales.

Profitability: The point beyond which margin exceeds SG&A after depreciation and the business is creating value.

Profitability ratios: Financial ratios that measure the profitability of the business (profit margin on sales, return on total assets, return on equity).

Prospectus: A document that is issued at the time of sale of a stock or bond that outlines the nature of the stock or bond and describes the company; the legal requirement for disclosure in a prospectus is "full, plain, and true."

Public statement: A disclosure of earnings that anyone can see, constructed so as not to reveal key business information (such as contribution margin).

Purchasing: Buying inventory and other assets for a business.

Quarter: A three-month period.

Quick ratio: A liquidity ratio calculated as (current assets minus inventories) divided by current liabilities; sometimes called the acid test ratio.

Raw material: Unprocessed inventory, such as metal bar stock, chemicals, and bulk plastic.

Real interest rate: The actual interest rate minus the inflation rate, reflecting the increase in effective purchasing power.

Receivable: Money coming into the business from sales of goods already shipped; a current asset that is typically measured in days of sales to show how long it takes to collect money from customers after the sale is booked.

Regulation: Legal limitations on how a business can be conducted.

Reliability: The ability of an asset to perform its function within specifications for a period of time. Reliability is generally consumed over time by operating an asset, and reliability is restored by doing maintenance.

Repayable grants: A liability related to long-term debt.

Reporting period: The time interval in which financial transactions are reported; typically monthly for internal management with quarterly and annual summaries.

Retained earnings: Money that remains in the business (as opposed to leaving the business and going back to the owners as a dividend) but is not kept as a separate cash reserve. Incremental retained earnings are net income minus dividends reported annually.

Retention strategy: Incentives intended to keep employees from seeking employment elsewhere.

Return on equity ratio: A profitability ratio calculated as net income divided by shareholder's equity; crucial to the shareholder and, thus, a driver of the share price.

Return on investment (ROI): The time value of money for an equity investment, i.e., the return provided by the entire cost of the investment; similar to interest, which is the time value of money for a debt investment.

Return on total assets ratio: A profitability ratio calculated as operating income divided by total assets.

Returns: Goods sent back to a supplier because of poor quality or wrong shipment.

Revenue: Money that comes into the business.

Risk: The chance that something in the future will not turn out as predicted; in particular, the prospect of a lower than expected financial performance of an investment.

Sales, general, and administrative expenses: Operating expenses not directly related to production. These costs of running the business are approximately fixed and may be referred to as indirect expenses or overhead.

Salvage value: Residual value (what someone will pay) for an asset once it has reached the end of its useful life.

Segregation of duties: A business control to ensure that more than one person is involved in a transaction, e.g., the person who approves a purchase is not the same person who receives it.

Share: A unit of ownership in a company.

Share capital: Shareholder direct investment in a business.

Shareholder debt: The name given to funds put into a company by shareholders as debt rather than as equity. Interest on shareholder debt is an expense that reduces taxable income in a company, whereas dividends are paid from after-tax income of a company.

Share price: The market value of a share; for publicly traded shares, a stock exchange will publicly display the price at which shares are bought and sold.

Shareholder: An investor in a business.

Shareholder's equity: Share capital plus retained earnings; also called equity or capital.

Short-term credit line: A current liability; typically, a demand loan that can be called by the lender at any time; can be considered to be negative cash.

Short-term investment: A current asset that can be borrowed against to raise cash.

Sinking fund: Funds put in trust, i.e., held by a trustee, for purposes of repaying the principal portion of a bond.

Speculative investing: A style of investing that tries to identify stocks that might have very high future growth, for example, due to the discovery of a drug.

Stakeholder: A person or organization in society that is affected by an organization.

Stale inventory: A common name given to inventory that is obsolete or otherwise unusable.

Statement of cash flow (SCF): A financial statement documenting all the flows of funds into and out of a company; used to predict the position of the credit line.

Statement of retained earnings: A financial statement documenting the value that has been retained by the business at the end of a reporting period.

Stock exchange: A regulated market in which shares of particular companies are bought and sold, with public disclosure of price. Companies must apply to be listed on a stock exchange. Listing carries obligations of public disclosure of financial results and significant changes.

Stock market: See stock exchange

Straight-line depreciation: A method of depreciation that reduces the value of an asset by equal amount per time period over its lifetime.

Sum of the periods depreciation: A method of depreciation that reduces the value of an asset by a higher amount in earlier time periods, declining over the life of the asset.

Sunk costs: Costs incurred in the past. Sunk costs are not counted for present worth analysis, which only considers future cash flows.

Taxes payable: A current liability; booking an obligation of a tax payment that has yet to be made; similar in nature to an accrued expense.

Times interest earned ratio: A leverage ratio calculated as earnings before interest and taxes divided by interest charges.

Timing: Recognizing expenses and revenues in the same reporting period so that management has a clear picture of whether value is being created in that period. Sometimes, the end of a reporting period comes between the times of related activities. This could offset expenses and revenue so that they appear in two different reports, which would create the appearance that expenses are occurring that are not related to creating revenue. For example, postponing expenses related to work in progress as an asset until the period in which the sale is booked as receivable revenue at which point, the value of asset in finished goods inventory is converted to a COGS expense.

Total asset turnover: An activity ratio calculated as annual sales divided by total assets.

Total debt to total assets ratio: A leverage ratio calculated as total debt divided by total assets; also called debt ratio.

Tragedy of the commons: When externalities come under pressure from overuse.

Transaction: A monetary exchange with a debit on one side and a credit on the other.

Trust busting: A common name given to government actions to break up a monopoly, known as anti-trust laws in the US and anti-combines laws in Canada. The name comes from the fact that enterprises were legally organized as trusts when the first actions were taken early in the 20th century.

Widget: A whimsical generic term for a unit of product.

Windfall: Unexpected business revenue reported as a gain in other income.

Work in progress: Partially completed product held as an asset.

Working capital: Current assets minus current liabilities

Write-down: A reduction in the book value of an asset as decided by management; entered as a loss in other income.

Write-off: A write-down of an asset to zero value.

Index

Credits

Chapter 1

34878582 from www.clipart.com. © 2009 Jupiterimages Corporation

34886399 from www.clipart.com. © 2009 Jupiterimages Corporation

Chapter 2

30323992 from www.clipart.com. © 2009 Jupiterimages Corporation

7672354 from www.clipart.com. © 2009 Jupiterimages Corporation

Chapter 3

32192840 from www.clipart.com. © 2009 Jupiterimages Corporation

34880756 from www.clipart.com. © 2009 Jupiterimages Corporation

Chapter 4

19018421 from www.clipart.com. © 2009 Jupiterimages Corporation

34826247 from www.clipart.com. © 2009 Jupiterimages Corporation

Chapter 5

178193 from www.clipart.com. © 2009 Jupiterimages Corporation

34886344 from www.clipart.com. © 2009 Jupiterimages Corporation

Chapter 6

Photograph of inside of NYSE by Ryan Lawler, August 15, 2008. Published on Wikipedia at:
http://en.wikipedia.org/wiki/File:NYSE127.jpg

Chapter 7

34782152 from www.clipart.com. © 2009 Jupiterimages Corporation

7234865 from www.clipart.com. © 2009 Jupiterimages Corporation

34878670 from www.clipart.com. © 2009 Jupiterimages Corporation

Chapter 8

39174818 from www.clipart.com. © 2009 Jupiterimages Corporation

Chapter 9

34854616 from www.clipart.com. © 2009 Jupiterimages Corporation